MY INDIAN FAMILY

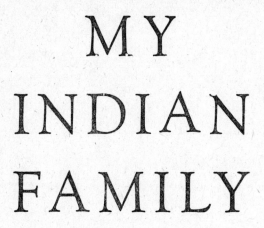

MY
INDIAN
FAMILY

Hilda Wernher

THE JOHN DAY COMPANY · NEW YORK

This book is published simultaneously
in the Dominion of Canada by
Longmans, Green & Company, Toronto

Fifth Impression

Manufactured in the United States of America

MY INDIAN FAMILY

~ I ~

*I*F anybody had suggested to me that I'd accompany my own daughter on her honeymoon I'd have thought him crazy. Any mother would. Yet here I am. Yesterday, forty-eight hours after our landing, Mary Ann was married to Rashid in strict privacy. As he has been on a year's accumulated leave in Europe he has to hurry back at once to his job in a small town upcountry. He works all day and there are no Europeans around. So I am to accompany them.

"Mary Ann would be too lonely without you, Mother," said Rashid just before Aden, when marriage on arrival had been decided upon by those two. "Life in India is not easy."

"But we love India!" Mary Ann's tone and expression left no doubt. "Don't forget we've been there before. We know how things are."

"If you didn't I wouldn't have the courage to carry you off as I do, darling. To a certain extent you know what awaits you. But only to a certain extent. On your previous trip Mother and you were distinguished visitors. You lived in State Guest Houses or good hotels. Now, however—" he does not finish the sentence.

"Now we shall know the real India," Mary Ann concludes, "and that's what we always wanted."

She is ever watchful to dispel his apprehensions and misgivings concerning our future life. My darling girl! Though her marriage is not what I would have wished for—far-reaching differences of religion, country and background prove a great handicap to happiness in the majority of "mixed" marriages—I try to live up to her courage and good will. How she looks forward to "real India"! And that brings me back to the strange and so utterly un-European start of this, our future life: that I am party to my own daughter's honeymoon!

Time is so short that we can't go in for shopping. We leave tonight. In a few months we shall come to Bombay for a shopping expedition only. This afternoon we are to drive on Malabar Hill,

I

then down Marine Drive to Colaba and back by the Strand. After dinner a last glimpse to the west across the Arabian Sea—and then India!

en route April 1

Travel in India holds the same drawbacks and fascination as on our first trip. The countryside is parched, its flatness boring. There are occasional hills but their desolate grayness does nothing to improve matters. The train jerks and rattles; yellow-reddish dust pours in despite gauze wire. At Bombay a tin full of ice was placed just underneath the fan. In consequence the temperature is more than bearable. Twice the ice has been renewed en route, owing to efficient beforehand organization by Rashid.

But even his efforts are not able to change traveling customs. There is no connecting corridor in the wagon. Each compartment is self-contained; the people sharing it are thrown together for better or for worse, without the alternative of stepping into the corridor or nosing about in other compartments, let alone in a sightseeing car. It matters very much whom you have got in your own compartment on a thirty-six hours' journey. It is for this reason that I am not only sharing my daughter's honeymoon but even her compartment!

When the question cropped up first I flatly refused. I said I'd feel too ridiculous for words and there was a limit to everything. But Rashid pointed out that, were I not to share, one or two strangers would do so. This was irrefutable logic. So here I am, thoroughly uncomfortable and nearly dislocating my neck in my efforts to look out of the window at a right angle. Mary Ann enjoys my discomfort. Says she: "Many a time have I felt *de trop* when people crowded round you, each wanting your time and attention and taking it away from me, your poor neglected child. Now it is for once your turn to feel *de trop!*" While she is whispering this into my ear we both laugh so much that Rashid protests and says that, being at last the proud possessor of a family of his own, he doesn't want to be left out of things altogether.

Dislocation or not, I like to look out of the window. There are the wide plains with occasional huge trees. And, where there are banyan trees or nim trees, there is usually a village and a station. An Indian village or small-town station never fails to fascinate me.

2

There is the hustle and bustle of brown limbs clad in whites, reds, yellows and greens; the proud bearing of women balancing water jars or heavy baskets on their heads, their statuesque yet swaying grace rivaling Egyptian friezes; the shouting in languages entirely unknown; the difference in male headgear even in people who otherwise dress alike: multi-colored turbans; white and black caps, a few fezes; children's and adults' gold-tinsel embroidered caps; the khaki turbans of postmen; little pink or strawberry-colored twisted berets—how shall I ever be able to distinguish which headgear means which sub-caste or denomination! One indication is, of course, the two water huts, at each small railway station within a few yards of each other: one bears the inscription "For Hindus," the other "For Muslims." When during our first visit we asked where Europeans or Parsis came in, we were told that they could drink the "Muslim water." No non-Hindu can be allowed near the water a Hindu is to drink lest it be polluted. Meticulous care is taken even among Hindus to keep the water undefiled by individual human touch. There is a man attached to the hut, whose duty it is to keep the jars clean and replenished. I dare say he is a Brahman. On arrival of a train he fills a medium-sized gleaming brass vessel from the big jar. Most travelers who approach him outside the hut—they are not allowed in—present their own equally gleaming small vessels into which he pours water. Others drink from their cupped hands which he has to replenish time and again. But before a man drinks or even holds up the vessel which is to contain his drinking water, he washes his hands under the running water the warden pours for this purpose; with clean cupped hands he then receives two or three times enough water to rinse his mouth. Only then does a Hindu consider himself clean enough to quench his thirst.

In many stations a pump is provided. However short the halt, there are always lots of passengers rushing up to wash and scrub themselves from head to foot. They need no towels. Life is less complicated in such warm climes.

"Won't you talk to us, Mother?" Rashid is anxious never to leave me out. Age is treated with far more respect in the East than in the West. I shall have to get used to that! "We were just discussing our arrival. I have both written and wired to my cousin to get the house in order and my old servants back. He has the keys. I only hope everything will be all right. Unfortunately I'll have to go to the laboratory almost at once and can't stay to settle you in."

"Don't worry! Anyhow I'm going to the hotel for the present. No, really, that's settled."

"But Mary Ann will be all alone!"

"I am no baby! You have married an independent woman of the West, poor dear!" Mary Ann takes my side. "And Mother is still more independent; you'll have to get used to that. She will come to us to dinner, to our first dinner. How grand it sounds, doesn't it?" She laughs, full of happiness.

Rashid has to give in. I think that's what he likes most at present, to adore her and give in. Having won her must seem like a dream to him. His life has been sad so far. He never knew his mother because she died when he was a baby. His father, to whom he somehow doesn't seem attached, married a second time but Rashid was brought up by a maternal uncle. He was married young against his wish and went to Europe immediately afterwards. His wife died while he was taking his Ph.D. degree. Later he took his D.Sc. (London) and was elected F.I.C. for his brilliant research work. He is the head of the Rampore State Central Research Laboratory, which is a great thing for a man of thirty-seven. His work seems to have been all in all to him, so far. He has never known a real home. Marriage to him means everything he has not had all his life.

The sun is setting over the dusty plains. Last night when we watched him from the Gateway we looked towards the West. Today the train takes us right to the East, into our new life.

Hotel Akbarabad, April 2

My room is enormous, with three verandas one of which is overlooking a lovely garden. The outsize bathroom is tiled and much better than I expected. It contains a European tub let into the floor and all the showers, brass buckets and dippers for Indian baths. I've had an "East-West" bath, making use of both ways. After some rest I enjoyed breakfast equally very good. Asked to order my lunch in advance I reject all western suggestions and order chicken *pilau*. I shall be lazy the whole morning. There is need for a lot of mental adjustment. Mary Ann is no more with me. And I have a son-in-law. Such a strange feeling! Would Richard have approved

4

of my allowing the match? How could I have refused? Mary **Ann** is of age. Even if she were not I could have postponed the marriage but not disallowed it. Who am I to know what is best for her? She may be happiest in the difficult task she has set herself. If only—

Later

I did not have the lazy morning I had expected. A note from Mary Ann was brought while I was writing. Would I come at once in Rashid's car and bring her some breakfast? There is much work and she needs me.

No breakfast? It is past ten by now. That seems to indicate that there is no cook and no provisions! Driver and boy were at the station to meet us.

The hotel supplies me with Mary Ann's breakfast, plus some tins of fish, baked beans, corned beef and pineapple I take for luncheon emergencies. Why does the manager smile? Well, let him. I have at present no time to find out. Soon I am driving over a bridge, then along two or three quite pleasant roads. The car turns into a big gateway. To the left lie the laboratories, to the right about eight or ten detached or semi-detached bungalows in a garden whose profusion of roses enchants me. There is only one big bungalow; it is the one the driver takes me to. Here is Mary Ann's new home!

Entering my daughter's drawing room I stop for sheer amazement. Mary Ann is just instructing an astonished boy how to use his broom made of sticks. I voice my astonishment, as I have never known my offspring's efficiency in that particular domain. While we are laughing I unpack the breakfast. "I have no time to sit down. Rashid says there may be callers quite soon! We must drive to the bazaars at once, buy what is most needed and rush home again. What'll we give callers?"

"Lime juice and biscuits will be best. That'll mean no trouble. What a mercy we have all those biscuits!"

"Let's see whether there are enough glasses and spoons."

There aren't. Stocktaking in dining room and kitchen shows that, though Rashid's cousin held the keys, many things seem to have taken leave. Hurriedly we draw up a list of crockery and cutlery. Back in the drawing room Mary Ann looks round. "We must make

5

the room look nicer. These curtains are awful. Let's buy some matching stuff."

I agree. The room is painted a lovely deep blue, the settee and two armchairs are matching, the cane chairs don't spoil the general effect. But the brown print curtains at six windows and three doors ruin it all. "What about your bedroom?"

"No time now!. We must hurry."

Before driving away we want to tell the boy what he should do during our absence. Not knowing Urdu or Hindi, we can't. Mary Ann imitates sweeping and points to the rooms left and right of the drawing room. Suddenly the boy understands. A smile breaks over his face and, in his turn, he imitates Mary Ann. The scene between inarticulate mistress and comprehending staff ends in general merriment.

While driving to the bazaars Mary Ann explains the chaotic conditions. "Rashid's cousin is out of town and returns only this afternoon. His elder brother—he who received us at the station, do you remember—opened letter and wire, but he hadn't the keys. So the house was only unlocked this morning with Rashid's keys."

"And meals?"

"The old cook has left town. Rashid says there will be a cook to prepare lunch."

"You can open the tins I brought."

"Only in emergency. Rashid is so unhappy about the whole muddle. He wants at least to produce a lunch on time for me, poor darling, so we must give him the chance."

I look at my wise child and resolve not to interfere with her plans even by suggestions. This is her show, not mine. If I compare the elaborately padded return from my honeymoon trip with this first morning of hers I feel ashamed. But she enjoys it all. Her generation is more active than mine.

"This afternoon there'll be three more servants, those we get from Government. The boy you have just seen is ours, driver and cook too."

Hearing his profession mentioned the driver turns his head. He has been with Rashid for many years, and seems already to feel responsible for Mary Ann. What he says we cannot understand, so we just shake our heads. Then he points to shops. Ah, he wants to know where to take us! Mary Ann says: "Plates, spoons, knives, forks, curtains," but now it is he who can't understand. Helplessly the three of us look at each other. Finally Mary Ann has the bright idea to say "sari." Where there are saris there must be curtain materials.

"Cloth shop?" retorts the driver. He turns into a narrow street with nothing but cloth shops to right and left, all four or five feet above street level and to be reached by little ladders. Open drainage everywhere, but no bad smell.

We are deposited in front of the biggest shop, which boasts of two show windows. Hindus are the proprietors, with religious signs painted on their foreheads and the very pink berets I wrote about a day ago. To our great relief one of them talks a few words of English. Soon we have chosen lovely blue cloth for curtains, exactly matching walls and furniture. Now Mary Ann buys more saris for herself. "I don't want to frighten people by wearing European dress, and Rashid will like it so." Silk for blouses to match comes next.

"We'll have to find a tailor. I'll wear one of my white blouses this evening."

"Tailor, memsahib?" One or two words from the shop-owner to a boy. Half a minute later a tailor from across the road takes Mary Ann's measurements. "Which first, memsahib?" Mary Ann chooses the blue color scheme. The shopkeeper admonishes the tailor. "Four o'clock," he repeats in English. "You'll have the blouse at four o'clock, memsahib."

"Does he know my address?"

The shopkeeper smiles. "Everybody knows it, memsahib."

Meanwhile the driver has climbed up the ladder to see how we are faring. Several other men come in his wake, apparently with nothing else to do but to look at us.

"Oh, the curtains!" Mary Ann turns to me. "I should so like to hang them for the visitors today! We could manage without the bottom hems but the top ones must be done. What a pity!"

"Have you more work, memsahib?"

"Yes, the hems of the curtains."

Another tailor from across the road is summoned; the new curtains are entrusted to him, the old ones serving as patterns.

Mary Ann is delighted with these swift developments. "Can I have these curtains too at four o'clock?"

"Oh no, memsahib, not at four this afternoon! You now shopping —then Ismail Khan fetch!" He repeats the same more elaborately to the driver; thus we learn at last our driver's name.

"How much will the sewing be?"

The tailor asks two annas per curtain. Whereupon shopkeeper, driver and tailor talk all at once with true oriental delight in bargaining. The price is reduced to one anna and the tailor departs followed by two boys carrying the material, for he is far too great a man to carry anything himself.

We now ask the obliging shopkeeper to translate to Ismail Khan that we want to buy crockery, glasses and cutlery. This is done and soon we drive across the market square whose picturesqueness I have no time to describe now. The car stops in front of a tiny shop displaying soap, rubber shoes and gramophone records.

"That must be the wrong shop! He hasn't understood after all!" We are afraid that we must return to the cloth shop for further translation. But Ismail Khan shows his perfect understanding by making the shopkeeper bring out glasses, spoons and plates. Thereupon we proceed to the shop, reaching it this time by means of a soap box. While we choose one item, the previous one is already being packed. The service is marvelous for a shop so small that we three seem to crowd it out. With equal rapidity the bill is produced. I am about to take it when Ismail Khan interferes. "No, memsahib," he says, "Sahib pay!" He wants to pocket the bill for remission to Rashid. "No, Ismail Khan, I pay." "Mother pays," decides Mary Ann. Very reluctantly he lets me have the bill, counting the change and testing each silver rupee against the stone floor.

On the way home we stop before the friendly cloth shop. Our curtains are waiting for us. How they have managed to hem eighteen pieces in so short a time I fail to understand. Just before we start again I remember another thing. "What about the bare tables?"

"It's so late already, mummy, we have to hurry home."

"But bare tables!" I quickly sum up with my eyes the possibilities of the shop. No table cloths or lace of any kind! Well, something dainty white will do. I snatch some georgette checkered white-in-white and off we drive, the car fully laden.

As soon as we arrive at the bungalow Ismail Khan takes himself off, pointing to the laboratories and saying "sahib." Apparently Rashid needs him. We are left with the one boy, Ghafur, who cannot understand what we want him to do. But when shown the new blue curtains he rises to the occasion in more than one sense and begins to fix them. Mary Ann carries the remaining purchases to her room. I stand with the white georgette stuff in front of three tables of different size, planning to hem these dainty table cloths by hand as quickly as I can, when I see an Indian lady crossing the garden towards out house. Hem or no hem, the tables must be covered! One, two, three cuts, tearing, stretching, finished! When Mary Ann re-enters all the tables are resplendent in their new glory. I hastily explain about the approaching visitor. She takes up the raw edge of one cloth and drops me a little curtsy. "Who has always preached at me about tidiness? And what would grandmother and great-grandmother say if they saw a daughter of the family spread unhemmed cloth? But all the same it looks gorgeous. Thank you, mummy." While holding her to me for a second I try to visualize my mother's and grandmother's attitude. But it is utterly impossible to even imagine either of them in such an unheard-of situation. When has a bride of the family not returned to a home all spick and span prepared by kindly hands?

"I'll get lime juice and biscuits ready. Do receive the lady by yourself. This is your house."

After washing some glasses and plates at the tap outside the kitchen, drying them with a towel that I take from Mary Ann's luggage and resolving to return to the nice shop for many dozens of dish cloths and dusters, I arrange things on a tray, handing it to Ghafur who has meantime emerged from the drawing room. I try to convey as best I can that I shall go in first and he is to follow with the tray. He begins a long and excited speech which is entirely lost on me. From his expression I gather, however, that he does not want to carry the tray. Well, I can't have such nonsense. Were he a high-class Hindu he might object to carrying our food; but he is a Muslim and has no such excuse. I try to look stern and say *"Ao!"*—come—which is one of the few words I remember from our previous journey. He trots behind me with a disapproving expression.

The visitor is seated on the settee with Mary Ann and rises to greet me with joined hands. She is a smiling youngish woman in a white cotton sari with red border and understands a few, very few words of English. She points to one of the semi-detached bungalows

9

as to her home, to herself as Mrs. Lavanyia and talks about her husband as "sahib" in contrast to Rashid whom she calls "burra sahib," by which we understand that he is her husband's boss. Meanwhile Mary Ann has risen to hand her visitor lime juice and biscuits. But the lady declines, again with folded hands and laughs all over her face. Ghafur begins to talk volubly, this time addressing himself to her. Pointing to me, he seems to say that he had refused to take the tray but that I forced him to. Mary Ann, always quick at grasping situations, questions her visitor in one word: "Brahman?"

Mrs. Lavanyia bows smilingly and Ghafur beats his hands together in relief. Mary Ann has guessed right. A Brahman cannot, of course, take food in a Muslim-Christian house.

But Mary Ann does not want to let her first caller go like that. She rushes to her room to produce chocolates which are likewise refused. Wanting to convey that we have nothing else to offer as yet, she opens drawer after drawer, pointing to their emptiness and shaking her head in pretended sadness. The visitor understands perfectly and takes both her hands as though to say that she wants Mary Ann but no food. Suddenly my daughter exclaims: "Fruit! Can you eat fruit?" "Yes," signifies Mrs. Lavanyia. Mary Ann dashes out and returns with two huge mangoes, the rest of our Bombay supply. Just as she is about to apply a knife to one of them the lady cries out: "No!" She points vigorously at knife and plate, shaking her head in token of their joint Muslim-Christian polluting qualities. Then she leads Mary Ann's right hand to take up the remaining mango—which has not yet lain on the plate—and hand it to her, and, in her turn, points out that she will take it home and eat it there.

The whole procedure has endeared Mrs. Lavanyia to me. She seems so full of good will. Again she begins a long speech, her intelligent face all aglow with eagerness. Really, this handicap of not understanding is awful! Between us Mary Ann and I master nine languages with a smattering of some lesser ones thrown into the bargain. What use are they now? We can only shake our heads.

But Mrs. Lavanyia has a brain wave. She sends Ghafur to her bungalow and he returns almost at once with two of her sons, nice boys of eleven and twelve who learn English in school. They are to serve as interpreters. Only now can our conversation be said to start in earnest.

Mrs. Lavanyia says that she and her family are extremely happy to welcome Rashid's wife and her mother. Her sahib and Rashid were school friends. Now the one serves under the other. When Rashid went to Europe for his postgraduate studies Lavanyia saw him off at Bombay. Both husband and wife had been sad to see Rashid, to whose success and qualities they pay the greatest tribute, without a home of his own. That is why they are so glad to behold Mary Ann who will give him home and sons. She is to go to Mrs. Lavanyia for whatever she may need; good grain, a she-buffalo, servants or advice. Rashid has many enemies who will, in one way or another, want to create mischief. Mary Ann should not give them handles by taking them into her confidence. All help or service she may need the Lavanyia household will be honored and glad to render. And will Mary Ann with Rashid and Mother take dinner with them tomorrow night so that they can welcome the bride?

Mary Ann accepts the invitation provided Rashid has not made other arrangements in the meantime. "We shall love to come. It is very kind of you to ask us. How is it that we can eat in your house but you can't in ours?"

Mrs. Lavanyia smiles and answers that Rashid—she calls him either "the burra sahib" or by his full name Dr. Rashid Ali—will explain these things better than she can. She rises to go. "I was very happy to hear that you bought saris, memsahib."

"How do you know? It was only an hour ago."

"The whole of Akbarabad knows by now. They all like you for it. May we now take our leave?"

After their departure Mary Ann and I long to compare notes about all the bewildering things we have been told. But a look at my watch interferes. "One P.M.! Your lunch! Let me get the tins! Will biscuits do instead of bread?"

But when we cross the courtyard to go to the kitchen a salaaming gray-bearded cook meets us. Two kinds of meat, rice and vegetables are on the fire. We retire speechless. What a baffling country! The appearance of a cook was to be expected; but that he starts his work without as much as presenting himself to the mistress of the house is amazing. And where have the eatables come from? Anyhow, lunch is secured.

I prepare to go. There are lots of *tongas*—diminutive gaily painted

Victorian brakes—outside the compound. Ghafur whistles and, a moment later, a *tonga* drives up.

"Do rest after lunch, mummy. You deserve it."

"Same to you, darling!" I look back at Mary Ann standing on her front veranda. Will she always be as happy as she is now?

Later

After an excellent chicken *pilau* and an equally good rest I describe the morning's activities in my diary. But I don't do them justice—it would require many pages to do so. That gradually appearing possessive pride of Ismail Khan in Mary Ann! Is it because his master won such a charming bride or because of our impressive purchases? Indian servants love their masters to throw their weight about; it adds to their own dignity. The man in white muslins who sold us the crockery, wearing one of those little round caps embroidered in gold tinsel, looking every inch a patriarch with his long gray beard! Ismail Khan said "Musulman" and behaved very differently in that shop than in the Hindu; himself displaying different wares to us and feeling obviously quite at home in a Muslim shop. Many black or gray-bearded men in the street wear the same muslin and gold-embroidered caps. If our shopkeeper is a Muslim they must be Muslims too. I've never yet seen such Muslim dress, neither in Egypt nor in Palestine and Syria. Well, I'll soon find out what they are. What unbelievable variety of types and costumes on the market-place of this little town! I don't think I'll ever get tired of watching them.

April 3

Yesterday, while I was still writing, Mary Ann and Rashid came at about 6:30 and I gave them late tea. Mary Ann looked like a *cinquecento* Madonna in her blue sari. Rashid almost burst with pride and happiness. "Do you mind her wearing saris, Mother? She looks so lovely! And it makes her more of the country."

"Of course I don't mind. There's no more beautiful dress for women. No Paris frock can compete."

"But I don't wear it properly as yet. Look, it's always slipping off my head."

"Why should you want to cover your hair?" Rashid looks at

12

glossy brown waves framing an exquisitely shaped little head. "Modern women in India go bareheaded."

"I am terribly old-fashioned then. I like it that way. It makes me feel like Arabian Nights."

"Rashid, you have married a perfect romanticist. Let me tell you that as a child Mary Ann liked nothing better than to dress up in chiffons and gauzes rifled from my drawers, pretending she was a veiled princess either from the East or from Fairyland. I don't think she went even as a grown-up in any other costume to fancy-dress parties. Did you ever, child?"

"Never. I like it best, and no costume looks more beautiful. You mustn't lay the stress on the princess stunt, mummy; my chief delight was being veiled, and feeling remote and mysterious. Now that I have at last my veil, don't tell me to drop it, rather advise me how to keep it on my head."

"I thought I had a western girl for a wife! Next thing you'll say you want to keep purdah!"

"God forbid! I want to get women out of it!" This has always been Mary Ann's dream.

"There is less and less purdah in our days. Hindus don't keep it anyhow and conditions among Muslims are improving quite a lot. Only ignorant people stick to keeping purdah."

"Why don't you ask that nice Mrs. Lavanyia how to keep your sari from gliding?" I suggest to Mary Ann who leaves her hand on her head all the time. "You have no idea, Rashid, how kind and eager to help she was."

"Yes, Mary Ann told me. But, Mother, both of you should be careful if you will forgive me for saying so. Don't trust such people too much. We are not in Europe. They may make mischief by gossiping."

"But she said you were good friends!"

"So we are. I have known Lavanyia all my life. He is a splendid fellow and, though he is a Brahman, he is very devoted to me."

"Have you found his wife so much worse?"

"Found? I have never set eyes on her and probably never shall."

"You have not seen your friend's wife?"

"It's her fault, not mine, darling. Don't look so full of reproach! Mrs. Lavanyia would never dream of appearing before me."

"But she's a Brahman, isn't she?"

13

"Yes, of course, like her husband."

"Then why? Didn't you just say that Hindu women don't keep purdah?"

"They don't. I didn't lie. But there is a long cry between not keeping purdah and appearing before men."

"Well, is not-appearing before men not called purdah?"

"Oh no. Would to God it were! Women in purdah never get any air but in their courtyards. When they drive or go out they wear a *burqa* covering them from head to foot except for slits for the eyes. They can't go shopping by themselves. They can't appear when male servants are present. They must keep to the *zenana*, the female quarters of the house. Mrs. Lavanyia leads a very different life. She moves freely about, her face uncovered. She goes shopping. I have no doubt she sees any servant or tradesman she wants to. But she does not see better class people, her husband's friends. That is all. You can't call it purdah."

"How interesting this all is! Shall we ever be able to understand all these differentiations?"

"You will very soon. By the way, Mother, your initiation begins tonight. My aunt comes after dinner with her two sons, my cousins. You will then see what real purdah means! No male eye except blood relations may see her. And my car must be made purdah —hung with curtains all round—before fetching her."

"Is she the aunt who was so good to you when you were here as a child?"

"Yes, she is. Those six years in Akbarabad were among my happiest, though all was not gold even then. But Auntie was never anything but kind."

"It will be lovely to meet her."

"You may be disappointed. I don't think you have met anybody like her. She is what is termed an ignorant illiterate woman, keeping the very strictest purdah. She has never seen any European. I wonder whether she will feel shy with you. When I went to see her this morning and told her all about Mary Ann she said she'd love her dearly."

"I shall love her too if she lets me. And as for her ignorance: had she had our opportunities she would know all we do or more. Perhaps she does, only other things."

Rashid puts his hand on Mary Ann's. "That a European girl says such things! Mother, how is it you made her so different from anybody else I've ever met in the west!"

"I didn't, Rashid. She made herself. Time and again I've been amazed at my own child."

"Yes, didn't I lead you an awful life, mummy?"

"Just listen to this. When she was about thirteen she fractured her ankle in two places rather badly and had to lie for weeks with her leg suspended, which was very painful. Never did she complain, but said always smilingly: 'Now I've time to think!' And the outcome of this thinking? One afternoon, at a time when she was already limping through the room, of course still heavily in plaster, I found her gone. Gone! Can you imagine my frenzy? At last I saw her walk up to the steep road. She had been to see classmates living half a mile away and had insisted on walking. Why? Because——"

"Now you must let me tell things, mummy. You see, I'd always been very much the 'veiled princess' in my thoughts, very remote and apart from others. I'd been delicate and terribly spoiled both by mummy and nannie, who was still with us. I loved beautiful things and music and lots of books and chocolates and soft voices like mummy's. I hated rushing round and bad smells and unmusical speech. They hurt me. I wanted to protect myself from all ugly things. When I was small I pretended to be an oriental princess retiring behind her veil; later I shut myself off from my classmates, many of whom came from poor homes, for mummy had wisely chosen a famous modern school not tolerating class distinction. Well, when I was in bed for so long, I thought it all out and came to the conclusion that I had to mend my ways and deliberately train myself to do the things I disliked most if I didn't want to grow into a selfish ass. I disliked walking and, still more, walking alone. I disliked the shouts of Rosie's brothers and the cabbage smell and oilcloth of their living room. So I went. It was all quite simple and logical."

"Quite simple! And why didn't you tell Mother? Now I've caught you! You said you always told her everything."

"So I did. But there was nothing to tell before I had carried out my plan, was there?"

Rashid seems overwhelmed less with the past than with the future. "Darling, promise you will no more run such dreadful risks.

15

Now you have a husband, don't forget! If something happened to you——"

"There won't!" Mary Ann speaks in soothing motherly accents. "I promise to be a good girl."

I am on the point of observing that she wasn't particularly bad even then, but I check myself.

Meanwhile it has become much later than we knew. We rush back to dinner, which is served under the stars on a table placed in the center of the big courtyard.

As soon as we have finished Rashid hurries both cook and boy. "Take everything away and go! Auntie will be here soon."

"Then who will serve the fruit and things?"

"Her sons, my cousins. She never allows me to do anything for her."

Mary Ann calls me aside. "Listen, mummy. You know how foolishly people in India think about western women. They say memsahibs are haughty and insist on being served by everybody and never do anything themselves. I want to show that it's not so. I'll serve them myself."

"You are absolutely right, dear. Shall we set the table now so you need only bring the dishes later?"

"No. I'll do all there is to do in their presence. Rashid, where are you?"

"Trying to find two sheets or so to hold up for Auntie's passage from the car to the veranda. She might bring them herself, though."

"No, I don't want that. Here are the sheets. We'll keep them for Auntie's purdah, shall we?"

"Other houses have a special curtain for such occasions. But we'll never have such old-fashioned things."

"Rashid, you are the modern Westerner and I the Oriental. No, darling, not now! I hear the car. Let me go with you to receive her."

"Certainly not, sweetheart. Though you are not in purdah, Auntie would never be able to understand a lady of the family standing on a front veranda not curtained off. You sit at the entrance of the courtyard—no, in its center. She is to welcome you, not you her. I'll bring her up to you."

But when the small white figure sheds her *burqa* and advances towards the courtyard followed by two tall sons Mary Ann cannot contain herself and hurries towards her. One second later they are wrapped in each other's arms. The three men and I look on. Nobody speaks.

Later it is my turn. Auntie clasps me with her right arm and kisses one of my cheeks, then with the left and kisses the other. Finally she brings forward her two sons who take my hand between both of theirs.

The eldest, about five years Rashid's senior, is Waliuddin, the second Faizuddin, who was in charge of the keys. Both wear the Indian *chervani*—long frock coat with stiff upright collar—and the white close-fitting narrow trousers Muslims wear. Auntie tugs at Waliuddin's arm. "We are very happy to welcome you and Sister to our family, Mother." His English is halting, his smile kind and winning.

We sit down round the table, Auntie keeping Mary Ann's hand in hers. But for her brown little face, the heavy golden earrings and necklaces, she is a "Lady in White." The Muslim tight-fitting trousers show her fine legs to far above the knees. She wears a long muslin shirt over a close-fitting bodice and a veil on her head. Her beautiful bare feet have skipped out of her gold-embroidered red velvet upturned slippers.

She looks smilingly at Mary Ann. Then she says something. Mary Ann regretfully shakes her head. Auntie repeats her words for translation. Rashid laughs. The sons begin to argue with her as though they didn't want to translate what she says. Resolutely she takes things in her own hands. With expressive gesture she makes as though to read and to write, pointing questioningly to Mary Ann.

"Mother asks whether it is true that Sister is very learned and can read and write. She cannot believe that Frankish ladies all do."

Smilingly Mary Ann nods assent. "But it doesn't matter, Auntie," she says, abandoning her newly acquired Ph.D. to the winds; "other things matter much more." And she caresses the old woman's hand.

The answer is duly translated to and entirely approved of by Auntie who, again by gestures, asks from Mary Ann whether Mother, too, partakes of such knowledge alien to women.

Mary Ann, with a twinkle in her eye for my benefit, replies: "Mother writes much better than I do. For she even knows how to write books, not only how to read them."

The audience are obviously impressed but not overmuch. "I cannot write or read books," is Auntie's comment. "A woman's book to write and read in are her children and grandchildren. Many pages this book has by the Grace of God. And every day there is something new to read and to write on each."

The two learned women look at each other. Can any book or book-knowledge surpass the simple dignity of these words?

For a moment Mary Ann rests her head on Auntie's shoulder. "I am glad to be here, Auntie."

"We are all glad you are, Sister." This is the bass of Faizuddin. His English seems much more fluent than that of his elder brother.

Both men have kept on their high black fur caps, the predominant Muslim headgear of India. In the West one shows respect by taking off one's hat; in the East by keeping it on. But the air is close. Mary Ann ventures: "Won't you take your caps off? They must be so hot."

"Thank you, Sister. You are very kind. But we cannot do so."

"Rashid is without, in front of his aunt and mother-in-law."

"Oh, I!" Rashid laughs. "I've always been the black sheep of the family. Auntie tolerated me, though." And he translates the words for her.

Mary Ann rises. "Where are you going, Sister?" That is Waliuddin.

"Just to get some fruit."

"No, this is our duty. Do remain seated!" Both men are pleading with her."

"Certainly not yours! If anybody's, then Rashid's. But today I shall serve you."

She has already gone. We see her move about behind the wire gauze of the dining room. Then she turns off its light and, carrying a large tray, steps into the moonlit courtyard.

I look at the four Indians while the bride approaches with her load. They seem spellbound. True, there could be no prettier picture than Mary Ann in her silver-dotted blue sari, her immense eyes in the ivory face full of animation, her happy smile bringing out all three dimples at once. But what keeps them fascinated seems rather to be the fact that this learned girl from the West makes it a point to serve and to honor them.

Rashid seems intoxicated with happiness. He turns to me. "This morning I told Auntie what an angel Mary Ann is. Now she can see for herself."

When the visitors rise to go, Auntie hands money to the bride, which Mary Ann accepts with a kiss. Luckily we have learned on our previous journey that in India a bride is given money, not presents. Otherwise what a shock it would have been!

Auntie tenderly kisses both of us and asks when we shall come for dinner. To our surprise Rashid answers rather vaguely. He will send a message in a few days' time.

Then we four get into the car, Auntie and I duly curtained off. Mary Ann and Rashid stand arm in arm on their front steps to see us off. I deposit Auntie and her sons in a moonlit quarter full of quaint romantic streets and lanes through whose narrowness the car can hardly proceed. When taking his leave Waliuddin says: "We should never have dreamed that memsahibs can be like Sister and you, Mother."

April 4

Mary Ann finds me over my diary. "Listen, mummy, you have hurt poor Rashid very much. He has begged me not to tell you but that's nonsense, since I tell you everything anyhow."

"Good Heavens, what have I done?"

"You've never kissed him yet. He has been waiting for it ever since our wedding. He says that he doesn't expect to get as many kisses as I do that one daily kiss is certainly his due. He says that Auntie looked astonished that you kissed only me and not him good night. And, what is worse, he takes it as a sign that you dislike him."

"Have you not told him that this is nonsense?"

"Of course I did. But you know what Indians are, even Rashid. They all have hidden inferiority complexes coming to light in the most unexpected ways. We have often been discussing this, haven't we? Well, here you have it in practice."

"Yes, I see the point. Somehow they always distrust us."

"Until we have convinced them a hundred times by love and friendship that we mean well." Mary Ann laughs. "How wise we sound, mummy! And we'll need all that precious wisdom of ours. It is much easier to discuss such things with Indian fellow-students at home, than to practice them in India."

19

"I can't see any trace of wisdom in my having made such a mess of things with Rashid. At your wedding I thought much of Daddy. Had he lived he would have patted Rashid on the shoulder and led him to me; it would have been easy then to embrace my son-in-law. Of course I knew I ought to do something of the kind but I felt too shy. Sorry, darling."

"That's more or less the explanation I gave Rashid. But he is afraid that you don't like him, and gives as proof that you prefer staying in the hotel to living with us."

"This would teach 'Punch' not to speak of mothers-in-law as he does! Well, I'd never have thought that Rashid wouldn't understand. It is for his sake much more than for yours that I don't want to spoil your honeymoon more than I can help."

"Oh, you incorrigibly western soul! What am I to do with such a mother! An Easterner wants all his folk around him, the closer the better. You are the first and only mother he has known in his life. Moreover, he is afraid that people might say you stay away from us because you dislike him. You see, in the East a mother is not supposed to be as independent as you are."

"And what does my wise child want me to do?"

"Conform to Rashid's wishes, naturally. It's all right for us to have our own notions about privacy and non-interfering of parents and so on. But we are here. Here people are used to parents' interference. We must gain their trust, so we have to act according to their notions, not ours."

"You are right, darling. Will you take me in, say, the day after tomorrow?"

"Of course, Honored Mother, but you have to learn that age means everything in this country; you should not ask me but simply issue a statement: 'I come the day after tomorrow!' Why not earlier, by the way?"

"Today there is that dinner at Mrs. Lavanyia's, isn't it? And tomorrow at Auntie's, I take it."

"No. I don't know why but Rashid seems to postpone that. He says there'll be a big dinner party given by somebody whose name I have forgotten but who's the greatest man of Akbarabad, and we must wait for that. Come sooner, mummy. There are these three new government servants and I don't like their looks. I want you to back me up against them."

"I think you are doing splendidly. Neither I nor any of our friends at home would have had enough sense to behave as you do, honestly. I am proud of my little girl."

"So you're coming tomorrow?"

"I command you to take me in! Is that all right?"

"Splendid, Honorable Mother."

Bungalow, April 7

For some days I had no time to write. There is a difference between going back to a quiet hotel room all by oneself and the many activities of settling in this house. There are lots of callers. There is the language difficulty; I am afraid we are exploiting the Lavanyia boys, but they seem to feel very proud of their job as interpreters. There are the new servants. Above all, there is the continual need of trying to understand things one does not understand in the least.

Take sweeping and dusting. Somehow we were always too busy to watch activities in the morning. But when, for two days, we had watched Ghafur emerge from the servants' quarters in the rear, at a quarter to four P.M.; seize his broom made of sticks and the duster; proceed to the drawing room and shut doors and windows tightly; use his broom on the carpet and flap his duster in a contemptuous way at the furniture, all in the hermetically shut room; finally emerge with the conviction that cleanliness had been restored: when we'd watched this procedure through the window for two consecutive days Mary Ann interfered. She opened doors and windows while he was "at work." He promptly reshut them. She showed how to dust a chair carefully and shake the dust from the cloth afterwards instead of whirling it up by flapping. He shook his head in disdain of our method. Meantime, the remaining staff had assembled, all of them taking Ghafur's side. Treating us like children who don't know any better, they pointed out that a room can only be cleaned if shut airtight. Even the Lavanyia brothers, hastily summoned, joined the enemy camp. Mary Ann and I finally beat retreat. There is a book we both have read, in which an American-Swiss girl married to a Brahman describes her experiences with her Indian staff. She comes to the conclusion that, whenever she lets her servants have their own way, results are much more satisfying than if she enforces hers. To save our face we say that Ghafur can continue his routine; but woe to him if the room is found dusty.

21

And now comes the miracle; the room is decidedly cleaner after the airtight performance than before! How? We don't know. This is one of the things you try to understand and can't.

Another mystery, though not quite so impenetrable, is Faizuddin's timetable. He is a lesser government official in the grade of only Rs.65/- while Waliuddin draws Rs.90/- for more exalted work. We thought this was very low pay; but Rashid explained that many state officials live on less, quite comfortably considering their requirements, and that Faizuddin is being anyhow much overpaid. I am afraid we have to agree to the last dictum as far as his zeal for office is concerned. Every morning about nine, after Rashid has left, he finds time to call on Mary Ann and me in order to inquire whether he can be of any use. Poetry, shooting and friends seem to be his favorite pastimes. "That is why he can't get promotion," says Rashid. "Auntie and Waliuddin worry terribly over him."

To Mary Ann and me Faizuddin is a godsend. We ask him lots of things and usually get sensible, reliable answers; but we have soon found out that we must not ask anything concerning Hindu life. If we do Faizuddin draws himself up and says there must be, undoubtedly, such Hindu customs, of which he has no knowledge. He and Waliuddin show both in dress and by wearing the old-fashioned pointed beard that they are every inch good Muslims. Rashid with his clean-shaven face and European suits seems from another world.

The first thing Faizuddin did was to teach me my own exalted status. I had inquired after his mother's health: "How is Auntie today?"

"She is well, praise be to the All-Merciful! But forgive me for saying so, Mother: it is not for you to call her 'Auntie.' This is for Sister and Brother to do, and for Waliuddin and myself. You are not one of us: you are of her rank. So you have to address her as 'Sister.' Will you forgive me for having spoken? It ill behooves a younger to correct those above him in rank."

"Forgive? But I'm grateful to you, Faizuddin! Please tell me anything I do wrongly."

"You and Sister can't do any wrong." And he beams toward the door through which Mary Ann enters.

I *must* get, or rather write, that Lavanyia dinner on the 3rd off my chest. It was so interesting and if I wait any longer I forget too much.

Rashid had had to attend a meeting presided over by some member of the Council of State in town for a few days. He said he would fetch us in time for the dinner. But eight became eight-thirty and yet he had not returned. There was a man waiting for him on the front veranda. I didn't look properly at him. He was wearing *khurta* and *dhoti* of snowy white and I had thought he was some lesser employee of the laboratories. On Rashid's return he turned out to be Mr. Lavanyia waiting to escort us to his house. I later asked Rashid about his dress and got the answer that nearly all Indians, both Hindu and Muslims, who wore European suits in daytime adopted the *khurta*—a collarless shirt of finest muslin—after the day's work was over; the Hindus getting into their *dhoti* for further dress, the Muslims into *pyjamas*, as they call their wide white cotton trousers for home wear. It is not a sign of poverty for a man to wear the coarse cotton *dhoti* just as the poorest people do, for this is the Hindu dress prescribed by religion: an uncut, unhemmed piece of cloth.

Mr. Lavanyia takes us to his house, never looking at Mary Ann, only at Rashid. In a smallish room a table covered with a white cloth and surrounded by only three chairs awaits us. The table is not laid. Why? We are late as it is. Surely they expect us, Mr. Lavanyia waiting for us over an hour! And where is our hostess? But I remember that she does not appear before Rashid.

The three of us are left alone. Then the inner door opens. Mr. Lavanyia and his two sons enter, each carrying a round metal tray fully laden. The brothers whom we have seen only in western shirts and shorts wear *khurta* and *dhoti* now. Our host places his tray before me; then he takes the two others in turn from his sons and places them before Mary Ann and Rashid. There are more than a dozen little metal vessels on each, looking like handleless cups of various sizes. Each contains a different kind of food. A generous helping of rice and different bits of relishes and chutneys are on the tray proper. We know how to eat Indian fashion. If we were invited to Indian meals on our previous journey we ate without cutlery with the right hand only, never committing the inexcusable crime of using the left one which is considered unclean. This is not difficult at all; you take a piece of the hot pancake-like bread—*chappati*—into your right hand and use it as a kind of spoon. But so far we had always got a spoon for rice. And, above all, we had never been honored with an invitation to an orthodox Brahman house where outsiders are not admitted to meals, if admitted at all. I try to be on my best Indian behavior and look sideways in order to imitate Rashid. Mary Ann has been invited by fellow students to many a Brahman meal at Hampstead or Bloomsbury and is, therefore, perfectly at ease.

Mr. Lavanyia gives monosyllabic orders to his sons, who reappear in relays with hot bread for each of us. "*Puri!*" says Mary Ann to me, "I have told you how delicious they taste, better than *chappatis*." So they do. *Puris* are apparently also pancakes; but they are crustier, fried in butter, the size of a woman's hand and incredibly good, piping hot as they are brought in. As for the food—only vegetables, cereals, milk and fruit, of course, since Brahmans never defile themselves and their house by meat or eggs—it is simply delicious. I recognize potatoes prepared in three different ways, as well as rice and *dhal*—pulse—the staple food of southern India and people hailing from there. All the other dishes I can't recognize. I do not know what I am eating except that these are delicacies of the first order. There is a dish of something unknown swimming in curd; something else which tastes like jam prepared from fruit of paradise; lots of vegetables I have never tasted; something like *ambrosia* in cream which is so good that Mary Ann and I exchange glances of mute admiration. On our way Mr. Lavanyia had explained that he had instructed his wife not to put sharp spices and curry powder into the food lest Mary Ann and Mother should not be able to eat it thus "hot." What Indians call "not hot" usually burns our mouth and makes us gasp for breath and water. But this time hot spices have really been used with discretion and we can eat everything, or rather only taste it. For when we have but sampled the many dishes we can't eat any more. Rashid's vessels are replenished as soon as he empties them, from other vessels which the Lavanyia brothers, always on the run, hand to their father. We can't empty ours. Remembering Rashid's warning to eat much—if you don't, all eastern hosts think you didn't like the food they provided and take offense —I empty my bowl of a creamy concoction whose refinement of

24

taste is simply indescribable. "Mango-fool" is Mr. Lavanyia's reply to my questioning look when he refills the vessel. "Impossible! We have eaten mango-fool so often. This is a thousand times better!"

"Brahman mango-fool is different!"

When the three of us say we cannot possibly eat more, we wash our hands. One boy holds the basin and soap dish, the other the three towels, while their father is pouring water. Mary Ann and I are relieved that Rashid is first, for we can learn from him how to behave. He has his right hand rinsed until it is clean, whereupon it clasps the soap and manages to get itself lathery without aid of the left hand; then the soap is rinsed before he puts it back and has his final rinse. We follow suit as best we can and I resolve to practise this self-sufficient washing process of one hand only for future occasions.

We rise. When the men move towards the veranda I thoughtlessly make a step or two in their direction. Mary Ann pulls me back. The brothers curtain the door off after the two men have left. Now I understand. We shall see our hostess.

But she comes not alone; with her are about a dozen other ladies. Mrs. Lavanyia advances ceremoniously carrying a round silver tray of intricate and beautiful workmanship on which several small silver objects are placed. She deposits it on the table and begins to take up one little box after the other. First, she paints the round red mark of Hinduism on Mary Ann's forehead. Then she puts a coconut wound with a white thread into Mary Ann's lap; then some grains of rice; then three silver rupees; then *hukum*-red dye. There is no mistaking the meaning of this ceremony but we don't feel embarrassed. Children mean everything in the East, and all good wishes center round this fact. For a woman to be barren is worse than death. Mrs. Lavanyia makes Mary Ann hold up the folds of her sari with all the symbols of fertility and wealth it now contains. Then she takes a lovely silver filigree bottle and anoints her right hand with fragrant rose-attar—oil. Later she garlands her with a heavy garland of Indian jasmine and roses, wound with real silver threads. That is all, as far as I can remember; but I dare say I am mixing up the sequence, for it all goes very quickly and I look on spellbound. Now Mrs. Lavanyia turns to anoint me and garland me likewise; I also get the red *hukum* mark on my forehead. Thereupon we are made to sit down while the other ladies group them-

25

selves on the floor, which has been covered by snowy white linen. Introductions begin with the help of the two sons. The tall lady is Mrs. Motilal, with her sister; both are remarkably good-looking. Mrs. Jarwarkar is the first wife—did I hear rightly?—of the cellulose expert. I do not remember the others; surely we will meet them again soon. There is a storm of questions waiting for us and the poor interpreters have their work cut out. Where did Mary Ann and Rashid meet? How long did they know each other? How is marriage celebrated in Europe? Where is mother's "sahib"? And no other children besides Mary Ann? No brothers and sisters either? Oh!

We explain how the two met several times in London, lost sight of each other and met again; how we decided on a second visit to India when Rashid proposed to Mary Ann and how, all of a sudden, both resolved to marry on arrival in Bombay. But while describing marriage ceremonies in the West we hear our host calling us from outside the purdah. As pre-arranged among the three of us, Rashid says it is time to go. We take our leave, joining our hands in *pranam* —the Hindu greeting which means, as far as I remember, "Our souls touch each other." All the ladies leave the room through the inner door before we do, lest the lifting of the purdah for our exit reveal them to male eyes.

At home we comment on the trouble the Lavanyias have taken for our sake. "Do you realize that they can't use again any vessel or goblet we used? And that they can't even wash up our things in their house?"

"How is it we can eat there but they can't here? Mrs. Lavanyia said you'd explain this to us."

"The chief point is that Brahmans are not to pollute themselve by eating with non-Brahmans or by using the same utensils. T is why they can't eat here; for we would eat at the same tabl serve them on our crockery. But even suppose we didn't, we let them eat alone and on brand-new crockery: they not eat food prepared in this house or use crockery that s on our shelves or went through our hands. Brahman men so mes take a bare cup of tea with me, but they are very careful n to let their ladies know."

"But what about our eating with them?"

"Well, did we? No member of the family ate with us for they

26

can't do so. We had our meal in splendid isolation on special crockery in the parlor—as far away as possible from the courtyard and kitchen they are having their meals in. But Lavanyia did us all the honor he could, for he served us himself instead of letting his sons, let alone servants, do the job. I am sure both he and she'll hear a lot about it from their caste."

We are very impressed with all we have heard. How truly kind the Lavanyias have been to take so much trouble and court their own people's disfavor all for our sake. True, they do it because of Rashid, not because of us. But our obligation remains the same.

It is time to go to bed. I kiss Mary Ann, who pulls my sleeve quite unnecessarily. I haven't forgotten.

Rashid holds out his hand as usual. When I kiss him he stands quite motionless for a moment; then he puts both arms round me and holds me close. "Now I have a mother," he says under his breath.

I feel ashamed for not having had the sense to kiss him before.

～ 2 ～

April 9

WE have three *sircari*—governmental—servants. They are attached to the bungalow, not to Rashid personally; the Superintendent is entitled to three servants to run the bungalow. There is Jagdish, the *chaprassi*, whose place is more or less the front veranda. The *chaprassi* receives callers, carries messages, posts letters and, I think, shops; for, if the ladies of the family are in purdah, servants do all the shopping. All the same, Rashid explained that the *chaprassi* is supposed to do rather the official side of work than work itself. Jagdish sweeps of his own accord drawing room, study, front veranda and part of the cloister surrounding the big inner courtyard; but he stops where the dining room begins, for he is a Brahman, a first-class Brahman and we call him "maharaj." This is a respectful mode of address to one of his rank, and all first-class Brahman servants are addressed thus. Hindu households able to afford a cook will always

27

engage a first-class Brahman to prepare their food according to the sacred laws although they themselves may be of lower caste than he.

In the ordinary way a Muslim-Christian household like ours would not come by a Brahman servant; but this is a Hindu State and the government officials and servants are Hindus with a wee sprinkling of Muslims under which heading Rashid falls.

Maharaj reads the Sublime *Gita* for about two hours every day on our front veranda. "Would you ever have believed that I'd have a Brahman chanting the *Gita* and sacred hymns in my service, mummy?" says Mary Ann, the part-time student of Europe's best Indologists. "It is like a dream!" So it is.

We are careful not to interfere with arrangements before we understand the mysterious motives behind them better than we do now. The *khansama*—cook—sweeps the cloister from maharaj's terminus along the dining room, the pantry we have freshly installed and the kitchen. He is a Muslim, of course. Ghafur, our own servant, does Mary Ann's bedroom; the dressing room which she shares with me; Rashid's dressing room; both bathrooms. He waits at table together with the *khansama*.

One of the two other *sircari* servants is the *chowkidar*—night watchman—a tall *Rajput* by the name of Tejsingh. He appears at six P.M. to relieve maharaj and guards the house at night. His headquarters are the front veranda, but every hour he starts on his rounds. In the morning he does my room before leaving. Because of snakes he carries a long staff. There are lots of them in our compound; government doesn't grant enough money for undergrowth and weeds to be controlled, and so the snakes have many hiding places. Rashid beseeches us to be careful. There is a serum against cobra- and Russels viper-bite, but none against the deadly little *krait*.

The *mali*—the gardener—the third of our *sircari* servants is said to be the best snake-killer; he breaks the backbone with a stone. He is a middle-aged man called Ram Pershad. He too is a Brahman but, it seems, not of so high a rank as Jagdish. People address him also as "maharaj" but Rashid doesn't; so we follow suit. He arranges the flowers in all vases every morning; we learned on our previous journey that in India the gardeners and not the mistresses do this job. And how well they do it! The same genius for color and proportion prevalent in Indian crafts and home industries lives in the works of art created daily anew by the simple gardeners.

28

I'd like to write more but there are visitors all the time.

April 10

"Dak—mail—memsahib."

Maharaj cannot read Latin writing, so he brings the letters to me to sort out.

"Take these to memsahib, maharaj."

"Choti memsahib?"

Choti means small, little. India, like the Orient as a whole, respects age and precedence above everything. In a State the senior maharani is the "burri maharani," the great one or just "the" maharani, while her junior colleague is the "choti maharani." Were Rashid's father here he would be the sahib or the burra sahib; Rashid would only be chota sahib. As it is I am the memsahib and Mary Ann the choti memsahib. But I don't like it. This is her house, not mine.

"To memsahib, maharaj. My daughter memsahib is."

"Thou mother art. Thou great memsahib."

"No, maharaj. House hers is. She memsahib is. Her mother I am."

"Masahib?"

Maharaj has found the solution. *Ma* means mother. An hour later everybody calls me by my new name. Only Ismail Khan says ostentatiously "Mother sahib." Is it to show off his English? Or is it because a Hindu and not he gave me the name masahib? Somehow I feel as though Ismail Khan, Rashid's co-religionist and trusted servant for years, dislikes maharaj profoundly.

April 11

Yesterday the "big" dinner at the "big" man's took place. He is Seth Chandralal Premchand, the uncrowned King of Akbarabad and, perhaps, the whole State. His Highness values him very much. Delhi does too, apparently, for he is due to be knighted next year or so. He owns the mills of Akbarabad and, I believe, others near Rampore, the capital.

Rashid had told us to put on "full war paint," minus the paint, of course. He's delighted at our both not making-up and does not want to believe that at home we do! So I've donned a creation of cyclamen and silver while Mary Ann put on one of the saris Rashid gave her; pale lemon chiffon, heavily embroidered in gold and crystal, with a gold brocade blouse and golden sandals. To me this ensemble looks like a disguise, for one of her best points is her girlish charm which does not need regal attire. But she looks absurdly young in spite of it. Rashid is lost in admiration. Whereupon we both protest that, tonight, he is the best-looking of the family. For the first time we see him in a white silk *chervani*. How much better his finely chiseled features are brought out in this way! He carries the ceremonial Muslim black fur cap under his arm, for at an official function—that is what the dinner party amounts to—he has to wear it.

When we arrive in front of the biggish house Mary Ann and I are nearly taken aback before the grandeur which awaits us in this small town. The party is held on the lawns, not in the house. A very wide expanse—later I hear it is the two hard tennis courts combined—has been covered with gorgeous carpets, predominantly red. Settees and armchairs form pleasant groups. All guests are assembled already, presided over by the *subha*—collector—who from his seat of honor overlooks the whole scene. The host's private secretary waits for us near our car, the host at the beginning of the carpet. He is placing Mary Ann to the collector's right with himself on her other side, me to the collector's left with Rashid as my neighbor. Drinks are served, Mary Ann and I asking for soft ones as usual. I chaff Rashid about his whisky, threatening to tell Auntie; for drink is strictly forbidden to any follower of the Prophet. We want to laugh together but the collector begins to talk to me. He is a nice elderly Hindu and tells me in excellent English how they all appreciate Rashid as scientist and friend. I feel maternal pride and explain in reply that we had been deeply impressed by Rashid's ideas concerning social and welfare work; and that we were keen to see them put into practice as soon as possible. Meanwhile Seth Chandralal, our host, has taken up some of the other guests for introduction to Mary Ann. Now he brings them over to me. I can't remember any name or even face. There is the *naib-subha*, the collector's understudy; the Superintendent of Police and his Deputy Superintendent; the City Magistrate; the Superintendent of Public Works; the Superintendent of the Governmental Hospital with two or three medical colleagues; quite a number of rich textile *seths*—that is what Rashid tells me—and the Inspector General of Education. I note that there is nobody representing the Akbarabad B.A. and M.A. College, nor the newly started Teachers' Training College. And I note another thing too; apart from us there is no woman!

All the men are dressed in *chervanis,* mostly of white silk, with a few black ones between. Only the host is in dinner jacket, probably in our honor. They wear elaborately wound multi-colored turbans, the *seths* the little pink tightly-wound berets I noticed on our journey. Apart from Rashid's there is only one black fur cap, which indicates that there is only one other Muslim present.

All the men say friendly words of welcome and the whole atmosphere is one of benevolence and well-being. It is a lovely sight. A huge drawing room has been shifted to the garden; we are surrounded by well-sprinkled lawns and roses, by flowering trees and ever-changing fragrance. We face the house; tonight it is nothing but background. Concealed searchlights illumine both garden and guests. But they do not disturb. The stars of the tropical sky dominate the scene.

When the butler announces dinner we don't move towards the house but walk leisurely across the lawn, along a well-kept path gleaming white in the searchlights and then through a rose garden. At last we reach our goal. On a second carpeted lawn surrounded by hundreds of rose bushes, a huge table decked with silver and crystal awaits us; the most beautiful dining room I've ever seen.

Our host takes the head of the table. Mary Ann and Rashid sit to his right, and I and the collector to his left. The others take their seats, presumably according to rank, for those at the far end of the table are certainly the youngest present. Dinner is being served at once. I recognize the hotel manager and some of his staff—European food is prepared for us, and so the hotel was called in. Since our host is a *Jain,* food is strictly vegetarian. But we are served with six to eight impeccable European courses, plus all sorts of things in small silver vessels standing in front of each guest; salted unknown nuts and known almonds; all sorts of mysterious salted cereals, some solid, some reminding me of puffed rice. There is no wine, but orangeade and ginger beer are served. I talk with the collector in answer to his cautious but unmistakable questioning as to Mary Ann's and my background. What was my husband? And my father? As I tell of my childhood in Francis Joseph's Vienna and of its rich and graceful culture, the whole scene seems to me unreal, as though I watched it on the stage, as though I were a spectator and not an actor. Here I am in the middle of India, talking of Imperial Vienna to an unknown man at a table surrounded by other unknown people whose true feelings are hidden from me. One of them is my child's husband. Richard, father, mother—you and my friends who are with you in the worlds beyond—do help us to find our way in this new and unknown life! Whilst thinking these thoughts the feeling of unreality disappears and I become aware of an affectionate smile from across the table. It is Rashid, wanting to catch my eye. Suddenly I feel at home.

Seth Chandralal rises for the toast to the bridal couple. It is a carefully prepared speech he reads out. He deals at length with Rashid's manifold merits; his scientific qualifications which not only are the highest in this State but are shared with him by only a few in the whole of India; his research work with its many ramifications: cellulosis out of bamboo fiber, vegetable oils, cotton research, sugar research and the benefit the State is deriving and will still further derive from this research; the fatherly interest His Highness takes in Rashid, who is an outstanding ornament and credit to the State; the esteem and affection Rashid has won for himself both from his colleagues in the Municipality and the town in general. All who felt themselves Rashid's friends had been proud of his friendship but sad to think that a man so deserving of the best in life was alone, with nobody to make him happy and look after him.

Now the speaker turns to Mary Ann. He says they have heard about her many accomplishments, so astounding in a girl of twenty-three: her Ph.D., her thesis considered important enough to be published in installments in a learned journal; her social and welfare work, especially the aid she gave refugees in many ways in spite of her youth. They have also heard of her and her mother's previous journey through India and the amount of well deserved honor accorded to Mother on that occasion, with Mary Ann to share in it. Thinking of these accomplishments and status, they were, if it was permitted to speak quite frankly, taken somewhat aback when first hearing about the marriage. They were afraid that such accomplished ladies from the West might find life in this upcountry town too restricted in scope and too dull; and also afraid that, not feeling satisfied with conditions, they would make Rashid dissatisfied as well. This has often been the case if an Indian married a western girl; but it is not right to blame such consequences on the European partner who has been brought up in ways unsuited to life in real India, where she cannot easily be happy. It was, therefore, with a certain apprehension mixed with their joy that they looked forward to making Mary Ann's and Mother's acquaintance. Only the joy, however, remains. For in spite of being such accomplished and even famous ladies from the West both Mary Ann and Mother have already won the hearts of the townspeople by their modesty and gentleness. If anybody had feared they would be proud and stand-offish he has been disproved. Both ladies extend their courtesy and kindness to everybody and this is deeply appreciated by high and low. It is true that they are thousands of miles away from their own relatives and friends; they should not, however, consider themselves alone. Rashid's friends are now theirs, not only for his merits but for theirs. And they are needed, sorely needed. "We know we have much to learn. Education is lacking. So is social spirit and welfare work. Women are living in purdah. Purdah means ignorance and ill-health for India. We men cannot change these conditions. Only educated women can, a woman who enlightens her untaught sisters behind the purdah. It is for you, Mrs. Rashid Ali, with your many accomplishments and your kindness of heart, to teach our women and take them out of purdah, that cancer on the body of our fair motherland."

There is a prolonged burst of applause along the whole table. Nobody seems to pay much attention to the speaker's closing sentences. When Mary Ann's clear voice says: "I promise you I'll do all in my power to help women out of purdah" there is much clapping and renewed approval. How progressive these men seem! It's too good to the true!

Rashid rises to reply to the speech. He has discarded the fur cap. His well-groomed head and proud bearing come out to full advantage. He looks like one of his handsome Arabian ancestors who rode into India many centuries ago—minus the beard, of course. I discover my son-in-law to be a really good *extempore* speaker. He seems deeply affected by his happiness and the tributes paid to him by his elders, but he keeps his voice steady throughout. He speaks of the hard life behind him. Though he comes from one of the best and oldest families in Islam with a pedigree of many hundred years, he had to fight with his guardian to be allowed education, very much unlike Mary Ann and myself. Until his fourteenth year he had learned nothing but to recite the Holy Koran; this seemed enough education for the upcountry family village in which he grew up. When he finally got his way, he went to school in Akbarabad; but later he had to pay back every penny spent on his education, as many Indians have to—perhaps because education is not yet considered as indispensable as bed, board and clothes which every family provides for children. Always has he been full of ambition, for himself and for India; always has he wanted to work for the education and progress of his country, and to fight communalism, her worst enemy. Enjoying perfect communal harmony in Akbarabad—a remarkable fact due to His Highness' enlightened attitude towards all his subjects, whatever their denomination—he knew that all those present agree that communalism must be overcome if India is to prosper. There are so many realms of life to be developed! Personally speaking, he has not been able to do so much, so far, in spite of the kind words said about his merits. But now, his loneliness having come to an end and with such a helpmate at his side, he will be able to give his best. It is considered bad taste to speak about the achievements of one's own wife: but he would commit a sin of omission were he not to tell his friends of her all-round knowledge and tolerance far beyond her years which, always anew, astonish and impress him, the much older man of science. He feels his life beginning only now. This new life has brought him, apart from his wife, his mother. Not hers only, but his. He regards her as such. There is no need to speak about Mother's merits and distinctions about which they have had the opportunity to read on several occasions. What matters is to have somebody like Mother with them, somebody who has studied and understood the majority of races and denominations and is thus the embodiment of enlightened tolerance. With her and Mary Ann's help Rashid hopes to live up to his friends' belief in him. He expresses his own and his family's grateful thanks for the wonderful welcome given them by Seth Chandralal, the collector and all of them.

When Rashid sits down his eyes are wet. It must be one of the high lights of his life. So much genuine friendship and affection round him—and Mary Ann! How proud he must feel to hear expressed in front of her the great regard his people hold him in! He looks at her, then at me. His face, usually lined beyond his years, seems young today. Dear Rashid! For me too this is a great moment. The three of us feel closer than before.

As soon as our car begins to move out of the *seth's* compound, Mary Ann asks: "Where are the wives and daughters of the men who are so keen to fight purdah? Why didn't they bring them?"

"They wouldn't dream of it!"

"But they said——"

"But they clapped——"

"Mother and Mary Ann, my dear ones both, *do* try to understand, though it's disappointing, I know. We Indians talk and talk, but we don't do things. That's why India is as she is."

"Don't you dare to speak ill of Indians in front of us, you bad man!"

"Well, they might change with you to make them, sweetheart. Is that more acceptable?"

But we know that his words cannot be laughed away.

April 12

We are still speaking about the dinner at Seth Chandralal's and asking Rashid about things we can't understand. With the exception of the wives of two European members of the Council of State (if on tour in Akbarabad), or Bombay ladies who happen to be visiting, women never appear at such functions. The two lady doctors of the *Zenana* Hospital, one a Bombay Parsi, the other a Madrassi Brahman —which means that they have been brought up in modern ways— are never invited except to purdah parties. Why? That's how it has always been. Are they club members? Of course not. Women aren't.

The professors of the College and the Teachers' Training College? They are not invited to such functions, which are strictly limited to high officials, rich industrialists and shop-wallas plus persons of distinction who may be in town. They are, however, welcome and popular members of the club together with the smaller fry like Lavanyia and the junior hospital doctors. Why are they not invited? Are they not the best educated people in town, in some ways far superior to industrialists and rich cloth merchants? Of course they are. Rashid, the modernist, makes no bones about it. "I hate all these barriers and distinctions. The sooner we get rid of them the better."

He puts his theory into practice. It is a sight for sore eyes to

35

watch him deal with his many callers. He makes it a point to receive humble people with the same or greater courtesy than "burra sahibs," a fact which endears him to both of us more than we can say.

April 13

It is very hot. People on the boat kept asking why we had chosen the hot season to come out. Our plan had been to travel right up to Kashmir which we had to miss on our first journey. We were to spend the hot season there and also visit the all-important excavations in Mohenjo Daro, while Rashid was to work hard in his laboratories. Later we were to have met in some hill-station not too far from Akbarabad to decide about future plans. Instead of all this we are here and it is hot.

My room giving on the front veranda where *chowkidar* sleeps or, rather, is supposed not to sleep, I don't keep my chief door open at night which makes the smallish room stuffy in spite of its fan. Rashid and Mary Ann sleep out in the courtyard. In India—as perhaps everywhere in hot climates—one's bed is not a fixture as it is at home in Europe. After sunset servants ask for today's orders, and beds are moved accordingly. One sleeps on this veranda or that, in the courtyard, front garden or cloisters, on the roof and, at times, even in one's own bedroom. This daily tribal migration is most entertaining because it constitutes the same reliable topic of conversation as weather does at home. Will tonight's breeze—if any—be caught best to the north or east of the house? Will the morning chill be too much for sleeping out in the courtyard? Are blankets necessary or portable fans? Cold or hot?

There is no end to fascinating speculation and reports of own cleverness, so much so that the game reminds me of golfing or fishing yarns. Also you can always tell your kith and kin "I told you so!" and they tell you exactly the same thing in return. An aviator flying low at dawn would see many a dishevelled figure carry bedding and even mattress into the house for further slumber while the rest of the tribe sleep on outside. Rashid and Mary Ann have to carry no burden; a second set of beds and bedding awaits them inside.

Rashid took it for granted that I'd sleep out in the courtyard, too. When Mary Ann told me so we both commented on his kindness, and on the different views of privacy held in East and West. She transmitted my reply: thanks and no.

But Rashid wasn't satisfied. "Mother, I can't feel happy outside if I know you don't get a breath of fresh air in that room of yours. The courtyard is so big! You could take the farthest side. Believe me, we'd never disturb or see each other."

"It is very sweet of you to think of it. But you know how we people are. Both Mary Ann and I'd feel terribly uncomfortable."

"If *I* don't feel uncomfortable why on earth should your own daughter? You have slept in the same room for twenty-three years."

"I'm afraid we haven't. We always had separate rooms. We even knock at each other's door. Really, dear, I can't possibly sleep in the same courtyard."

"Why?"

"It is difficult to explain. We *are* like that. Call it self-consciousness, if you like. Mary Ann would keep on wondering what I hear and think. I'd know that and should feel awful. Both of us wouldn't sleep."

"Yes, Mother is right. It's simply not possible."

With Mary Ann on my side Rashid has to give in. "But promise that you'll come out if it gets too hot for you to bear; or would you prefer to sleep on the roof?"

He is a dear.

April 15

Commotion at the back door. There are ladies, including Mrs. Lavanyia; lots of children; many servants. All are talking to our *mali* who motions them to speak softly.

It is 3 P.M.; the men are in the laboratories. What can this mean? Why does the crowd come through the back door?

The Lavanyia brothers explain. Among the many snakes of the compound there is a cobra of huge size. A few minutes ago he has been perceived on our lawn outside the front veranda. *Mali*, the expert snake-killer, is ready to kill him if such are Mary Ann's orders. But they have all come to beseech Mary Ann not to have him killed. It would mean ill-luck, if not worse, to the whole compound. Men owe gratitude to the cobra, perhaps not in far-off countries, but certainly in India.

Mary Ann is at once at the height of the situation. "We know

37

what the cobra did for Lord Krishna, and that we must do him honor."

"Didn't I tell you memsahib would understand in spite of her being from beyond the Black Waters?" Mrs. Lavanyia looks proud.

"He comes only for milk," says the mistress of one of the bungalows; "he never touches any one if he gets it."

Mary Ann nods assent. "Of course he will get his milk. He is my guest, isn't he?" Then, remembering the Jungle Book: "This is *nag*— is his *nagina* also here?"

"There is no *nagina* in the compound, memsahib." Her unexpected knowledge fills them with wonder.

"Ghafur, get one cup of milk! No, wait! I'll go myself if I am hostess to *nag*."

When Mary Ann reappears with a deep handleless cup in both her hands we all follow her to the front veranda. Here *mali* wants to take the cup from her. But she shakes her head. "I'll take it myself."

I've never yet lived through a similar moment. What am I to do? Stop her? Perhaps I could, not through authority but through pleading. I could say the simple truth: she is my only child and all I have. And Rashid loves her so.

But I don't. I have no right to. Her life is her own. If she follows the kindness and wisdom of her heart there can be no danger. It is as though, in this moment, she were one with the soil and soul of India.

We look into each other's eyes, feeling securely rooted in our lifelong comprehension of each other. Both of us are deeply religious, though not in a "churchy" way. Christ means everything to us. In crucial moments we are, therefore, quite without fear.

A smile on her lips, Mary Ann slowly crosses the garden-path with the cup and sets it quietly on the lawn. Then she returns. Silently the whole crowd re-enters the house. Nobody is permitted to see the cobra take his meal. They move into the courtyard. But before leaving, each one, not only the servants but also the ladies from the bungalows, bow down to touch Mary Ann's feet.

Half an hour later *mali* brings the empty cup. Mary Ann directs it should be kept apart for similar occasions. "It really seems we are at last in real India, mummy!" says she.

38

This morning Rashid had to leave, very much against his will. His Highness is on tour and wants to meet him at Nullgarh, where a big sugar factory is to be erected in accordance with Rashid's recommendations. His absence will last four days. He had to take the car, and we lead a quiet life. The parting was hard on both of them.

Mary Ann and I are dealing with our neglected mail. Since our arrival we had practically no time to write letters; so we are using Rashid's absence to make amends to our friends at home. Mary Ann enjoys writing to her professors about her wedding and life in "real India." She says she'll write a second thesis in a few years' time about "East-West relations in practice."

April 18

Faizuddin comes with a dinner invitation for tomorrow. Auntie complains that we've found time for other people but not for her. Now Rashid is away there is no excuse.

We accept with joy. Auntie has impressed us deeply, and we long to see her at home "reading the book of children and grand-children."

There is a wire from Rashid. He'll return in two days' time.

April 21

It is night when we set out for dinner at Auntie's in a gay one-horse *tonga*. There are no street-lamps, but the waning moon and, especially, the starry sky light the way sufficiently. The streets of the Muslim quarter are so narrow that they remind one of some of those *calle* in Venice through which a single gondola can just pass. I quite understand now why Ismail Khan couldn't drive up to Auntie's door the other day. In a *tonga* we do. Faizuddin makes us climb four or five wooden steps by means of something which suggests a chicken's ladder. Later we learn that this is the *zenana* entrance; the men's entrance is palatial in comparison. The last step brings us to a narrow slit in the wall, hung with a heavy curtain. A hand stretches out to lead us in. It is Auntie, waiting behind the purdah. Her incredibly soft hand is guiding us through what seems to be utter darkness. I sense more than I see goats, a cow or two, geese and chicken. Then we step out into a middle-sized courtyard, not paved like ours but with uneven mud floor. Auntie takes us to where two lamps are burning on a smallish table. Only then does she stop to kiss us on both cheeks. Waliuddin appears from the darkness and makes us sit down on two quite comfortable wooden armchairs. There are no more about. Both Auntie and he remain standing.

Just before starting from home, Mary Ann and I had renewed the vow we have made our guiding star for life in India: not to interfere with Indian customs and doings. Yet, when Mary Ann jumps up to offer Auntie her chair, I feel it is just the right thing to do. Such is the inconsistency of human nature.

Auntie laughs all over her face and puts Mary Ann forcibly back into her chair.

"Mother says she cannot sit while Mother and you are our guests, Sister," is Waliuddin's explanation.

"But then we have to leave at once, Waliuddin." Mary Ann has not yet made up her mind to address him as "Brother," the usual mode of address between cousins. "Do you really think we'll sit comfortably all evening while you two are standing?"

"We won't stand all the time, Sister. When Mother and you have had your meal we shall sit down."

"Why not before?"

"To do you honor, Sister. It is a great day for our humble home to receive for the first time ladies from the West. Before you came to Akbarabad, none of us had ever talked to a European lady."

"But we are now of your family"—she makes an effort—"Brother. You should not treat us ceremoniously like strangers."

"Just because you have honored our family by entering it we should treat you better than we do strangers, Sister. Do remain seated, I pray."

There's nothing we can do but meekly accept the situation. Too late we remember our vow. Whenever we violate it, the defeat is ours. India is stronger than mere interlopers.

Subdued, we sit in splendid isolation, watching a table being placed before us by two very young bedraggled-looking servant boys. A white cloth is being spread. Basin and jug appear. The servant hands the jug to Waliuddin, who pours water over our hands. Faizuddin holds the basin, Auntie soap and towel. When we have cleansed ourselves—a religious custom before meals wherever Muslims live—the two little servants bring dish after dish to the courtyard's inner door, beyond which there seems to be another courtyard. Faizuddin takes them over, carries them to Waliuddin, who sets them on the table before us. This indeed is honoring us.

Auntie, superintending the whole show with a benign smile, makes Faizuddin translate for us. "We have asked your cook how your western food is. So we have put but few chillies and spices into things, because we know you call our food too spiced. And here is the raw food you like so much. Look!" She proudly produces sliced tomatoes and cucumbers.

"How sweet of you to think of it, Auntie! But I am sure we'll love everything."

"So we shall, Sister," I say, trying to forget what Rashid would say if he saw us eating tomatoes certainly not disinfected with permanganate. As for Mary Ann and myself, we had already decided before our first journey to India to be sensibly cautious but rather to take risks for ourselves than the one of being impolite and refusing food kindly offered. We have to eat these tomatoes, come what may. As in the more dramatic case of the cobra, we understand each other. I think it is this attitude of ours which has made Indian contacts easy for us. Orientals are extremely sensitive, and writhe inwardly over rebukes and insults for days and years.

We eat delightful mutton *pilau*, reminding us of the best we tasted in Muslim countries or eastern Europe; lots of other meat concoctions, including quail and grouse, all too spiced to our taste, however; lovely curds, pale green with cucumber slices or dark with chopped dill, both refreshing in the extreme after the spiced meat; jellies reminding of red currant; rose jam of incredible flavor.

Halfway through, Mary Ann can't bear it any longer. "If you don't now sit down with us, Auntie, we'll stop eating, won't we, mummy?" She takes Auntie's hands and coaxes her as though she were to cry if Auntie didn't sit down. In the end everybody laughs. A third chair is produced for Auntie, finally a fourth for Waliuddin. Faizuddin is the only one to remain standing, being a younger brother. We leave it at that. Asia cannot be conquered in one evening. We have done enough for today.

The five of us are still alone. Rashid had spoken of lots of children in Auntie's house, some of whom he likes very much. Where are they? There must be their mothers, too. Rashid says that, to his knowledge, both Waliuddin and Faizuddin have only one wife each. He has seen Faizuddin's lady, heavily veiled; the wife of the eldest never appears. Then there are many other men, women and children in the house, all relatives from Auntie's village. Where on earth are all these people stowed away? They must be dying to see Mary Ann. Better not ask, though.

Faizuddin opens the after-dinner conversation. "We hear a lot of talk about you, Sister."

"Tell me!" Mary Ann is as eager to know as Faizuddin to tell. "What do people think of us?"

"In the bazaars they all say that you are uncommonly modest and chaste, not only for a lady from the West but even compared to the most pious daughters of Islam."

For a moment we are both knocked over by this truly astounding comment, calmly delivered by Faizuddin and listened to with approval by the others. Feeling that it should not be left to the young bride to go into details, I ask: "How is it that the bazaar people know so much about Mary Ann? She can't speak to them, practically."

"They see enough to know. Sister is always polite and gentle to everybody, however lowly as compared to her own rank and station. What makes them approve of her is the way she always holds her sari together under her chin lest her head be uncovered. This is a token of great modesty."

It is hard to remain serious during this eulogy. I look down so as not to encounter Mary Ann's eyes, expecting she is doing the same. In reality she hasn't yet learned to master her sari gracefully: that's why she keeps one hand at her throat when in the bazaars. That a defect is turned into virtue, that a modern girl from the West is praised for "chastity and modesty" by the most conservative of Indian communities—the Muslim—is, apart from anything else, rather funny.

Auntie waves her hand, apparently to the darkness outside the kerosene lamps' radius. Suddenly the darkness becomes alive. Dozens of persons seem to emerge from nowhere and, in their wake, some goats, portly geese and rabbits. It is as though Auntie were the Pied Piper. With one movement of her little hand a long retinue of followers comes into being.

There are about a dozen women, some dressed like Auntie in white muslin, some with colored veils, some with both vividly colored long shirts and veils. All of them wear white trousers, tight-fitting below the knee. They are not being introduced to us and we are left to wonder who is who. There are also an uncle (Auntie's generation) and two cousins, all from her village. They take our hands in both of theirs and make welcoming speeches before seating themselves near, though not at, our table. A few string cots are brought for the audience to squat upon cross-legged. They look at us, taking in every detail of our appearance, especially Mary Ann's. Some smile at us in a friendly way. None dares talk.

If they don't, their children do. About half a dozen toddlers scramble round Auntie, climbing up her knees, tugging at her trousers and veil. With a baby seated on each arm, kissing both in turn, she seems perfectly happy—"reading and writing her woman's book." But one of the toddlers, a lovely little boy with an aureole of almost fair curls, strides over to Mary Ann, finger in mouth. After a minute or so of close scrutiny he seems to decide that she has passed the test, climbs upon her lap without further ado and nestles against her, thoroughly contented.

This charming spontaneity breaks the ice all round. "Look at Akbar! He is the first to kiss Auntie Mary Ann!"

There is general laughter and clapping of hands. Akbar seems to be a great favorite, and no wonder. In his little white shirt as only garment, he looks a perfect angel against Mary Ann's soft pink sari.

By the law of imitation the other toddlers follow suit. They lean against Mary Ann's knees, all clamoring to be taken up. But she doesn't want to relinquish Akbar, who has gone to sleep peacefully against her shoulder; so she caresses the others with her free hand and laughs at their futile efforts to dislodge him.

Auntie, bereft of the toddlers but busy kissing the two babies, leans over to me; "It will be sweet for thee, Sister, to have grandchildren. There is nothing sweeter." For the first time she gives me the *tum*, comparable to the French "*tu*."

"Akbar is Faizuddin's youngest," explains Waliuddin. "But he doesn't know it. The other day somebody asked him to whom he belonged, and he ran up to me."

"That comes from spending all your time away from home,

43

Faizuddin," chaffs Mary Ann. "Your own son doesn't know you! How many more have you got?"

Tribal divisions are disclosed before our eyes. Faizuddin has four, Waliuddin, five: the others belong to Auntie's village relatives or are nondescripts. It is now the turn of the eldest among them to greet the bride. Hamid, Waliuddin's first born, a handsome lad of fourteen in a far too showy brocaded pink *chervani* and a fez recites an Urdu poem he has composed for Mary Ann. Waliuddin translates with visible pride. The bride is being likened to both new and full moon, to a nightingale, a rose and the Fountain of Wisdom. Her mother is the "Star of the West," whatever that may be, whose rays have led rose, nightingale, etc., to the East. As far as I can make out, this must be one of those flowery poems on strictly Persian pattern. Hamid glows with pride when both of us duly thank him. So does his father—where is his mother?—and, above all, Auntie.

Not to let him reap all the harvest, another boy produces a quotation from the Holy Koran, prettily illumined by himself. "Thank you very much indeed," says Mary Ann. "I'll have it framed in gold and hang it over my desk."

"And what will you frame my drawing in?" asks Faizuddin's eldest. "I've copied the Father of your Country, so you should not feel lonely out here." And proudly he produces a remarkably good pencil portrait of—Franklin Delano Roosevelt!

We are completely nonplused. After such great effort, how are we to disclose that we are not Americans? The decision, however, is taken from our hands. Faizuddin explains: "We know, of course, that your country is Australia, not America. But there was no photograph to be had of the Father of Australia. America is next to your country, so we took the Father of America."

That's that. Austria is often mixed up with Australia in this part of the world. After all, Faizuddin and his son did the best they could for us. Given a choice between Chamberlain and Lebrun, we'd certainly choose Roosevelt. We distrust appeasers who, blind to reality, lead the world to disaster.

After this interlude I take a good look round. The smaller children have been put to bed meantime in the simplest manner imaginable: six of the toddlers lie huddled against one another on one cot, four of the bigger ones on another. Pillows, sheets, nightshirts don't

44

seem to be necessary. They are sleeping peacefully under the stars, unmolested by all the talk around them.

Only the more or less grown-ups are left. A very thin woman with a beautiful but emaciated face places a big silver *pan*-box before Auntie's feet. Auntie squats on the ground to prepare *pan*, chewed after every meal by Muslims and most Hindus, and invariably served as mark of esteem to guests and officials. Betel-leaf is spread with quicklime and *catechu;* astringent betel-nut, chopped, is placed on it together with cardamom and other fragrant spices; the little green packet is rolled in a triangle, secured with a clove used as pin, and chewed at length. The combination of leaf-juice, *catechu*, nut and lime brings about a brilliant red color, staining the mouth—not to mention streets and walls, for *pan*-chewers have a habit of spitting all over the place, because of the *pan's* astringent qualities.

"It is Faizuddin's wife," Auntie answers, when I inquire who has brought the box.

Auntie serves me ceremoniously with *pan*, whose taste and looks I loathe. On our first visit to India I devised a method to deposit the triangle deep down between cheek and jaw, throwing it out of the car window as soon as we got away. It works, if the interval between *pan*-ceremony and exit is not too long. Not knowing, however, how soon we can leave tonight I keep the *pan* in my hand, talking nineteen to the dozen so nobody will detect my malingering.

The lamps are burning quite low now, while the starlit sky seems more dazzling than ever. At home we behold the Milky Way on blessed summer nights; here the whole sky seems one huge global Milky Way. Against the tissue of a myriad needlepoint stars, shines forth the pattern of familiar constellations.

Mary Ann bends to me: "Mummy, isn't it unbelievable that we are now here among these people, that they have opened home and heart to us? How could we ever explain to our friends at home an evening like this? Look!"

She is right. How could we ever explain in Normandy or Holland, in Hampstead, Belgravia, South Kensington, in Paris, Vienna, Prague or Schenectady, these nameless women who hide their faces from their own husbands, these children put to bed in the simplest of manners, these hosts who, for respect, don't sit down to meals

45

with their guests, this sovereign matriarch commanding her tribe in utterly totalitarian fashion? How to explain that Hamid, the fourteen-year-old, still shares his grandmother's bed, together with Akbar, her favorite among the toddlers? That the almost painful cleanliness of raiment in our honor cannot conceal usual carelessness? Above all, how to explain that we now belong to this tribe as members of the family? It is unreal, fantastic—but true.

"Look, mummy!" Mary Ann indicates by her eyes a charming face we have not yet seen. It is a girl in the gorgeous court dress of old Delhi Mogul days, accompanied by a gray-haired woman. They must have just come in. Auntie rises to embrace both.

"This is our Auntie," explains Waliuddin, "who has a house across the road. And this is her youngest daughter Sakri. She is wearing her great-grandmother's court dress to welcome you. Come forward, Sakri, to show your finery."

The girl seems like a being from another world in her wide ruby satin skirt, a cloth-of-gold close-fitting bodice, a golden veil and the Delhi court jewel, almost the size of a hand, over her brow. She looks the dreamed-of Oriental beauty, with huge almond eyes, fair complexion, incredibly slender waist and graceful movements. But what makes her outstanding is a look of great sweetness, resigned, sad sweetness. What reason for sadness can there be for a young girl as beautiful as she? While I look on, fascinated, I see tears veil her eyes when she takes Mary Ann's proffered hand. In a flash I understand. She must have loved Rashid, must have hoped to be his wife on his return from the West. How terrible!

I only hope Mary Ann isn't aware of things but, as usual, she has been even quicker than I to sense the situation. "I'll ask Rashid about Sakri," she murmurs in French while Faizuddin takes us home in the *tonga*. "I knew the instant she looked at me. I'm so very sorry. What makes things worse is that she is so sweet, not at all 'the rival.'"

~ 3 ~

R ASHID is back from Nullgarh, tanned, tired but happy to be home again. His Highness has approvel of all his plans and encouraged him to put things on as broad a basis as possible. He'll have to return to Nullgarh before long, but this time he wants to take Mary Ann with him. "It was so terrible without her, Mother! I felt like a lost dog." Then he puts his arm round me. "And also terrible to be without my Mother. You know, I've been so lonely all my life that only now I realize how much I've missed."

Poor darling! Wells of unused affection surge to the surface. Mary Ann's and my life have been so different, always surrounded by tenderness.

At first his face clouds when we speak of our unchaperoned escapade to Auntie's. Then he brightens visibly. "Now it's done, I'm glad you went. I did so dread to take you there! I know, of course, that both of you are far too kind and broad-minded to look down on my people. But I kept on thinking that you've never seen anything like it. If I think of my own discomfort in beholding the squalor, the dirt, the badly brought-up children—it's such a pity, for they are dears, really—what must your feelings be? I've more or less grown up under such conditions; you've not even heard of them. So I was afraid of taking you there. That's why I always put off Auntie's invitations. I was ashamed. Now you know."

"But we loved it all. They are such sweet people, the children, Auntie and the whole lot."

"Sweet? They're backward and as obstinate as anything. It's not poverty, far from it. The boys are not sent to the best schools, as far as schools go here; the girls not at all. They are to grow up as ignorant as their mothers, if they don't die before of dirt and disease."

"Don't be so hard, darling. Things can't be as bad as all that."

"Worse! If you knew how I've tried to alter them! I've begged and begged to let a proper doctor look after the children, at least; I've offered to pay for one boy's tonsils and one girl's adenoids to be removed. But no! Some bazaar quack is called in, or Auntie administers her home-brewed mixtures; an operation, however slight,

47

is taboo. So the boy continues to be poisoned by laryngitis, and the girl will probably grow up an imbecile because of her adenoids. Or do you think it is a good thing for a big boy like Hamid to go about in fancy dress instead of shorts? But Auntie spoils him beyond imagination. He parades in all hues of the rainbow as though he were a dancing girl."

"You are right, of course. Yet there is beauty in it all."

"I can't perceive any. I only see criminal ignorance. What'll ever become of this wretched country if people don't want to improve? It is very well for you two to be generous about deficiencies; but if, like myself, one has had to fight one's way out of that utter squalor and mess, one gets bitter and depressed seeing that those one belongs to prefer to stick to the mud."

Rashid's fiery speech suddenly seemed to me to explain the fierce modernism of many educated Indians I have met.

April 25

I'm worried about money. I wanted to buy Mary Ann a little car, so she wouldn't be cooped up when Rashid has to take his away. It isn't necessary, but it would be pleasant. Next thing on the list is an electric refrigerator. In Akbarabad you can't rent them on a monthly basis as you can in big towns and hill-stations; you have to buy one. We need a good kitchen stove, too. Cooking Indian fashion over an open charcoal fire without an oven is not satisfactory in the long run, though cook is turning out quite nice cakes and cookies, baked in a saucepan. We need lots of other things, too, and I was looking forward to getting them in Bombay. Now my bank has written that, owing to further restricting laws on the Continent, the greater part of my already much-dwindled income does not reach London as it used to. This is a glum outlook. I've spent most of what I brought along on things connected with the impromptu wedding and suitable presents to Rashid on Mary Ann's and my behalf; assuming that there'd be more coming in this quarter. Well, there isn't. I feel bad about having to tell Mary Ann. She'll mind because of Rashid; not that she needs to; he loves her for what she is, even if she were the traditional beggar-maid of literature. But this is the East. A girl's material background is much commented upon. And what'll happen if there is a child? I thought I'd provide all the necessary equipment and upkeep of the nursery, so that Rashid's relatives can't say it's expensive to have married a western girl. I understand he has to provide for quite a number of his relatives. I shouldn't like his marriage to interfere with these duties. In the average Indian mind a Westerner is a person coming out to India to pocket a salary and enjoy a status he'd never have dreamed of at home. Take, not give. That is the average notion, though many Westerners have given great love and selfless effort to India. We've always been keenly aware of this mental attitude, and have tried to disprove it; that's one of the reasons why I accepted nothing, not even chances for interesting work on our first trip, however tempting some of them were. I don't want money from India. But now I worry. If only I could spare Mary Ann!

April 27

Mary Ann told me she asked both Auntie and Rashid about Sakri. Auntie admitted that all of them had planned the match while Rashid was in the West. He, on the other hand, was genuinely puzzled, even indignant. "What? This girl to think of me? I've certainly given her no reason to. I remember that in a letter Waliuddin wrote on Auntie's behalf, he suggested something of the kind, but I set things right at once. An uneducated purdah girl for me! Even before I knew you, darling, I'd never have dreamed of doing such a thing. It's preposterous."

Still, Sakri's problem isn't solved. Rashid is certainly the only modern man she has ever beheld. No wonder she lost her heart to him. Sakri means "the sweet one." That is exactly how she looks. "Isn't it awful we can't help her?" says Mary Ann. "But I'm the last person who can."

April 30

I've always held that in India there is a Hindu patina spread over everything. Most Indian Muslims are very different from Muslims in Arabia, Africa, Turkey; pageantry, utterly alien to Islam, is practised under Hindu influence. Even Muharram, the Muslim month of mourning, is in many places gay with processions, immersions and fireworks. The same thing happens to Christianity, and courageous clerics admit as much. Hinduism influences everything.

Thus it happens that in our Muslim-Christian house, the untouchable sweeper can't set foot on the step separating the cloister from

49

the courtyard. He sweeps the latter; but when Mary Ann told him to wash the cloister with disinfectant—after all, that is sweeper-work —he himself said smiling that he wouldn't be allowed up this one step. This philosophically resigned acknowledgment of his own degradation drove Mary Ann and me frantic. If even Christians like ourselves submit to the man-made laws of untouchability, how can one expect Hindus to forgo them? This house is Muslim-Christian; there isn't the slightest reason why we should bow to untouchability. Mary Ann and I resolve that, for once, we'll fight this thing through —against India. Consciously taking the sweeper by his sleeve, she makes him step up to wash the cloister, ordering him to draw water from the tap outside the bathroom. We both stay to await further developments.

To our amazement the first protest doesn't come from maharaj, the high-class Brahman. It is Muslim Ghafur who perceives what is afoot. He runs into the kitchen to call cook, his co-religionist. We see them put their heads together, look at us doubtfully, then deliberate anew. Finally Ghafur trots over to the servants' quarters, returning with Ismail Khan as leader of their joint Muslim *démarche*.

"Mothersahib, memsahib, we know Europe in, sweeper great man is. But here India is. Here sweeper small man is, small, small." Ismail Khan is pointing to the ground. "His work courtyard is. House his work not is. He house unclean make. That good not is."

"Holy Koran says all men brethren are. Thou knowest that thou Muslim art, Ismael Khan, not Hindu. Holy Koran in, caste not exists."

"We Holy Koran know, memsahib. But this India is. Hindu bad men are. House against they talk will."

Both parties remain adamant. The sweeper, who has relinquished at once his exalted position of washing up the cloister and looks as though his only wish were to run away, is sternly ordered up again by Mary Ann. Maharaj and the gardener appear from nowhere. Maharaj, the first-class Brahman, is the only one among us entitled to protest. Yet he doesn't, which gives us the second surprise of the morning. He merely advises the sweeper to proceed with his work without forgetting the corners. But he looks wistfully at us, not with pity, but with a kind of new tenderness. There's no knowing maharaj, the disciple of the Sublime *Gita*.

Ismail Khan, the ultra-Muslim, having meanwhile enlisted Brahman support against his own tolerant religion, returns with the Lavanyia boys who try to convince us that this sort of thing "is not cricket." Nobody works. Each and all talk, long after the sweeper has taken his dejected departure. There seems commotion on the compound. Mrs. Motilal's sister crosses the garden to enter Mrs. Lavanyia's house; soon the second Mrs. Jarwarkar follows her. Servants are sent out to the Laboratory or from bungalow to bungalow. We half expect Mrs. Lavanyia. Instead, Rashid is home unexpectedly early for lunch.

"What has happened? Lavanyia and Motilal came to tell me that your good heart had carried you away, and that there was trouble brewing."

We explain. "I entirely agree with you, my dears, no need to emphasize that. As you say, this is a Christian-Muslim house, and the spirit of intolerance has no place here. Personally I shouldn't mind in the least having my food prepared and my bed made by an outcaste, provided he kept himself clean. I'd rather enjoy it, because it would teach others a lesson. But we can't afford to do what we like. We are not free. I'd lose my job if we carried the thing too far."

"Rashid—you don't mean to say they'd sack you—you, with your qualifications unique in the State—you, their scientific pride—for having the cloister of your private residence swept by a sweeper! It's preposterous."

"Nobody'd sack me. There'd be no need to. My job would crumble away all on its own."

"How?"

"Well, first people wouldn't visit this house any more, or, if they had to, they wouldn't accept food and drink and probably wouldn't shake hands. Not only Hindus, mind you; Muslims and others as well. A man in my position can't afford that. As you know, I have to entertain for the Laboratory and, more essential than entertaining, receive all sorts of people on official business. If they refuse to shake hands with me, where am I?"

"And secondly?"

"Secondly, they might ostracize me also in the Laboratory. You see, darling, not only our house is polluted in the eyes of people: it's us. You, Mother, I. If we do things they consider untouchable, we become untouchable too."

"Yes, I understand, as far as Hindus are concerned. And I understand that in your position you can't, and ought not to, risk ostracism. After all, your research and work is to benefit India." Mary Ann looks bravely at Rashid, though her voice is very low. "But why Muslims and all the others? It doesn't make sense. Not only do they betray humanity without any need, they betray even their proper religion."

"I agree. But don't think too badly of them. Their business would suffer, their social relations collapse, their children be shunned at school. That is why Muslims have, in cases like this, to knuckle under to the Hindu caste system. The ignorant among them—alas, the vast majority—forget about the tolerance of Islam and are caste-conscious without being aware of it."

"It's ghastly."

"So it is. So ghastly that I sometimes wish I'd not come back here. I'm so fed up, so discouraged at times. Shouldn't we go back to Europe, or to the United States, the three of us?"

"And who is to work for India if those who can, quit?"

With Rashid, the last word is Mary Ann's. Not so with India. India has indeed won the day.

May 1

Our sweeper has been given a beating, not too hard, but just to teach him manners. By caste Hindus or Muslims? No. By his own people. They reproached him for bringing danger on their outcast caste.

May 2

Faizuddin calls while Mary Ann in the courtyard is dealing with the *dhobi*—the washerman. He listens as she counts and proves to the *dhobi* that his account is at fault. When he has gone, Faizuddin can't contain himself any longer: "Why does Brother make you work like that? It is man's work to deal with the *dhobi*."

"We think very differently, Faizuddin. We'd consider it a disgrace if the woman were not able to deal with everything concerning the household she is mistress of. The man works all day at his job; why should he have to bother with the house as well? We try to have things nice and ready for him when he comes home."

"What a delightful country Europe must be for men! Here it's

52

very different. Our ladies bother us with trifles at the moment we get home."

Coming from Faizuddin, this is too much. Mary Ann looks studiously out of the window as she asks: "By the way, Brother, I always wanted to ask you how on earth you have so much time to come here, instead of staying with your wife, when you are free from the office."

"What am I to do at home, Sister? There is nobody for me to talk to if Waliuddin is out. The ladies have to look after the children and the house."

"Why not help your wife look after the children? Don't you think she'd enjoy it for a change? After all, you are their father!"

Faizuddin, somewhat sheepishly, replies that only ladies know how to take care of children, and that men must visit their friends.

"You know very well what I mean, Faizuddin," concludes Mary Ann.

Does he? I wonder. Individually, he grants her all the laurels on earth; generally speaking, his male superiority complex remains unchanged.

May 5

For two days Mary Ann had a touch of fever. A blood test was made; it's not malaria, thank God. Dr. Ram Chandra, the superintendent of the Government Hospital—he is an M.R.C.P. (London) —says that Europeans often have unexpected attacks of fever before getting acclimated in India. I've heard so myself and it does sound plausible. But she is all right again now, lying in my little room, which both she and Rashid declare more peaceful than theirs. Rashid has been frantic with fear. "Give it to me, darling, give it to me!" I heard him coax her once.

May 9

Maharaj, to whom we are untouchable beyond imagination, has changed a great deal since he came to us. We never asked him to do anything he didn't volunteer to, except the posting of letters or such things. Very soon, however, he tried of his own accord to relieve us from work we undertook ourselves. At first he couldn't understand why we washed silk underwear and blouses at home; but when we explained that the *dhobi's* pounding methods would

53

reduce these tissues to shreds in no time, he ceased opposition. His religion and caste rules prohibit any kind of dirty work; so he cannot help us. But he lingers outside the bathroom door, and the very moment clean water has rinsed away every trace of polluting dirt and soap, he takes things one by one across the threshold and suspends them in the courtyard, as he has seen us do. It's all quite voluntary, and we don't mention it to anybody. He has also practised ironing by himself—which is clean work—so as to take this task off our hands. Whatever we wash he irons, proud to handle the new electric iron.

But his efforts are not viewed by everybody with equal favor. Whenever Mary Ann smiles approvingly at him, commenting on his new efficiency, we can be sure that pinpricks will follow. The cook will say that the bananas maharaj brought home from the market are one anna too expensive. Whereupon Ismail Khan will volunteer to do the shopping. Or he will tell Rashid, whom he valets, that maharaj is being seen in gambling-dens every night. This seems highly improbable, since he never asks for an advance as most of the others do, and begins his day looking immaculately fresh and rested. It's a regular campaign. We can't see its point, since he is a government servant and doesn't aspire either to Ismail Khan's or cook's job. Is it communal resentment? Or just jealousy?

May 12

We've been entertaining quite a lot. Two dinners, five teas. Once Rashid sent word at 3:30 P.M. that four *subhas*—collectors—on tour would come to tea at five. Would Mary Ann be able to manage? In Akbarabad, this is not an easy job, especially if, like the three of us, one declines to buy sweets from the shops where flies can too easily infect them. There is the additional difficulty of bread. Indians ordinarily eat *chappatis* or *puris*—unleavened bread. Barring the bazaar bakers—not patronized for the same reason as the sweetshops—decent bread is only obtainable against standing order at the Railway Buffet. On these occasions we can't send for extra bread, because there isn't any. Cook was out, having his afternoon rest at his place in town, as always. So Mary Ann and I had to rise to the occasion. I prepared *croutes au fromage*, using biscuits instead of toast. That same morning cook had fried the delicious Indian sweet known as *jellabi*, for which we often paid a high price in Tottenham Court

54

Road or Regent Street. But we had no cake. In the whole of Akbarabad, you can't get any. And we *had* to get one or two more sweets! At home, such things don't matter overmuch; in the East, where a host is honoring his guests by doing things as well as possible, it would be commented upon unfavorably if the tea were poor. The guests might think that Mary Ann didn't take the same trouble for just Indians as she would have taken for Europeans. There's always that wretched distrust and inferiority complex lurking in the background. So a sweet we had to have. Baking is easy if you have an oven, but we didn't feel equal to baking on a *sigri*—a small open charcoal fire—in a saucepan, heaping live coals from another *sigri* on to the saucepan's lid for dual heat. We were alone to set the fire going, and didn't quite know how to do it. So we gave up the idea of baking, and turned out a French chocolate cream, hoping it would set in time. Fortunately, cook arrived in time to prepare both spinach and onion *bajyia,* one of the Indian tea-time savories. Mary Ann dressed hurriedly and saw to things in the drawing room. Ghafur returned particularly bedraggled-looking from the bazaar, and had to be sent off for a complete change. The guests had already arrived when I left the kitchen. Anyway I took a quick bath and came just in time for tea. But it turned out a sumptuous tea, and Rashid was proud as anything, especially when later we explained to him all the contretemps.

The strangest tea-party of all was for the Jarwarkars, husband with number one and two wives, in Indian terminology, "burri *bai*" and "choti *bai,*" plus two sons of school age; the girls, being mere females, were left at home. It happens quite frequently in India that a man marries two sisters. Often the first wife herself makes her husband marry her junior sister, lest he marry a stranger who will fight her. Clan-feeling being stronger than even caste, a sister can be depended upon to remain loyal to the first wife. In the Jarwarkar family, however, things seem to have been different. People say that when number two was visiting number one, the husband fell in love with the girl and immediately took her for his second wife. It's not our concern. But we made up our mind to be ceremoniously correct about serving the burri *bai* before her junior colleague. We also decided that the twofold husband wasn't to get a thing to eat before both his ladies had been served. Except in modern circles, men are always served before women. For Mary

Ann and myself an exception is made, but this exception, due to our being Westerners, doesn't alter the rule. True, we know that a Hindu woman considers it correct to serve her lord first and that, somehow, all Orientals have similar customs. But this is our house. We can stage an object lesson in different treatment of women, by serving tea in western fashion.

This time we are having two cakes, three kinds of sandwiches plus several Indian savories and sweets. Mary Ann is pouring; I take the first cup to the senior, the second to the junior, now the ruling wife (the elder is said to live all by herself somewhere about their court-yard). Both ladies refuse, both motion me unashamedly to take the first cup to their joint lord. I remain adamant, saying that "West in," ladies come first. Mary Ann seconds me; Rashid says to the ceiling —he can't address the ladies directly—that it is high time things were altered in this country. Mr. Jarwarkar, an educated man, laughs and says he'd like to try the new regime for once. But it's no use. Burri *bai*, seeing that I don't give in, rises, takes the cup from my hand and presents it ceremoniously to her unfaithful lord, thus carrying out to the letter the Code of Manu, as far as the conduct of wives is con-cerned. The same procedure is repeated over each dish. Man comes first. Again India has won the day.

May 14

Mary Ann and Rashid have left for Nullgarh. I wish it were more of a honeymoon than the Nullgarh flat countryside and Rest House can provide. Anyhow, they were very happy and excited to set out together. They wanted to take only maharaj and Ismail Khan, whom Rashid commends as a good cook; I was to have been left with Ghafur and cook. But news came that either His Highness or high officials of the State would visit Rashid's camp in Nullgarh. I insisted that they should take cook with them, for emergencies. Mrs. Lavanyia kindly volunteered to provide my lunch and dinner.

May 17

"How many mothers do you have?"
"Three."
"And how many brothers and sisters?"
"Five brothers and seven sisters."

"Are all of them at home?"

"Only two small brothers. Another studies for the LL.D.; and others go to school in Lucknow."

"And the sisters?"

"Four are married. I and two younger sisters are still in my home."

This conversation takes place at the Akbarabad Mission, where I've been to tea. A young girl with an older companion, the daughter of a rich landowner, has called in a purdah car to discuss some embroidery work her mother wants done at the Mission's workroom. When the Padre leaves for the club, his wife brings the visitor to the drawing room, safely female after his departure.

Live and learn! I've been to many houses in which dwell two or more wives; but I'd never have dreamed of coolly, like my hostess, putting the question: "How many mothers do you have?"

When we are alone again I tackle the subject. Mrs. Blackwell shrugs her shoulders. "I always do it, because it sets the poor dears at ease from the start. They know how we feel about plural wives, and they would be too embarrassed to mention their family life if not encouraged. As you know, to ask about people's relations is the only polite way out here to start conversation, so I show that I take plural wives for granted, and all embarrassment vanishes."

"I see the point. Thank you. You've taught me something I didn't realize."

"When you'll have been in this country as long as I have. . . ."

"How long have you been here?"

"Twenty-two years. My husband twenty-eight."

"Always here?"

"Here or roundabouts. So you see we've spent all those years in one of the most conservative regions of India."

"Is that the reason why you expect most men to have several wives?"

"Yes. I'm used to it. It's not true, however, that only Muslims practise polygamy—I'm sorry to mention it, your son-in-law being a Muslim himself, but then he is so different. A very great number of Hindus have two or more wives."

"Because the first wife doesn't bear sons?"

"In some cases. But very often just for the pleasure of it. Look at the young Dewan of Portan, just thirty miles away from here! He is

57

twenty-eight; he has a lovely wife who gave him three splendid boys; yet he goes and marries another girl some weeks ago! What can you expect from such people? Pagans remain pagans."

I wonder. Maybe things in this region are as Mrs. Blackwell says. On our first journey I found, generally speaking, plural wives rather the exception than the rule. People can't afford them. I also think we shouldn't judge these things by western standards. After all plural marriages are strictly legal both in Hinduism and Islam. A man having more than one wife does nothing improper according to his religion. At the same time it is felt nowadays in both communities that plural marriage is not desirable from many points of view; reform movements both Hindu and Muslim try to put an end to the custom.

Mrs. Blackwell knows many things about India that I don't; I could learn much from her; moreover, it would be but natural that we two European women should become friends. But her mental attitude is not mine. I appreciate her kindness of heart and all the work she does in school and dispensary. Yet to her, non-Christians are incapable of higher feelings. She'll always believe the worst of them, never giving them even the benefit of the doubt. But I don't want to be unfair to her. Perhaps, on closer acquaintance, I'll get another impression.

May 21

Mary Ann writes she and Rashid had their first quarrel—over maharaj, of all things! Rashid must have believed some of Ismail Khan's lies. Mary Ann stood up for maharaj, which seems to have driven Rashid irrational. "How can you take a mere *chaprassi's* part against me!" he cried out. "If you do, you can't love me!" Mary Ann says it was all completely crazy on his part. Out of pique or annoyance, or to regain her composure, she went into Nullgarh all by herself, without letting him know, and spent two and a half hours with the wife of the *naib-subha*. On returning she was picked up on the road by Rashid, who had been driving round frantically to find her. Well, well,——

"Camp Nullgarh, May 21

"My darling Mother,
    "I'm writing to you in great distress. Mary Ann will have already

58

told you about our first quarrel. In itself this wouldn't be too terrible, since all newlyweds are said to have their quarrels, and to enjoy reconciliation. But what distresses me is that I don't know who is right. I'd love to say I'm not, but I can't. Since matters of principle are involved, and it is necessary for my peace of mind to find my bearings, I'm writing to my dear mother. Let me frankly state my case; do tell me exactly what you think of it all. I'll try to understand every word you say, and I know you'll try to understand me. This is a most unusual letter to write to one's mother-in-law, but so are you unusual. I know you will not take it for granted that Mary Ann is right simply because she is your own child, as nearly all mothers would do, especially in this country.

"This is what happened. We had a quarrel over maharaj, Mary Ann taking his side without paying heed to my point against him, which was briefly that he is dishonest. I am not going into the matter, for it's much less important than the ensuing consequences. When going for my inspection tour, after the quarrel, I couldn't think for distress and temper. Let me frankly admit the latter; for Mary Ann, my darling Mary Ann, whom I love more than I ever can say, had stood up against me and hurt me on account of a scoundrel like maharaj. I tried to work, but I couldn't do a thing, all the while thinking of my Mary Ann I'd left for the first time without a kiss. Well, I soon realized that I'd never be able to work or think or breathe if there was anything between us. So I drove home again, that is to the Rest-House. Imagine my shock when I found Mary Ann gone without a message! It was unkind and inconsiderate of her in the extreme; she knew how I'd be cut up over not finding her. But, even apart from that, how does it look! This is not Europe; a lady of good family doesn't walk nearly a mile all by herself into town! Mary Ann knows full well that people, seeing her walk all alone, must comment unfavorably on my not accompanying her, or not letting her have the car. And, what is worse, they will talk harshly about her and call it immodest for a newly married and beautiful woman to walk all by herself where men can stare at her. At the time I didn't think it out that way; I was too worried about my darling's whereabouts. I drove into Nullgarh and went into all the shops I could think of; I paraded the streets leading to the houses in which we had visited, since I couldn't very well call to say, "Is my wife here?" That may be possible in the West—

though it shouldn't happen even there—but out here a husband is expected to know his wife's whereabouts. I certainly don't insist on my wife's asking my permission to go out, as Indian ladies have to do; but out of consideration for me she should let me know where she goes if I have to be away from home all day long, and cannot even be sure of what my wife does, how am I to work and keep my head?

"When I had driven round like a madman, and was again on my way to the Rest-House, I found my darling at last. Relieved as I was beyond measure, it was an awful feeling to see her walking by herself in the road like a common woman. She had visited the wife of the *naib-subha*. There are young men in that house, the *subha's* sons from his first marriage. What will people think of her going without my knowledge—for had I known I'd have obviously taken her by car—and spending hours in that house!

"Well, darling mother, there it is. Am I so terribly wrong and backward to want my wife to tell me when and where she is going? And to be hurt if she takes other people's, let alone servants', part against me? If she loves me, how can she do that? Please tell me what you think about it all.

"Is it not too hot for you? Are you sleeping in the courtyard at long last? Can you stand Hindu food twice a day for so long? I'd be much happier if you'd engage a cook to look after you properly. Promise you will if you feel you'd prefer your own food. It is a shame you are all alone, but it was you who wanted to remain behind.

"My work is progressing quite well. The Laboratory will become more and more the center for all sorts of chemical combines. In fact, that's what it is already.

"Mary Ann sends her love. By the grace of God her health is good.

> "Respectfully and devotedly,
> "Your loving son,
> "Rashid."

Akbarabad, May 24

"My dear Rashid,

"Thank you for your kind, frank letter, and the trust you place in me. I'll try to answer as you expect me to. But let me say at once that I can't state who is right. Very rarely in life you'll find that one person is quite right and the other quite wrong. There are two different points of view, owing to differences of background, country, and so on. Both of you must try to understand each other.

"I'm indeed sorry that Mary Ann went off as she did without letting you know her whereabouts. She must have realized it would hurt you, and she shouldn't have done it.

"On the other hand you, too, ought to realize two different things: first, that you hurt Mary Ann considerably over the maharaj business, and that she may have gone to cool off before showing you how much you had hurt her; secondly, that for a European girl to go out by herself for a walk or a visit is as natural as breathing. One doesn't think about it; one just does it as one has done it all one's life and has seen everybody else do it. True, she knows that India isn't Europe; she has given up many things she was used to on that account; you know that. But, being upset—and she must have been—one forgets new surroundings and acts as one would have acted at home.

"Now, why was she upset and hurt about the maharaj business? Let's get to the root of it all, because such situations will turn up again and again.

"You were upset, and more, because Mary Ann defended somebody you attacked. (That he was 'only a servant' doesn't count with you, seriously; your kindness towards underdogs is one of your qualities I appreciate most.) You say: 'If she loves me, how can she do that?' My dear, this is one of the fundamental differences of outlook between East and West. Westerners go in for *abstract* right, and they'll stand up for it a hundred per cent. Easterners have often your own feeling: right or wrong, the person who loves me must stick by me. Do try to see and to acknowledge this fundamental difference! I'm not speaking now of whether Easterners or Westerners are right in their respective outlook; I'm merely pointing out that this outlook is different. If you can understand *that*, you'll spare yourself and those you love much future distress. It is not that Mary Ann does not love you if she stands up for somebody else; according to western mentality her love for you has no right to interfere with her sense of justice. Difficult as it may seem for you to realize at first, dear, it is the very best in Mary Ann's heart which makes her

61

oppose you if she thinks—rightly or wrongly—that you are being unjust to somebody else. Don't you think it'd be much easier and pleasanter for her not to antagonize you? But, if she did, she'd be unfaithful to the very best in herself and her background; to stand up for *right as such*, regardless of the personalities involved.

"I'm afraid this sounds very abstract, but I'm sure you'll understand.

"I'm so glad you are satisfied with your work. Even in my ignorance I'm very proud of you.

"Don't worry about me, my dear, please. I'm quite happy as I am. The Lavanyia food suits me, since I don't care for meat anyhow; and I get salads and fruit on my own, all drowned for hours in permanganate, as I promised you! Yes, I'm sleeping out in the courtyard. It's lovely to look at the stars whenever one wakes up.

"Much love and kisses to both of you,
                                        "Your affectionate
                                                    "Mother"

May 27

"How do you like my food, memsahib?"

"I just love it. Apart from being extremely good everything tastes so very clean and natural."

"It is Brahman food. And we prepare everything at home. Milk, *ghi*—clarified butter—and curds are from our own buffaloes. You should also keep a buffalo. Dairyman's milk is bad."

"I suppose we should. But it's not only your dairy produce that tastes so clean."

Mrs. Lavanyia laughs and addresses her sons volubly. She talks so quickly that I can't make out a word except "tell her." What is it to be?

"My mother says she wanted memsahib to know for many weeks past that flour should not be bought ready-made in the bazaars as memsahibs do. That way it can never be clean. People are talking a lot that at Rashid Ali Sahib's house, which is so great and rich a house, food is not clean."

"Not clean?"

"Muslim cooks never are. And how can your food be clean if you buy flour already milled? How can you know the grain was properly picked over and cleaned before milling?"

Indeed, how can I? This is a thing we've never bothered about in the West. We buy flour, not grain.

"Mother says we cannot ask memsahib to our kitchen and court-yard to show you how cleaning is being done, because we do belong to the Brahman caste. But we shall now fetch our servant who is just picking grains; in memsahib's front garden she can do this, and memsahib can look how she does it."

I sit on the farthest corner of the bench among our many rose bushes, to remove my polluting presence as far as possible from the Lavanyia grain. The woman picks carefully, grain for grain, dis-carding a lot which to me seem quite good. If all the stuff she discards goes into our "ready-made" flour, I can understand that people think our food unclean.

"Thank you very much. I've learned a lot. Do you clean every-thing like that—pease, lentils, caraway, peppers, juniper?"

"Indeed we do—sugar, too. The spices have their special season to be cleaned and stored. But we cannot show you. Not only are we Brahmans, but Madrassi Brahmans. The Deccani Brahmans are not so particular. Mrs. Motilal will be happy to show everything to you. We'll tell her."

"With pleasure. But I'd rather wait till my daughter's return. I know she'll be most interested. We've often wondered how we could learn about housekeeping in India."

"I shall be at Mrs. Motilal's to explain everything because I can't show things to masahib and memsahib in my own house."

It is a great departure from anything they've practised so far. These people *do* treat us well.

May 28

Mary Ann writes they have had a busy time. His Highness has been there and she had him to tea. She says tea was as good as pos-sible under the circumstances, with nice sandwiches as the mainstay and three cakes hurriedly ordered from Bombay. The worst is that they have no ice "but I've learned the Indian art of cooling drinks by evaporation, or by suspension from a tree. You'll make eyes, mummy."

His Highness seems to be a fatherly kind of man with elaborate manners and a quick grasp of things. He is sixty-three, but looks much younger, keeping himself fit by tennis and vigorous riding.

63

He seemed very pleased with all Rashid had to show him and praised him much to Mary Ann. On taking leave he said that, on his next visit to Akbarabad, he would again come to tea and meet Mother, too.

I wonder. Shall I stay on here indefinitely?

Mary Ann doesn't any more mention the quarrel, nor does Rashid in his affectionate P.S. I think everything is all right again.

May 29

I've had a disturbing dream. Though out in the courtyard, I dreamed I was sleeping in my own little room when Rashid came through the dressing room to my door and knocked. "May I come in, Mother?" he said; "I can't bear it any longer all by myself." I got out of my bed at once, snatching up a wrap, and unfastened the door. For a moment he did not move; then he put his arms around me and held me close, as though never to let me go. Big sobs shook his whole body. I stroked his head and kissed his tear-stained cheek, all the while murmuring terms of endearment. But while I did so, feeling we belonged to each other as we never had, there was only one thought uppermost in my mind: where was Mary Ann? Rashid had come from an empty room to cross the dressing room and enter my door. Both of us were alone in the house.

I awoke panic-stricken. What did that dream mean? Where was Mary Ann?

Then I pulled myself together. Even to think such thoughts is wrong. Whenever my bad heart gives trouble, bad dreams are liable to appear, in case I sleep on my left side or can't catch proper breath. That must have been one of them. I had better forget it.

June 4

I've been ill all these days. Fever like Mary Ann's, non-malarial and without explanation. But in due course old pleurisy began to hurt; after all, it must have been some cold. My illness started on May 29 and may have occasioned my upsetting dream. Dr. Ram Chandra came twice a day, doing a medical as well as a friend's job. "Tell me all you want done, Mother, or else Rashid Sahib will kill me on his return." He went to the Lavanyias to see about my food; sent a staff sister from the hospital to look after me; searched Seth

Chandralal Premchand's library for books I might like. There remained but one think he wasn't ready to do for me, and did under protest only.

Visitors poured in the first day, without inquiring if they might, without any ado; suddenly they crowded my room, chatting, conjecturing, saying that Mary Ann and Rashid ought to come back at once. I was flabbergasted at their entering at all; used to the blessed silence of a sick-room at home, I couldn't believe my eyes. Telling the sister not to admit visitors didn't seem to help. So when the doctor returned at night I asked him to put up a notice on the door of my room: "No visitors allowed."

"Mother, this will create misunderstandings. In this country people visit patients as a mark of respect and friendship."

"But I'm ill! I've fever and pains, have to change my position constantly on account of hot-water bottles, quite apart from the heart-trouble. One can't see visitors under such conditions."

"I know this is the way of the West. But here people think a patient cannot recover without tokens of love and friendship, the more the better."

"Doctor sahib, indeed I don't want to appear unfriendly, but I can't smile at visitors just now. It tires me. You as a medical man must know this better than I do."

"I understand your point, Mother. But others won't, and they will take it badly. That's why I don't want to put the cardboard up."

"I ask you to do it. After all one has the right to be ill in one's own way."

"Very well, Mother. It shall be as you say."

The notice was put up, and the influx of visitors stopped abruptly. Sometimes I heard exclamations from the next room, but I didn't pay any attention to them. I was glad to be left in peace.

It is strange how age alters things. As a child and girl I could have any amount of fever without losing consciousness. Now I've a bare 102 and don't feel mistress of myself. It was particularly so on the third day. I'd dozed fitfully during early afternoon hours; awaking, I was wondering how high my temperature might be, for I couldn't collect my thoughts. I seemed to suffer from hallucinations. Did I not know that no visitors came in any more? Yet here I was seeing the room crowded with women and children. What is more, I smelled them: there was the heavy scent of *loban*—Indian incense—

65

mingled with the smell of cocos-oil and garlic. Surely my temperature couldn't be high enough to set all my senses wandering! Four women and several children were squatting on the ground and calmly gazing at me out of unfathomable dark eyes. One child approached the bed to touch the top-sheet with a timid finger. The odor of garlic became overpowering. At this juncture Ghafur tiptoed in. Seeing me awake, he pointed proudly to women and children and began introductions: "She my mother's mother is; she my mother is; she my brother's wife is; she my sister is. They here came so that masahib should not always alone have to be. Alone not good is."

India had again won the day.

And I liked it! I was touched by that genuine kindness, and ashamed of having had the notice put up. Such is the inconsistency of human nature.

June 7

Mary Ann came the very moment they heard of my illness. Ismail Khan drove her at what can be termed breakneck speed on such roads as these. Rashid will follow in two or three days. Maharaj has offered garlands and coconuts for my recovery in the Nullgarh temple. I refrained from asking whether Rashid knew about it.

But Mary Ann mentions things herself. "I realize only now how terribly careful I have to be. I thought Rashid was entirely different from that unbalanced and inferiority-complexed type of Easterner I've so often met among fellow-students. Indeed he *is!* Yet, if worked up, he gets nearly as bad as they are. Can you believe that after the drama of my going into Nullgarh he actually said: "If I were a Westerner you wouldn't treat me like that!" God knows I'd never have given a fraction of my present concern and carefulness to a western husband! It simply wouldn't have been necessary."

"Yes, it's astonishing, coming from Rashid. On the other hand, we'd do well to remember that, all told, no Westerner can ever put himself into an Easterner's position. Whatever our individual inferiority complexes may be about being ugly or stupid or self-conscious, we've never known a racial, a color, inferiority complex; nor have we ever been treated with the condescension—to put it mildly —which we have bestowed on Easterners. So we are not good judges as to what Orientals have been feeling in this respect for hundreds

66

of years. We might feel exactly the same in similar circumstances, for all we know."

"That's true. I always feel it's not Rashid personally who says such things; they don't belong to him. He's very open-minded, sometimes boldly so. But in such moments it is his people who speak out of him—the adequate expression would be his 'Blood and Soil,' but I do hate using Nazi-coined phrases. Well, when he quiets down, his individuality again gets the upper hand, and he's sorry for what he said. But I'm afraid that after that affair he won't ever like maharaj. And that's why I didn't tell him about your garlands."

"How did he take my letter?"

"He said it was a wonderful letter, and that he loved you dearly but, being no superman, he was afraid he couldn't always live up to the standards you've set him."

"Things are all right now?"

"Of course they are. Don't worry, and get well. You look so pale and pulled down!"

4

June 12

GRAY clouds are veiling the sun, but the heat is more oppressive than ever. The monsoon has already broken in Bombay, so it should break here soon. With all the others we are looking forward to the rains. This parched season has been again an object lesson of what the rains mean to earth, beast and man. I had my first in Palestine where it had not rained for more than two years preceding my arrival. From monsoon to monsoon in India there are no rains except small and very rare showers; so the monsoon is a seasonal wind. Blowing over most parts of India from the southwest, it is the wet monsoon in summer; from the northeast in winter, it is the dry monsoon, bringing no rain except in the south. Thus the rains fall approximately between June and September only; they are not evenly distributed, for the monsoon, although it pours down in torrents when it strikes the mountains, has little water to spare over sandy plains like Sind and Rajputana. Some deserts get only a few inches a year; some hill places nearly 500 inches. In those parts of the country in which rains are scarce there is a vicious circle of droughts, famine, disease, migrations of man and beast, Government relief, drought and famine. But even in those districts blessed by rains the uneven distribution brings much tribulation. There may be too much rain, the rice and grain-fields being damaged beyond repair; yet, from October to June the lands are increasingly parched. It is the same with man. Longing for the rains is of indescribable intensity. Somehow I begin to feel it too.

June 14

Rashid is back, later than he expected, but full of life and zest. With him here we'll have to give and attend lots of parties. There is a European couple staying at one of Seth Chandralal's guest bungalows, the Kirkpatricks, a high official of the Revenue Department on tour with his wife, children and staff. They've called. Both husband and wife are good talkers and, having knocked about on service a great deal, know a lot about India. She is much younger than he, a good thing, for she has still enough spirit of adventure to accompany him wherever he goes by car or bullock-cart. "Since my husband has to tour except during the monsoon season, we'd be separated for about eight months in twelve were I not to go with him. And he'd be all by himself in those wretched places he has to visit, never with a soul to talk to." Mrs. Kirkpatrick seems a very efficient organizer, a Yorkshire lass. She travels as an autarchy, taking everything with her and nothing for granted. This is the only way one can travel to out-of-the-way places, often in jungles. They are taking their own traveling kitchen and baking their own bread wherever they go. Mrs. Kirkpatrick promised to show us her portable oven for us to copy.

Tomorrow we're dining them. I must stop writing, for my head is full of chicken mayonnaise, undisguisable mutton under some fresh disguise—beef is taboo in the State, pork and bacon in a Muslim house—chocolate cream, and wishful thinking for a proper oven to prepare cheese soufflé, or something au gratin.

June 19

The past three days have been a regular nightmare. I hate describing them at all, and shall do so as briefly as possible; but the happenings certainly clamor for recording.

Mary Ann and I were busy on the 15th with our preparations for the dinner party. To meet the Kirkpatricks we'd asked Seth Chandralal, their host, the *subha*—collector—the D.S.P. and the Blackwells. It was about six P.M.; we were superintending laying the table and arranging salted almonds and chocolates, when maharaj came to the door of the dining room to announce, "Burra sahibs have arrived."

"What burra sahibs?"

"Burra sahibs."

Who on earth could that be? On the compound Rashid is burra sahib; at home, however, "sahib" only, since there is no other in the house. The *subha* is called *sircari*—governmental—sahib. So what?

"Who, maharaj?"

"Burra sahibs, sahib's uncles."

"They are here?"

"They are here with their luggage. On the front veranda."

Rashid is on some inspection tour or other, returning only about seven P.M. in the nick of time to shave and dress. We are busy with preparations. And, above all, we don't know all the rules and etiquette for receiving Rashid's paternal uncles. Why didn't they wire their arrival or write in time?

"Send Ismail Khan's eldest boy at once in a *tonga* to Auntie's, maharaj. Here is money. He is to say that sahib's uncles have arrived, that sahib is out and that Mother and memsahib ask Waliuddin and Faizuddin sahib to come here at once in the *tonga*. If they are not at home the boy is to find them. When you have dispatched him, tell cook to get tea for two ready on a tray. Ghafur is to carry it to the drawing room, also jug, basin, soap and towels for washing their hands. We'll wait about deciding where they are to sleep until sahib's return."

After maharaj's departure Mary Ann turns to me. "I wish Rashid had told me more about his people. But he always avoids speaking about them. We're in for it, mummy. Please come with me to welcome them. I'm afraid to go alone."

"Nonsense. You are quite capable of carrying off difficult situations."

Flushed by work and excitement, looking extremely girlish, Mary

Ann covers her head demurely with her sari, and off we go to the front veranda. Two slender figures arise from the wicker chairs, one with a white, the other with a black beard. Both are immaculately buttoned up in *chervanis* that are tight-fitting like gloves. "So this is our daughter! And this is Mother! Pray let us step inside. It is not fitting for a lady of our family to appear outside the purdah."

The voice of the elder uncle is pleasant, the English halting but easily understandable. Leading the way, without any doubt as to our following him, Rashid's eldest uncle reaches the cloister and, with a graceful gesture of his hand, motions us to be seated. To western mentality his behavior is very cheeky; to eastern, not. Women don't count, this is his nephew's house and, as the eldest uncle, he is boss of the whole show.

As far as bossing is concerned, Abdul Sattar, Rashid's younger uncle, seems to rank next. In loud tones he orders our servants about, says he will now take his bath, enters Rashid's dressing room only to emerge again with the latter's silver-mounted brush and comb, plus his most beloved hair tonic. Abdul Sattar is taller than Rashid, yet much less handsome. His features are weak, his expression is sulky; he doesn't create a good impression.

While Mary Ann is pouring tea, the elder uncle, Fakhruddin, says how glad he is to make her acquaintance and Mother's; how he will enjoy staying with them, and his nephew for the summer, at the end of which his wife and daughters might join him, Abdul Sattar traveling home to fetch them here. "Then all of us will live together, as a family should. But you must change your dress, Daughter—it is not fitting for a Muslim lady to wear a Hindu sari in front of him who takes her father-in-law's place."

"I didn't think you'd prefer a western dress, Uncle."

"Who speaks of western dresses? Do you mean what Mother is wearing? Of course not. My daughter has to appear before me in proper Muslim dress; trousers, shirt and veil. Let me not see you again in a sari!"

Fortunately Waliuddin and Faizuddin arrive at this moment. But for their advent we'd both have spoken our minds.

Taking advantage of the greetings exchanged between the four men, Mary Ann murmurs: "Mummy, tell maharaj to stop the car before it drives up, and to direct Rashid to go straight into your

70

room. We'll join him there for decisions. We'd better send round to our guests to say the dinner can't take place. This is too ghastly for words."

But when we sit *in camera* Rashid, gray-faced, his jaw squarely set, insists that the dinner must take place. "What would our guests think? They are all high officials; one can't treat them like that. We'll have the dinner; the uncles can dine with Auntie. I'll fetch them here after our guests have gone."

"How will you get your uncles to agree?"

"Leave that to me. I know why they came. It's sheer blackmail. I'll explain it all tomorrow, darling. I'm so terribly sorry they were rude to you. My people are the limit."

"Let's not go into this now, dear. Don't worry about me. If you could only see how awful you look! Where are they to sleep?"

"Fakhruddin in the room corresponding to Mother's, the other side of the front veranda. Abdul Sattar on the veranda, outside his door."

"Together with *chowkidar?*"

"I don't care. I will not have them enter the house, anyhow."

"But how can you prevent them? And how will it be when the whole family——"

"Don't you worry, darling. They won't come. And now I must set to work. But I can only carry things through if you don't look so distressed."

How Rashid did it I do not know. The fact is that, some twenty minutes later, the four men departed in our car, and our dinner party took place according to plan—at least as far as externals go. Food and service were good; we had two men from the hotel in attendance. The evening was a success, for all those present were good conversationalists and enjoyed discussing East-West problems; but despite my children's playing up valiantly, Mary Ann's white face and Rashid's sunken eyes robbed me of any pleasure. After the guests' departure I retired at once to let them have some brief moments of solitude before Rashid's departure for Auntie's. When the noise of the car had died down, Mary Ann came to my room. "Rashid says he'll explain everything tomorrow at breakfast, which the three of us are to have very early in our bedroom, so nobody can disturb us. I don't know more than you, since there was no time for explanations; I only know that he's a poor lamb and that we must stand by him. What a mess it all seems!"

"It certainly does. I'm very sorry for both of you. But things will turn out all right. Rashid is capable of taking care of you."

"Yes, he said he'd arrange everything, and that I was to trust him and not worry."

"That is the best you can do. I trust him too."

"It's very sweet of you, mummy, not to say 'Haven't you enough of the real India by now?' By the way, I haven't. Things can't always be rosy. We were so happy until now."

"Bless you, darling, you'll go on being happy, don't worry."

But, looking at my child's strained face, in which only the enormous eyes seem alive, I realize with a pang that Mary Ann has grown from a girl into a woman.

At our conspirators' breakfast next morning Rashid, looking ten years older than yesterday, makes his report: "I came straight to the point last night. I said that, much as we should like to receive the whole family, it was not feasible on account of my work and other reasons; that I even had to ask the uncles to depart almost at once, since I couldn't entertain them properly with all the work and building I had on my hands. You see, though I well knew that unpleasantness couldn't be avoided in the long run, my people being what they are, I didn't want to be the one to start it; so I gave this plausible and polite explanation."

"Will not your uncles think it is I who turned you against them? After all, a nephew can't turn out his paternal uncles, least of all in India; so they and everybody else will say I made you do it. They'll blame it on the 'awful' West and that's what I don't like. I've tried so hard to make the West a success!"

"So you did, darling, beyond imagination. If all Westerners were like you and Mother——. But now to brass tacks; we have so much to talk about and decide. You are mistaken; nobody will think that you have anything to do with my line of action. You see, this is not happening for the first time. Long before I even knew you, as a matter of fact as soon as I had my first job, this kind of thing began. It is sheer blackmail. It's a shame I have to say this of my own people. I did so try to hide things from both of you, but now it has become impossible."

"What exactly do you mean by blackmail? Surely your uncles have nothing in hand to hold against you, no crime or peccadillo; love letters could only be shown to me, and I wouldn't mind."

"No, they have neither crime nor love letters to hold against me. But they can blackmail me all the same. That's where you come in, darling. They know that now they've got me."

"I don't understand a word. Where do I come in? How? Please explain."

"I'll have to start at the beginning, then. My uncles and, in their wake, the whole family, think I'm the milking cow of all of them. I don't object to making a reasonable allowance to the older ones; but I don't see eye to eye with a lot of idlers like my younger uncles and my own generation. Why shouldn't they work? Why should I have to keep them? Quite apart from financial considerations, it's bad for a man not to work. He's bound to become a rotter, especially in this country where his every whim is encouraged. My Uncle Fakhruddin has never done a stroke of work, and Abdul Sattar and their sons follow his example. The whole lot live in the family village, the last of an originally big estate. They live on my allowance, squeezing extras from poor tenants for whom they've never done a thing. Their fields and orchards run wild, because they're too lazy for any constructive work. They eat and talk and gamble; and if debts run too high and the police threaten, it is I who am to provide the cash. You can't imagine what my life has been. Seeing a letter of theirs, I hardly dare to open it. For the past few years I've stopped visiting by saying there are either no visits or no allowance."

"And where do I come in?"

"You are my soft spot, and they know it. For myself I don't mind trouble or odium; I'm past that stage. They knew I meant business, and stayed away. That's how I've had comparative peace in my house, at least. But now they know I'll do anything to save you trouble. Accordingly their plan is to create trouble for you, to make life in this house unbearable for both of us. They know I'll do anything to get them out."

"Rashid, why can't you continue to say either visit or cash?"

"Because they'd bring in Mary Ann, Mother. Mud flung against me doesn't matter. But I won't have Mary Ann's name dragged about by them. So I'll have to give in this time."

73

"Don't give in on my account. I'll stick things through with you. You don't know yet how militant I can be if I want to, can't I, mummy?"

"Darling—you're the best pal a man ever had—I do so hate your having to hear all these nasty things. What must you think of it all! You're not angry, are you?" Rashid's face is working. "It isn't my fault, indeed it isn't."

Mary Ann takes his hand: "We do understand what you went through all alone. But you aren't alone any more. We are with you to the last ditch."

"No more alone! Sometimes I can't believe it."

"But it's true. Now let us be practical. What are we to do?"

"You, darling? Nothing. Just leave things to me."

"But I have to know. How else can I face your uncles? What exactly did you settle with them last night?"

"Well, I got Fakhruddin off the idea of bringing his family here. I dare say he never meant to; it was just to frighten you. He has also agreed to depart within three days provided I equip him completely and increase his allowance. But we haven't yet agreed about Abdul Sattar. I won't give in on that point."

"What is it they want? And what does 'fitting out completely' mean?"

"In India hosts have to fit out guests before departure. Wealthy guests get some presents only; but people who are either poor or arrive purposely only with what they've got on, must be fitted out. One has to give at least one of each kind of garment: *chervani*, trousers, shoes, underwear, headgear. Abdul Sattar arrived without even a blanket, though I gave him a good one on his last visit."

"Does he go in for a blanket collection?"

"He? I'm sure he sells a new one at once."

"Do you mean to say that this is a practice all over India?"

"More or less, and with Hindus as well as Muslims. Of course not with really educated people. But a man loses face if he doesn't fit out those among his relatives and friends who need or pretend to need help."

"So if you need clothes or things, all you have to do is to go a-visiting?"

"Exactly."

"What a paradise for certain people!"

74

"That's why they don't want to work. As long as you've relatives, you're bound to have food, shelter and clothes, so why work? That is my uncles' case."

"What is it you refuse to do?"

"They want me to buy a partnership for Abdul Sattar in a cloth-shop. It is in the town next to where they live. They want him to earn money for their expenses. If I refuse, Abdul Sattar is to remain here with us. It's sheer and brutal blackmail. As though he ever would make money!"

"And what will you do?"

"Not give in. If I had all the money I had spent on setting up people in business and paying their gambling debts, I could deck you in diamonds and pearls almost from head to foot."

"Don't worry about that! You know I dislike wearing jewels. What will you do?"

"Leave it to me, I beg of you. Only don't worry. Please don't talk to the uncles. Do remain inside. Send food—Indian food, cook knows what—for both of them to the front veranda at ten or ten-thirty which is the hour for their midday meal. Let it be plenty, two meat dishes aside from *pilau*, two vegetables, and sweets. They are not to say they went hungry. Only don't meet them, please."

"But how can I have it said that your uncles are not received into the house, and have to remain outside even for their meals? What will people say? It really looks too bad."

"Then have the food served in Uncle's room."

"It is far too small. Please, dear, let us do things properly. Make it at least the drawing room."

"Promise not to show yourself! I don't want Uncle being as rude to you as yesterday. I'll try to come over for their meal."

Exclamations, shouting from the front veranda! Within a few hours our peaceful house has become a queer place.

Rashid attended his uncles' meal, while we remained invisible. Since he had to go back to the office immediately afterward, we didn't know what mood the tyrants were in. But we were not left in ignorance for long. Smiling, Uncle Fakhruddin suddenly stood at the door of Mary Ann's room in which we sat sewing.

"I want a talk with my daughter. To know her I have traveled

75

many days and nights [an exaggeration]. Will she not be the mother of my grandchildren?"

He sits down unasked. With his placid smile and patriarchal appearance he seems the very incarnation of benevolence.

"I see my daughter has not yet changed her attire."

No reply. Mary Ann is gazing into space.

"A Muslim lady must wear Muslim dress."

"I am no Muslim lady. I am a Christian."

"What? My beloved nephew, my son, married to an unbeliever? That cannot be true. It would be terrible were he to have committed such an unforgivable sin against the only true religion."

"It is no sin at all, since the Holy Koran allows Muslims to take brides among 'the peoples of the book,' both Christians and Jews." Mary Ann seems now bent upon putting the intruder in his place. "Moreover, Muslim husbands are requested to facilitate the fulfillment of religious duties for their non-Muslim wives. What about Mary the Copt, the Prophet's own wife—Peace be upon him——?"

"Am I to learn about my own religion, the only true one, from an unbeliever, my son's wife, who should not open her mouth in my presence?"

"You are to learn nothing. I'm simply quoting the fifth *surat* of the Holy Koran."

"How do you know, if you are no Muslim?"

"We learn quite a lot of things at home, especially how to know and appreciate other religions." (This is an exaggeration on Mary Ann's part. Most Westerners don't know or care about other religions.)

"Had I known that my misguided son had married an unbeliever!"

"You did know. He wrote to you from Bombay by registered mail."

"I took it for a joke. Was it not bad enough to have married a Westerner? For many centuries our blood has remained pure and undefiled. Now, for the first time, it is being spoiled."

I got up. "Really, sahib, this conversation ought to end. I'm sure Rashid will be very angry to hear about it."

"Will he? Well, I can tell you that the least he expects is for your daughter to become a Muslim at once; only then will people stop despising him. Marry a Westerner! Do you think that because of the airs you people give yourselves it is considered an honor to have a western girl in our families? It isn't. It's considered a shame."

After that, developments moved swiftly. We did not again see the uncles. They had their meals at Auntie's. Twice Rashid talked to them in her and her sons' presence to settle matters. He refused to talk to them in his own house. Fifty hours after their arrival, they left. Only Faizuddin saw them off. Rashid stood his ground. No partnership was purchased for the younger uncle. The victory was not theirs.

June 24

"Mummy, do you note everything in your diary?"

"Certainly not everything, darling."

"But you should! I rely on you as historian. It would be a thousand pities to forget the things that happen to us."

"Yes, who would believe that in our present small-town existence there should be so much excitement and even melodrama."

"Have you written about the Rani of Sangwar?"

"I'm afraid I didn't. I write quite casually about a thing that strikes me, or some line of thought. It's just for me. Nobody will ever read this diary except you. So there is no need for completeness."

"There is. Things are so interesting and shouldn't get lost. Have you written about the breaking of the monsoon?"

"Not that either."

"Mummy, what are you thinking of? The rains, and the joy of the people, and the rain songs! And at times the streets under water! Now we know why the shop entrances are built so high, to be reached only by steps or soap boxes. Do you remember how we wondered about it the first day?"

"Yes, it seems ages ago. Now we feel already quite initiated, don't we?"

"We have still much to learn. Astonishing things are happening all the time. Do you know what Mrs. Lavanyia told me this morning while you were gardening?"

"I wondered why she was staying so long."

"Well, it was a lengthy story. You know how she loves talking. It seems that everybody knows everything. People feel very much

77

with us. The Hindus say—at least Mrs. Lavanyia says they say, but perhaps it's only she—that I should beware of the uncles' evil eye. She says Muslims are capable of anything, and for all she knows I am in great danger."

"What nonsense! Muslims are just as kind to us as Hindus. The uncles were an individual case; such people do exist in every community. Could anybody have been sweeter to you over this affair than Auntie and her sons?"

"They did feel so ashamed, though they had nothing to do with it. I told Mrs. Lavanyia as much. She pulled an enigmatic face and said this was India, and I should be careful; some day I would remember her words."

"Funny woman!"

"Mummy, the better I know Hindustani, the less pleasant life becomes. In the beginning I didn't understand what people were telling me; I just smiled, so did they, and everything was all right. Now I begin to understand their gossip, and I don't like it. It's interesting, of course, and I learn a lot; but there is so much meanness in it. Everybody seems to talk against everybody."

"That happens in many parts of the world, though usually in a more sophisticated way."

"But here it's sometimes too obvious. By the way, did I tell you that people think you must dislike them very much to have shut them out during your illness? They say you'd have admitted Europeans, but not Indians."

"To reproach me of all people for color prejudice! Didn't you explain how, with us, nobody is allowed into a sick-room, and how Westerners would never dream of entering unasked?"

"I did, but you know it's no use. You must be extra kind, that's all."

"I'm sorry I was so unsociable."

"Don't worry. Things will mend soon. Tomorrow everybody will be at Mrs. Motilal's."

June 25

Red, black, green pepper; red and green chillies; ginger; saffron; cardamom; curry-powder; poppy-seed; clover; bay leaf; turmeric; coriander; both green and dried; nutmeg; cinnamon; dill; marjoram; thyme; leek; all kinds of nuts and raisins.

78

Ground rice, barley, millet; *jowar, bajri* and other flour ground from pulse; *mawa,* which is solidified milk or, rather, cream, used for expensive sweets—the Indian names of all these, and a good many others we rehearse before going to Mrs. Motilal's tea-party so as to understand explanations.

Our knowledge is greater than two months ago; yet there is much more to learn, quite apart from the Hindustani names for various condiments. India seems inexhaustible in grains, pulses, vegetables, fruits, herbs and spices unknown to us. There seems to be everything our planet has ever produced; and I remember that Asia has been the cradle of almost every cereal mankind knows. Some have relapsed into wild growth in the East, while raised and highly developed in Europe; others have been cultivated here for many thousands of years. Whenever I am faced with the great variety of flour here, as compared to the very few kinds we are using at home—after all we live more or less on wheat; corn and rice flour are the exception—I am amazed at the bounty of the blessing. Everything grows here. But it is usually not tended as it should be, owing to poverty and many other reasons.

According to western notions, food is extremely cheap. India-grown food, I mean. The moment you go in for imported stuff like tinned food or bottled sauces, things become expensive. I can now understand why the hotel manager smiled at my hasty purchase that first morning. I spent three or four rupees on a few tins; in a place where you get a pound of mutton for three annas, and a dozen huge bananas for two, this seems an expense only a greenhorn would go in for. In addition to lavish country produce the Bombay and Calcutta stores will send up every kind of tinned food, every brand of bacon and ham, game, sole and lobster packed in ice, and so on but we don't get these things. On the one hand it seems not right to spend a lot on such luxuries in a country in which people are so desperately poor; on the other, we want to learn about and live on Indian produce. Only then can one learn about a people's eating customs.

June 26

Mrs. Motilal and her young sister looked ravishing in yellow saris, with marigold and roses adorning their plaits. There was the second Mrs. Jarwarkar, the mother of the vegetable oil expert, Mrs. Sharma; Mrs. Ram Chandra, the hospital superintendent's wife; Mrs. Prabha

79

Lal, whose husband is professor at both colleges. Mrs. Sharma had brought two nieces from Bihar, at present staying with her. Mrs. Lavanyia presided, so to say. I don't know why, but this inconspicuous little woman, rather plain and plainly dressed, doing most of her housekeeping herself, is a kind of social arbiter. Whoever is received by her is *reçu*. The greatest ladies of town and surroundings call on her, and she is invited to each and all select purdah parties while other ladies, whose husbands have higher positions and are wealthier than Lavanyia, are not. Is it only because the Lavanyias are the highest-class Brahmans of all? Or is there some other reason?

The tea is overwhelming. We are served with no less than eight savories, let alone the sweets. For Mary Ann's and my benefit most savories are prepared by Mrs. Motilal's sister on a primus stove before our very eyes. The delicious spirals we eat piping hot and crusty are made of seasoned rice flour and fried in *ghi*—clarified butter. The vermicelli fried gold-brown consist of millet flavored with marjoram and dill. And so on.

But our culinary education does not stop with tea. Of course Mary Ann and I can't enter the kitchen; even Deccani Brahmans cannot go so far as that in breaking caste rules. But we are allowed into the storeroom, corresponding in size and position to the dining room in our house. Brahmans eat in the kitchen containing the sacred fire or in the courtyard, and don't need a dining room.

There is a huge grain-chest, filled with carefully picked wheat. More wheat is stored in a go-down. There is a rice-chest, filled with equally carefully picked rice. Whenever flour is needed, a servant picks over the necessary quantity a second time and takes it away for milling; the same applies to other kinds of cereals, and to rice. Flour of every description is kept in highly polished brass receptacles, holding from ten to fifty pounds. *Massala*—spices—are stored in beautiful triangular glass bottles, each more than a foot in height and neatly labeled. We count about thirty such bottles. The spices, carefully cleaned and sunned at the time of purchase, are ground every day before use in curries and the like. Cereals, rice, spices, onions, garlic and so on are bought once or twice a year in great quantities at their respective harvest seasons.

Everything is so spotlessly clean and shining that I involuntarily think of the quantities of Vim needed to polish such a lot of brass. But we learn that only ashes and earth can produce such polish, and at once resolved to try out that method. To say that Mrs. Motilal's utensils are cleaner than ours is a considerable understatement.

We sit down again. Conversation becomes very animated, following our praise and enthusiasm. Each lady gives good advice, or tells of a specially praiseworthy recipe as devised by her mother or grandmother.

"You're so kind. We've learned lots today," says Mary Ann.

"We have told you all our small knowledge, memsahib. Now you must tell us the secrets of the West."

"Yes, the secrets of the West!" There is general commotion. "We want to know so many things!"

"Which?" We are eager to be of service.

"Is it true that in the West women take precedence in everything and that men must obey their bidding?"

"Well, yes and no. Men certainly don't obey women's bidding; but women also don't obey men's. The question of bidding isn't in the foreground. There is partnership, comradeship, between man and woman." (At least there should be—is my aside.)

"What is that, memsahib?"

"Neither man nor woman is master. They share everything, good or bad. It's walking through life hand in hand."

"Hand in hand? Oh, that's called Free Love, isn't it? Already at school-age! My husband told me. The Chief Justice of America himself wrote how every girl. . . ." Mrs. Ram Chandra, blushing, looks around, proud of her superior knowledge.

I nearly explode. When will Westerners stop quoting Katherine Mayo to India, and Indians stop quoting Judge Lindsay's books to the West? Both describe *one* aspect only very incompletely; undue generalization has made this sexual aspect one of the chief stumbling-blocks between East and West. Judge Lindsay is cited as the ultimate authority on the utter depravity of the West; Katherine Mayo, on Hindu-Indian depravity. Both deductions being wrong, their widespread influence is preposterous.

We try to convey as much to our charming listeners, but in vain. To them—*per procura*, for they haven't, of course, read these books themselves—Katherine Mayo is all lies, and Judge Lindsay gospel truth.

Mrs. Sharma's nieces whisper with their aunt. The old lady turns to us. "Memsahib, tell us the secret of the white skin. How can we become white ourselves?"

Mrs. Ram Chandra, the educated doctor's lady, intervenes: "But that is impossible. We cannot become white. There is the pigment of the skin. . . ."

"Oh yes, we can." Mrs. Motilal is positive. "Not we, that is, but our children. If one does something during babyhood. . . ."

"That's what my mother's mother says," affirms the eldest niece. "She comes from Calcutta side, and in her own mother's time a great English lady visited, repeatedly, the *zenana* of an aunt of hers. That great lady told them the secret of the white skin. When in the West a baby is born, a bath is prepared immediately after its birth; this bath it is that makes the skin white."

"What do they put into it?" many voices ask at once.

"My mother's mother forgot. She was but a child when she listened to the great English lady."

"Do tell us, memsahib."

"I'm afraid we don't know."

"Masahib will know. She has had a child of her own. Look how white memsahib is!"

I don't quite know how to mitigate the disappointment. "Truly, we don't know of any recipe for making the skin white. Our babies get a bath immediately after birth to make them clean and sweet; but there's nothing in the water to bleach the skin."

"Oh, masahib, we told you so many of our secrets, and you will not tell us a single one of yours!"

"My dears, I'm so sorry. If I knew, I'd tell you with joy. We are more ignorant than you think us."

"And why should you want to be white?" adds Mary Ann. "God created many flowers of all hues. Is the red more beautiful than the blue or the yellow? All of them belong to His garden. You are beautiful as you are. There is no need for you to change."

The Indian ladies protest: white skin is the way to happiness and power. Mary Ann and I speak of the incomparable beauty and grace of Indian womanhood, knowing all the while that, as far as India is concerned, the ladies are certainly right. A girl a shade fairer than her otherwise prettier sister is the first to be married off. But we want to make Indian women conscious of their attractiveness, and skip the inter-continental color problem.

82

"Why didst thou not tell us that glass cleaned with ashes is cleanest?"

Cook shakes his head in utter innocence. "I know memsahibs bazaar-stuff like buying."

"Maharaj, why didst thou not say something? Now that Ghafur uses yellow earth the brass looks so clean."

"Masahib wisest is. Who son is to advise Mother?"

Both sides enjoy the gentle mockery of those eastern replies. Everything is as highly polished as at Mrs. Motilal's, a fact which is already known to town and district by the invisible unfathomable news service of India. We have learned the lesson, and our staff are pleased with our having learned it.

Indian servants are incredibly sensitive. Whatever their individual faults or merits, where their masters' life and thoughts are concerned they are like antennae. There's no use hiding anything from them; they know our thoughts before we do. I'll never forget one afternoon in a feudal State Guest House on our first journey. Since it was Sunday, we hadn't ordered our car for the usual afternoon drive; we wanted the driver to be free. At five P.M. European air mail was brought by a *chaprassi*, who retired before we opened the first letter. One of the letters contained the news of a dear friend's sudden death in Scotland. Mary Ann and I felt rather depressed, longing for home, yet not wanting to say so. At five-thirty the head-bearer knocked. "Will the memsahib and Miss sahib not take a drive?" he said. "No, we've dismissed the car for today." "I have taken the liberty to order it, memsahib. It will be here presently. It is not good to remain indoors too long. One gets sad. There is a temple the ladies have not yet visited."

How did he know? How *do* Indian servants know?

Anyhow, they do. When the uncles were here everybody, Hindu and Muslim, including outsiders like the postman and *dhobi*, did all they could to express their sympathy and concern. I wonder how I'll stand colder climes after this. Perhaps I'll long for the understanding and affection of Indian servants.

I'VE always forgotten to mention the club. Does this mean it doesn't impress me much? It's a nice building, though, erected in the same style as the other governmental buildings. I believe Government had it built; for in the first instance, it was meant for officials. Now businessmen and professionals have come in, too. There is a nice garden, leading to two well-kept hard tennis courts, a big lounge, a ping-pong and a billiard room. The radio is in the lounge; bridge is played there, as well as on the veranda surrounding the whole house.

The social life of Akbarabad is vested in the club. All members attend nearly daily, leaving only in time for their evening meal, which Indians usually take at nine P.M. Apart from Mrs. Blackwell and two Parsi ladies from Bombay—which accounts for their modernism—we are the only females.

"Why don't you encourage ladies to attend, Sethsahib?" asks Mary Ann of Seth Chandralal, the club president. "I remember with great pleasure your words about the necessity of ending purdah. Wouldn't the club be a good starting point?"

Seth Chandralal smiles. "I know what you are driving at, memsahib. You think I'm being very inconsistent. So I am. But don't forget that man has no say in the matter. It is our ladies who don't want to leave purdah. They think they will lose their good reputation by attending a mixed club. Get your Mrs. Lavanyia to join. She has great influence. But she won't."

"Indeed she won't." We remember her acid comment on Brahman ladies appearing before men other than their close relatives.

"Perhaps we could try a ladies' club in the room at the back. It could be curtained off."

"But that's not doing away with purdah, Sethsahib."

"It would be a start. The ladies would get used to driving to the club. Some enterprising ones might come across the purdah in due course."

"Sethani sahib wouldn't join?"

"Oh, no. Don't forget, memsahib, that she is a grandmother. The elder generation is very conservative. By the way, she hopes you will visit her again soon."

"With great pleasure." At first we had called on Sethani sahib after having dined or tea'd with her husband. Finding her very nice and intelligent, we have taken to visiting her on her own account. She can't talk enough about Bombay, where she spends at least four months of the year—shopping, going to the races, seeing pictures: in a word, out of purdah. Only here in her own home she has to stick to it. People would resent if she didn't.

We don't attend the club very often. But, at least, at the club we've met the college staff, debarred from the tables of the elect, but by far the nicest and most cultured people in town. How we dislike this attitude of "money or position alone counts." And how it reminds us of Main Streeters—or many realms at home!

July 4

"Don't speak so rudely to me, Rashid."

"Rudely? Good gracious, darling! Mother, did I speak rudely?"

"Of course not. Quite normally. Why do you think he was rude, child? He really wasn't."

"Oh, it's your fault, mummy. You always speak softly; so I suppose if somebody speaks 'normally' or raises his voice a little, I think he is being rude, because I'm used to you."

"Mother, this is really a grave lapse on your part. How can a mere man ever compete with you?"

We joke a moment or two; then I leave them to themselves, and sit down among my favorite rose bushes.

Old times come back. Mary Ann, about ten years old, complains of her teacher's having spoken rudely to her. I make her repeat the incriminating words, which she candidly does. Then I say: "But, darling, that is not rude! She spoke to you quite normally."

And then an avalanche rushing over my head, both from Mary Ann and her faithful nannie, who had been staying with us since my child's birth.

"It's all your fault, mummy! You spoil us so, that's why we feel everybody else is rude. If you scold, it is as though somebody else were kissing. You are never angry; you only pretend to be for educational reasons, and I, on the other hand, pretend to believe you're angry."

85

Now, thirteen years later, in India, I wonder. Did I make Mary Ann too dependent on warmth and affection, even in externals? Is it unhealthy for her? Or was I right to give her as much warmth as possible? So far I can't see that it did her any harm. She is a giver, not a taker.

July 7

The Rani Saheba of Sangwar has taken a fancy to us. Whenever she drives to town from Sangwar to shop or consult the senior lady doctor, she makes it a point to drop in for tea—a purdah tea, of course, for no men apart from her father, husband and sons have ever beheld her. The Sangwars belong to a princely family from Rajputana who keep a purdah stricter than any Muslim; for with them a father-in-law never beholds his son's wife; nor can a daughter-in-law appear with her husband before his mother.

Since our bungalow has no purdah entrance, her Chevrolet drives to the back door of our courtyard. All male servants—we have no others—are chased away; the Rani alights between sheets of gold brocade, held up high in front of their heads by her male servants, so as to exclude visibility; she steps into the courtyard with her female attendants, where Mary Ann receives her. A purdah lady never goes out without one or two female companions. Even at home a lady of good family should never be alone.

It would be quite useful for us to have an ayah for such occasions, but it seems such a waste. We have to retrench as it is, with increased allowances to Rashid's family.

Yesterday being a holiday, we went out to Sangwar for tea and dinner. Rashid stayed with the Raja, a jovial man of about fifty-five, who is extremely fond of shooting big game, gardening and taking colored films. Mary Ann and I had tea with the Rani in her apartments on the third floor; the Raja occupies the second.

The palace of Sangwar is a two-fold structure. There is a fortress-like building, windows starting only on the second floor level for fear of feud and siege. A modern wing has been added without any transition. Thus every floor contains both grim medieval and up-to-date rooms. As far as we can see, the latter are more for show than for daily use. The Rani has a lovely bathroom in pink and silver, pink tub and all; but she takes her bath under the shower and tap of her Indian bathroom.

86

The Rani had asked us to meet her widowed daughter, Her Highness of Raipuri, who is on her yearly visit to her parents. With her is her little son, His Highness the Maharaja, during whose minority a Council of State rules in Raipuri.

She is a very pretty woman of twenty-five, wearing the modern sari instead of the Rajput *gagra* and *lugri*—bodice and skirt—which become her mother so well. Widowed three years ago, she has to spend her whole life in utter seclusion, except for receiving lady-visitors and calling on royal *zenanas*.

"We don't miss anything; we Rajput women are used to such a life," she says with a smile to Mary Ann, "but to you conditions must seem unbelievable, memsahib."

"Not unbelievable, Your Highness; my Mother and I have visited many *zenanas*. We have the good fortune to have many Indian woman-friends. They are so delightful. But I wish——"

"You don't believe in purdah, memsahib?"

"I am afraid I don't, Your Highness."

"Nor do I, in general."

Before her marriage the Maharani had, for several years, an English governess, much beloved by her, who had certainly influenced her in many ways. "For us, however, there seems no other way."

"Do tell us about the West, masahib," interrupts the Rani. "Why is everybody divorced once or twice?"

I understand the two-fold implication. She wants to call her westernized daughter to order, and at the same time to deprecate the West. "At the risk of disappointing you, Rani Saheba, I have to say that in the West there are many more good than bad marriages—as everywhere else, I suppose."

"Then why all these divorces?"

"There are not so many, really. But it's the divorces people talk and write about, not the marriages. That's why you out here think that everybody is divorced."

"Yes, so we do." The Maharani bends eagerly forward. "But I know we are wrong. As masahib says, there are happy marriages everywhere, and in the West there is comradeship, which should make for better marriages."

"How can the western procedure be called marriage at all?" the Rani flares up. "A woman visible to other men is no wife."

This time the interruption comes from me, for it is difficult not to speak of the many Hindu wives who, losing their lord's favor, have to lead a miserable life at the mercy of their luckier successor or their utter dependence upon, and obedience to, those three males who, during their whole life, have authority over them, father, husband and son. There would be many more things to say; but somehow it doesn't seem fair, even on provocation, to say them to these women who are part of the system—especially not to that wistful young widow who must remain lonely to her death. So I interrupt, believing foolishly that historical problems will provide safer ground. "How long is it since *sati*-burning of widows on their husbands' funeral pyre has been abolished in Rajputana?" Queens and princesses of Rajputana are famous in history and legend for heroic *sati* to escape the Mogul conquerors.

The Rani proudly raises her head. "Not so long as in other parts of India. Our families were the last to capitulate before the interference of the British. I remember *satis* in my childhood, though they had, of course, to be kept secret."

"Rani Saheba—do you mean to say you are in favor of *sati*? Without the laws against it, even your own daughter——"

"Of course I am. It is a woman's right and duty to follow her lord in death. Why should foreigners be allowed to take this glory from her?"

What use is there in arguing? Reformers always say that woman is the retarding element, the one who clings to the past. They are right.

July 11

I'm again down with a bit of fever, this time without a cold, though everything is damp during the monsoon. Mary Ann is sitting with me when Rashid enters. Under kisses he murmurs something in her ear. At first she looks startled, then very pleased. Fondly she strokes his hand. "Mummy, he is such a good boy! I really can't tell you how good he is."

I don't know what it is all about, and there is no need to. All I know is that my child is happy with her husband. Bless him!

Mary Ann went out this morning without telling me where to. On her return she comes straight into my room. "Mummy, I went to see Dr. Cama. She says it's true—I'm expecting a baby, at last."

At last! I remember Mary Ann's girlish dreams. Now her wish is fulfilled, thank God. My darling girl!

"Does Rashid know?"

"Not yet. I'll tell him tonight."

"Say that I'm tired, and am to have dinner in my room."

"That's sweet of you, thanks. But I'm sure he'll rush to you to let you have the news. Don't let him know that you knew before him."

"Of course not."

It is as she says. At ten P.M. they burst into my room, where I duly lie abed. "Mother!" Rashid can't find words. They sit down on my bed, all three of us talking nineteen to the dozen. We are happy. And I go to sleep with thoughts of prams, nursery furniture and "*Frère Jacques.*"

Strange how western Mary Ann has become all of a sudden in her culinary longings. "Mummy, let's have kippers. Or the *Sachertorte*—Viennese chocolate cake great-grandmother's cook used to make. Or let's go to the *quartier latin*, to the students' tavern. We'll have *choucroute à l'alsacienne* with lots of sausages. Or fresh sardines. And a *coeur crème* or *camembert* for dessert. Oh, mummy, now I know what I want most: let's walk down from the Sorbonne straight to that baker's just opposite on the *Boul Mich'*. There we buy *pain au chocolat*, still fragrant and hot, and that's what I'd like best."

How can I get it for her?

Mrs. Ganpat Lal, one of the most advanced and prominent women of India, has paid a flying visit to Akbarabad. We had her to tea. She is beautiful in spite of being a grandmother, widely traveled, well-read, writer, speaker and social worker. Her main interests are betterment of conditions for the untouchables, remarriage for Hindu widows and women's education.

"Will you help us?" she asks.

"Of course." We tell her of our welfare work at home. We hope to get things going in Akbarabad, too. Then we relate our recent conversations about purdah, *sati* and such things. Mrs. Ganpat Lal lives in British India where, in big towns at least, views are more advanced; but she is quite familiar with reactionary parts of the country like ours.

"Education is everything. Example and education. Will both of you teach at the Akbarabad Women's Institute? So-called untouchables attend."

"Is it the one near the market place?"

"No, that's for caste-women. It would be a good thing if you taught there too. But I was thinking of the little Institute for Untouchable Women. Do take it under your wings."

We promise to do so. "Do you get much support in Akbarabad?"

"Yes and no. At the women's meeting yesterday I got much applause and a good purse for my work. When I turn my back, very few ladies do anything until I or another social worker revisits Akbarabad. Then it's again applause and money. Well, we *do* need the money, so I shouldn't grumble."

"It must be uphill work."

"It is, but things improve a lot. There are so many schemes for bettering conditions." Soon we are deep in rural reconstruction and education. If a woman of Mrs. Ganpat Lal's caliber were here—how different life would be!

July 27

At long last my bank has sent me some money. I've set aside a fair amount for nursery requirements; ordered a stove with a good oven and shelves for the pantry. The electric refrigerator will have to wait. But Mary Ann'll have all the copper and brass she wants for kitchen and storeroom. Moreover, we spent this morning pleasantly in buying a good number of saris for her, and several dress lengths of cotton cloth for me. I much prefer cotton saris to the silk or georgette she wears for afternoon and evening. She likes cotton saris of antique Indian patterns, with their incomparable blending of color and form, for all her morning wear. One day it is a shell-pink muslin patterned in honeycomb design, another, flowers in three different shades of blue on ivory ground; a third, a green sari with a Muslim border of mosques; a fourth, a yellow sari with a formal pattern of lotus flowers. These cotton muslins are softer than the softest silk; it is sheer delight to wear or look at them. Only now do I understand what eighteenth and nineteenth century books mean by eulogizing "Indian muslins."

This morning we bought four cotton saris, each one more delightful than the other. To look always fresh and tidy one needs one or two per day, so one can't have too many of them. In addition we bought two saris of handspun silk with handprinted border; one deep blue, the other strawberry. And finally a Benares sari for great occasions, gold-gauze shot with green, which, incidentally, is the Muslim color. How Rashid will enjoy seeing her!

July 29

An English friend asks for my advice. Her second daughter wants to accept the proposal of an Indian fellow-student in Cambridge. He is the son of a rich landowner in Bengal. Do I think a "mixed" marriage can be successful?

Sitting on the roof to watch the sunset, Mary Ann and I discuss the letter. She knows the girl better than I do.

"Each case is different. Generally speaking, I don't think it is easy for a western girl to come out to India."

"Why do you say that? Are you not happy?"

"Indeed I am, touch wood. But yet it isn't easy."

"What exactly do you mean?" My heart is beating fast.

"Local influences are often stronger than people. Joan's Bengal boy may be all right; but what of his people once she settles in Bengal? Will he not change under the influence of all he has known from infancy? We've often discussed the boys who, in the West, are modernists to the fingertips and, when they return, keep their wives and daughters in purdah, like any of the most old-fashioned of people."

"That's true."

"Rashid is different. Many others too. Yet if I were to have a wish granted, it'd be to live with him in Bombay or the West. Whatever might come between us would arise from reactionary local influences, not from his own self. He is really incredibly good, I realize it more and more."

"Joan's Bengali boy might turn out as well—though it would be rare luck. Rashids are no everyday occurrence, neither here nor in the West."

"Do write that Joan should first of all scrutinize the boy, and his dependability under duress; afterwards she should scrutinize herself. Does she only love the boy, and her own romantic notions of moonlight over the Ganges—as we all did? Or does she also love India? Really, mummy, I do think that it's not enough to love the man; one must love India as well, or else one can't stand the distress, the squalor and the many heartbreaking problems. In the end one might blame the country on the man, which would be a shame."

"It would. Has your 'real India' disappointed you?"

"No. I love it, as I did when I didn't know it properly—no, more. But at times it drives me mad. This town is rich; yet there is no welfare work to speak of, no maternity care, no Child Welfare Center. The schools are—well, what we know they are. The college professors are not regarded as social equals of rich shopkeepers, who might find it hard to read a book."

"And the purdah business!"

"That's worst of all. A country can't develop ahead of its womenfolk; so education and better health for women are more important than anything else. Look at the women in Auntie's house, or at the Rani of Sangwar! Mrs. Ganpat Lal and her friends do much; yet so much more is needed. I'll work to get girls out of purdah. But first I must have my little boy. Yes, it'll be a boy. You always wanted a girl, and had her. I want a boy, and will have him. Then there must be a sister, so he won't have to grow up alone as I had to. But afterwards I'll work to get girls out of purdah, and give them a chance. Meantime you'll carry on for me."

"Am I to stay here forever and ever?"

"I hope not. Nor am I and Rashid. But you won't leave me in the lurch, will you, mummy? This is not Europe. What should I do without you to talk to? And Rashid wouldn't dream of letting you go. Do stop for a while being a well-known this and that. Be just a mother and grannie."

"Indeed I will, darling. Shall I say with Auntie 'a woman's book to write and read in—'? How sweet it will be to hold your baby!"

August 4

The stove with a really good oven has arrived. I ordered it from

Bombay. Looking at it, I'm proud as a peacock. Mary Ann ought to have familiar food, for which she is longing. Since she loves chocolate above anything, I'm planning all sorts of chocolate cake. I might also be able to turn out éclairs, though I never did them; but how on earth am I to prepare the *pain au chocolat* you get at every baker's in Paris?

August 7

Mary Ann has had a terrible accident. Just before the car sped on to Akbarabad bridge, the door suddenly opened; somehow she fell out and rolled down the steep slope, suffering from internal hemorrhage and a light concussion. One doesn't know yet where the lesion is. There are two specialists in attendance, apart from the local doctors. They are hopeful, and say that, in some weeks, Mary Ann will be all right.

But I have not forgotten my dream.

I know that my child will die.

*   *   *

September 29

It is a long time since I opened my diary.

When all was over, I sent two cables home, asking that all friends be told about Mary Ann's death. Cables and airmail letters have been pouring in. Many friends ask me to let them have details of Mary Ann's passing and last words; others want to know about me, or even suggest traveling to India to fetch me home. I cannot bring myself to reply, though I know how anxiously dear friends are waiting for my news. It is as though I were paralyzed. I can bear up well enough in my immediate surroundings, but I can't write about things. It has been so all my life. When Richard died, it took years before I could speak about it. Now it will take still longer.

But if I can't write letters, there's another thing I have to do. I must record in my diary what has happened. I feel I ought to set it all down, partly so things shouldn't get lost, partly for India's sake. Through my child's death, and subsequent events, I have learned to know the loving-kindness and generosity Indians are capable of—not only friends, but each and all. This experience has been unique. True, I've had other sorts of experience too. Strange, bewildering things have happened to me, stranger than I can say. But

93

the chief feature remains the overwhelming sweetness and love Indians have lavished on a Westerner whom they had known only for a short time, and who had never done anything for them. These facts deserve recording. But the task is going to be a hard one. Perhaps it will be best to write the whole story without interruption. If I don't write in that way, I may never be able to complete my narrative at all.

Mary Ann gained consciousness two days after her accident. The specialists thought the worst was over. She had not lost her child, and the inner hemorrhage had, apparently, stopped. Everybody was hopeful, everybody but me. It was not my dream; I could easily have pushed that back. I just knew. But since others didn't, I kept this knowledge to myself. I thought the doctors just pretended optimism; after Mary Ann's death they assured me this had been genuine.

I had to do all the nursing myself, because Mary Ann didn't let anybody else touch her. Even in her initial unconsciousness she got restless if either of the two nurses approached her. I felt so sorry for them. During the three days of consciousness, one of them used to stand, motionless and unseen by Mary Ann, at the door of the dressing room. When changing the bed, taking off the icebags and so on, I just handed things to one of them without a word. I never left the bedroom while consciousness lasted. The moment I went, Mary Ann would get upset, even when her eyes were closed, or her mind was wandering; she would toss about and call herself hoarse: "Mummy, mummy!"

All the time she had to have a featherweight icebag on her head. Somebody, standing behind her, had to keep it in its place and, at the same time, shift the ice's weight gently in rotation, lest it be too heavy. The nurses, even invisible, were at once detected by her. Rashid immediately understood how to manage the ice. So did Dr. Chandra Lal, and Dr. Miss Cama, the Parsi lady doctor, who was extremely kind to me during those days. But, looking back now, it seems to me that it was nearly always maharaj who, standing behind Mary Ann, took charge of the icebag at all hours. I remember once having been struck by that fact.

"Thou must go for thy meals, maharaj. Thou art here too long already."

94

"How can I eat if my masters are in distress? How can I eat if my mistress is so ill?"

He didn't. Like myself, he knew, I think, that Mary Ann would die. And he knew that I knew.

The weather was hot and sticky, following a break in the monsoon. Blocks of ice had to be chopped into tiny fragments. During that procedure much ice melted in the heat. It was an anxious business, for there *had* to be chopped ice ready whenever maharaj lifted his eyebrows to indicate he'd soon need some. Then I would for a second appear at the door of the front veranda. *Chowkidar*, the Rajput night watchman, had made himself responsible for the handling of the precious ice, while Ismail Khan fetched ever-new supplies by car. In the same way, the moment I went near the courtyard door, cook appeared and I asked for orange juice, barley water, milk or whatever else was due. The only one of the servants who did not rise to the occasion was Ghafur. Perhaps he was too young to understand. He kept his hours, and didn't otherwise care whether his help was needed or not.

I can remember things only in a disconnected way. All the time I was wide awake, without feeling tired and with a kind of triple consciousness. Yet the effort to concentrate on everything Mary Ann needed was so great that I couldn't take in much else. Vaguely I was aware at times of drawing room and front-garden being full of people, without recognizing a single individual.

I also cannot place meals during those five days. The nurses and cook say that there were none. I only remember bananas; if I approached one of the doors of Mary Ann's room, there was always somebody who quickly peeled a banana for me or held a glass of orange juice to my lips. I didn't want these things, but they made me take them. Once I remember Waliuddin standing with a plate in his hands for what seemed an endless period outside the courtyard-door. I had no time to go out. When at last he got hold of me, he murmured that Auntie had sent that special dish for me to eat. I drew back; eating seemed utterly out of the question. For the first time, however, it entered my mind to inquire about Rashid's food; I heard that he, too, didn't take anything. Then and there I embarked on a kind of blackmail policy; every banana, cup of tea or glass of orange juice offered to me I accepted only if Rashid took the same in front of me. Soon he blackmailed me in return. We got so used to not taking anything if the other didn't that even today we look mechanically at each other's helpings and leftovers.

Apart from the nurses and Dr. Cama, there was no woman about the house. Purdah made ordinary female assistance impossible because Rashid, the doctors and our male servants had to be constantly in and out. Only after sunset there were women stepping softly out of the courtyard's darkness into the room, and moving back again into the night. It was the hour in which Rashid sat with his friends on the front veranda. I did not talk to the women, but they cannot have minded, since they saw how busy I was doing something for Mary Ann all the time. Sometimes I saw them; sometimes, too intent on Mary Ann, I hardly noticed their presence. If they could catch my eye they made a gesture of prayer or looked up heavenwards before disappearing again. As long as they kept out of Mary Ann's sight, I didn't mind these visitors. Among them I remember the Rani of Sangwar; a very poor market woman from whom Mary Ann had often bought vegetables, and who now had brought a whole basket of the most expensive oranges, a little fortune to her; the Maharani of Raipuri, suddenly standing before me and taking both my hands without a word; three ladies representing the Institute for Untouchable Women; all the Parsi ladies in town. But most of those who came I didn't even recognize.

All the European women were out of town. I longed to see one of them because I knew I would need help when the end came. Even death has its inexorable exactions. In the crucial moment, I would be alone for the laying out, the candles, the flowers and so on. It needn't have been so, for two unknown English women, residing sixty miles away, drove to Akbarabad on hearing the news. They spoke to one of the doctors outside the bungalow, asking him to tell me that they were at my disposal, should I need them. Somehow the message never reached me until weeks later. It was a pity; their help and presence would have been a great aid.

My attitude towards prayer has always been a little unusual. It hurts me beyond words that people of all creeds lift their eyes upwards mostly to ask for some favor or other. I'm against that petitioning spirit. One should think of God for God's own sake, not only as a means to get a better job, or as a source of hope during a time of illness. I remember saying as much to a very pious woman;

96

she looked at me in amazement and replied: "But I never go to Church without wanting something!" This attitude worries me. It seems to me that mankind will never evolve on such selfish and narrow lines. This is why I've never been able to pray "for" something on personal lines. For objective causes, yes; for me and mine, no.

Now, after Mary Ann's accident, I had the vague feeling—it was indeed no wish, rather a feeling of duty—that I ought to pray for my child's life. But it was impossible. Whenever I tried to, the words and thoughts formulated themselves simply into: "Thy will be done." "Remain true to yourself!" my child still seemed to say to me, even on her deathbed.

After a shock or in illness, people often return to their roots. During my long illness eight years ago—I was given up for many months—I could only grasp or utter ideas familiar from childhood and youth. The same thing now happened with Mary Ann. Whenever she was conscious she remembered her earlier life only. Rashid she knew instinctively; but she didn't know of India or her baby, of English or Hindustani. All she spoke was German or French, the languages of her childhood. It was heart-breaking to hear Rashid's ever-repeated question: "What does she say, Mother? What does my darling say?"

In the beginning I tried to translate for him as best I could, but soon it became impossible, for Mary Ann got restless the moment I didn't reply at once. At times, however, when she was fully conscious, she answered him in English; it was also in English that she once more said: "Mummy, I can't tell you how good he is!"—at which Rashid broke down. Her instinctive attitude left no doubt that she had been happy with him.

It was all the more heartbreaking that he couldn't understand what she was saying most of the time. I no longer tried to translate, but since he was always standing or sitting behind me, I sometimes laid my hand on his or leaned my head against him for a moment, as a token that I would translate all her words—later.

Another time it was he who comforted me. Mary Ann all her life had insisted on my singing to her every day; it was for her a ritual which she never dispensed with. Though she loved classical music, her favorites were the many folk songs I had sung to her in childhood. These she meant when she requested daily, "Mummy, sing."

97

During those five days, singing became increasingly difficult for me. Because I couldn't trust my voice, sometimes I sat silent, in spite of her pleading.

Shall I ever forget the day before the last? My child's eyes wide open but unseeing, her voice quite low but insistent. "Mummy, why don't you sing? I am ill, I have pains. It is such a little thing I am asking you." Then, with twitching mouth, in English: "Rashid, such a strange thing has happened. My mother doesn't love me any more. What can be the reason? Just now, when I am ill and in need of her, she has ceased loving me. Can you believe it?"

Rashid, steadying my head against his shoulder tried his best: "Mummy loves you so much, darling! I always was jealous of this love. There's no greater."

But Mary Ann did not hear him. She had stopped thinking in English. Softly moaning she lay there. *"Ma petite mère ne m'aime plus."*

Then I began to sing one song after the other, all those I knew she loved best, concentrating on one thing only: to keep my voice steady. Even in semi-consciousness Mary Ann would detect any tremor, any deviation from the usual. Suddenly I remembered how, if I had been sad, I had had to avoid singing in front of my father, between whom and me there had been a bond of complete musical understanding. In conversation I could deceive him; never, if I sang. "Where do the tears in your voice come from?" he would ask. I was thinking of him, and how I now sang to my child the familiar songs he had taught me; how he had waited and prayed for this child's birth with a fervor almost as great as that of a lover; how he had adored and worshiped the dark-eyed baby, he, a bulwark of the State, whose word was law to many; and then how he had had to go before she was even four years old.

I sang the Brahms, Mozart and Weber lullabies, which had lulled her to sleep so often; "Silent Night" and "O Sanctissima," which she always began to clamor for immediately after the Ascension, unable to restrain any more her longing for Christmas; songs of the mountains and the sea she would not again behold; Breton ballads, Gregorian tunes, "Vienna" and *"Au clair de la lune."* Within me I knew that now there would never be any grandchild to sing to, that my own child was now going from me; but I had to keep my voice steady. With God's help, I succeeded. I sang and sang. "Now

98

everything is all right again!" said Mary Ann at last, with a contented sigh.

I did not see the people who had gathered to listen. Later I heard that there had been hundreds out in the garden. "Christian Vedas," some of them said.

That last afternoon and evening of Mary Ann's consciousness! Those present, excluded from our German or French conversation, would have been amazed to learn that what we talked about was literature or, rather, one of its aspects.

It had started when Mary Ann awakened and said at once, as though in continuation of a trend of thought: "Nobody can ever take Christ from me, mummy! Christ in me is so strong! I'm flooded through with light and strength! It's He, not me!"

Then: "Mummy, promise you'll write about nothing else. That is what people need most. Not a narrow Christ of whom one is afraid. He came for all, Christians and non-Christians. He never excludes, He always includes. Why do books not say so? They should."

"Some do, darling."

And soon we were discussing the Gospels and the Zend Avesta, *Paradise Lost* and Plato, St. Theresa, the Grail Saga, Faust and the Divine Comedy. So we talked, finished each other's quotations, smiled if we had forgotten a line or two.

While talking, I reflected how during her short life she had, in one sense or another, always lived for the all-embracing Christ. Her present going to Him was but a step, a transition. For a moment I felt as though I would no longer want to cry.

That night Rashid realized that there was no hope left. I saw the change in him. He seemed like a man stricken. I found no time to talk to him, but I asked Ismail Khan to stay near his master during the night. "Memsahib very ill is," I said, "to God she go will." At least that is what I wanted to say, but I couldn't form proper sentences. English had left Mary Ann, Hindustani had left me. Even today I have not recaptured it.

So Ismail Khan sat in the cloister all night long. Rashid's bed had been moved there after the accident. I heard him sob all through the night. At about two o'clock, when Mary Ann was lying with closed eyes, I slipped out to him. He was sitting up in bed, his head in both hands. I sat down in a chair. He at once pulled loose the mosquito net and clung to me, his face wet with tears.

"I can't believe it, Mother."

"Didn't you know until now, darling?"

"No. And if I did, I pushed the thought back. We were so happy, Mother dear."

"I know. My whole gratitude is yours for having made my child happy. Remember her words 'I can't tell you, mummy, how good he is'?"

"Shall I ever forget those sweet words of hers? They are all I can cling to. Oh, Mother, I can't believe she will be taken from me. We had so little time together—a bare few months! That all should now end——"

"It doesn't, dear. Death does not end the bond between those who love each other."

"If only I could believe that! Do you believe in after-life, Mother dear?"

"I do more than merely believe in it. I *know* there is an after-life, and that death doesn't end anything."

"Is that what makes you so strong? People cannot enough admire your calm and fortitude. Nor can I."

For a moment I contemplated. Was I calm? Certainly not. But I couldn't afford to give way. What would become of Mary Ann's last hours if I did? What of Rashid?

"Don't you believe in after-life, Rashid?"

"I'm afraid I don't, Mother. To me, death means the end, though to my religion it doesn't."

"Can I ask something of you, dear? Mary Ann, like myself, has no doubt about after-life. To both of us, death means only a transition. Help her to pass over in the way she would want you to, could she but talk about it."

"How can I help?"

"Don't want to keep her back, now that you know she has to go. Don't hold her back by despair. Don't think of yourself. Think only of her."

"I'll try, Mother. I'll remember that in Islam, too, lamentations are forbidden, lest the departed soul be disturbed."

"Try. If those who love her think uplifting peaceful thoughts instead of wildly clinging to her, it will help her in crossing the threshold. God bless you, darling. Now try to sleep. A heavy day lies before you. Let me tuck you in. Thanks, Ismail Khan, for staying here all night."

A muffled sound. Even Ismail Khan, the imperturbable, cried.

I did again forget the light within me. It is easier to reach the heights than to dwell on them.

At dawn Mary Ann grew restless. "Mummy, this place has brought us misfortune. I never felt like that at home. We won't be happy here any more. This house oppresses me. Let's go!" And she wanted to get up.

I tried to calm her, but didn't succeed. "I'm so afraid I'll be kept here, mummy! Shall I ever leave this wretched place? Tell me!"

"You will, darling! I know you will."

"Are you saying so just to reassure me, mummy?"

"No, dear, I promise you—that you will leave Akbarabad soon. Mother is sure of it. You can believe her." Oh, the agony of it!

"Today, mummy?"

"Perhaps—today, my love."

"Now all is well. Why didn't you tell me before, mummy?"

"I tell you now, darling."

With a smile she dropped off. I remained, shattered.

Three hours later. The door to the front veranda was open. Ram Pershad, the gardener, appeared with roses and jasmine; every morning he brought three beautifully arranged bowls for Mary Ann. Seeing that she had recognized him, he said that he had been praying for her recovery, and pointed heavenwards to emphasize his words.

Looking steadfastly at him, Mary Ann did something truly astonishing. Slowly she greeted the Brahman gardener with a ceremonial *pranam*, joining her hands in front of her brow, and said in Hindustani, giving him his proper title: "Thanks for thy prayers, maharaj. I shall go to God soon, and they will accompany me on my way."

I think that, then and there, Ram Pershad decided to worship Mary Ann after her death. He still does so daily.

Never before had Mary Ann performed the big *pranam*, even not when greeting saintly Hindus. Was it her farewell to the soul of India?

Ten o'clock. The doctors wanted to administer an intravenous injection. She was restless and her eyes were open, though I saw that she was hardly conscious. It was essential that she should remain still, so the doctors could perform their task. Seeing a volume of Goethe, I asked Dr. Cama to get it for me, while I held Mary Ann's hands. Soon I was reading the forceful dactyls of Faust's last scene. She tried to recite with me, but couldn't. With little movements of mouth and eyelids only, she marked the rhythm.

Then, when I came to the final chorus mysticus:

"Everything transitory
Is but a parable——"

she exclaimed: "Only God is no parable, mummy. He *is* the only reality."

These were her last words. She closed her eyes, not again to reopen them in consciousness.

I sat alone with Mary Ann, holding her hand in mine. I knew that I was now only to think of her soul, which had almost left the body.

About six o'clock Waliuddin came to say that food was waiting in the dining room and that Rashid begged me to eat. I replied that, without Rashid, I wouldn't. I couldn't understand why there should be a meal all of a sudden. Only later did I learn that, in a Muslim house, fire is not lit and meals are not cooked for seven days after death has taken place.

Waliuddin sat with us. No word was spoken, no servant entered the room. There were omelette, tea and toast. I don't know whether we ate or not. I remember asking for a second glass of water, which Waliuddin brought himself. Then we dragged ourselves back.

All of a sudden a startling transformation came over Mary Ann. So far, her face had borne an expression of seriousness, even of suffering. Now, while her head slowly changed its position, she began to smile. It was an ever-deepening smile of such delight and wonder that words fail to describe it. I have never seen her, or anybody else, look as radiantly happy as Mary Ann did on leaving this life. Her eyes must have beheld the light of higher worlds.

While Mary Ann had breathed her last, I had hardly heard Rashid's agonized cry "Good-by, darling! Darling, good-by!" Now he was sobbing on Waliuddin's shoulder, and I suddenly became aware of him. I got up and went to him, but continued to try to follow Mary Ann's soul with my loving thoughts. I felt as if she approved, as if she said to me: "Remain calm; everything is all right."

After that, many things happened all at once.

The room seemed suddenly full of men: Waliuddin, Faizuddin, Auntie's relatives, the doctors, maharaj. Somebody said: "No, it is for Mother to close her eyes." This I did, and also bound her face with a handkerchief.

As soon as the men had led Rashid away, I saw a crowd of women approaching from the courtyard. Apparently it is the custom here to condole with the bereaved the moment death has taken place. Our own ways are different. I could not dream of letting anybody come in before Mary Ann's body was properly laid out and the sick room put in proper order.

I had but a second to decide what to do, before the ladies reached the door, crying and ready to embrace me. I quickly closed it in their face, saying in English—my Hindustani had left me completely —that I begged them to wait a little until everything was ready. Later I was told that most of the women thought I had gone out of my mind for grief, and was not responsible for my actions: only thus could they explain my apparent unfriendliness and my not beating my breast.

All along, I had realized I should have to do things myself; but I had not realized that I would have to do them *against* everybody— not because people were not kind, but because our customs were different. Nobody understood what I wanted. In India at the time of death people are used to each caste or group doing all that is necessary for its own people only. No outsider is ever called in to help. It was an altogether new situation, created by the absence of Mary Ann's and my "caste."

Waliuddin and Faizuddin came in to say: "Mother, Rashid wants everything to be as you decide. When is the funeral to be? During the night?"

During the night? Did I hear correctly? Then only did I remember that we were in the tropics, and that funeral or cremation had to take place almost at once. Perhaps this was the reason why there was no tradition for laying out the departed. But at night? Within a few hours?

"Tomorrow morning, Waliuddin," I said. "I want to keep watch and pray during this one night."

"As you say, Mother."

~ 6 ~

$\mathcal{R}$AM PERSHAD, the gardener, arrived at the door. Remembering Mary Ann's *pranam*, I nearly put my head on his shoulder. "I need many flowers, maharaj," I said. "All thy beautiful flowers I need."

He understood, and was looking about for the bowls.

"No, not bowls. Just flowers! All roses, pink and red. And jasmine. Flowers for her head," I said, "and for her hands, and for the whole bed. *All* thy flowers! Get the other gardeners to help thee."

In silence the last duties were performed.

Outside the locked door: "Mother dear, are you ready now? So many people wait."

Inside: "Where shall I put the candles?"

Two little tables—no, three. Quickly, between head and wall. White cloths on them—those we bought the first morning. On the middle table, just behind Mary Ann's head, I placed a reproduction of Fra Angelico's Last Judgment which I always have with me. Candles right and left—but something was not right.

I opened the door: "Ram Pershad, listen!"

"Yes, masahib. Here are the flowers, two big baskets full."

"Listen, maharaj, I want cypresses; big branches; to stand against the wall here on these tables. Dost thou understand?"

"I understand, masahib."

Roses on the pillow, encircling the head with its white georgette covering; the red ones nearest to her, the pink ones to the outer ring.

Red roses in and around her hands. Masses of jasmine everywhere. The green cypress branches on the tables behind the bed.

At last I went to take a shower, and to put on my only black frock. Just as I was ready, Rashid, unable to wait any longer, came through the dressing room.

"Mother, her smile is still there! I was so afraid that it would go. How is it that she can look so happy? Do you think she—is?"

"Yes, I think so, dear. Nobody could look as she does without being supremely happy."

"You can't believe, Mother, how dreadful and dreary death has

104

always seemed to me. But this room is just the contrary. It is filled with calm. And my darling is the image of serenity and beauty. I'll never be able to thank you enough."

"I've done only what we always do for everybody who dies."

Together we stood, Rashid and I, facing Mary Ann, while people passed behind us. I didn't want to turn to them. This was no moment for condolences.

"I shall return during the night, Mother," Rashid whispered as he was about to go back to crowds of visitors. "Then you and I will be alone with our darling, and you'll tell me everything."

But it was not to be. When Rashid came at about two o'clock in the morning, he found me drugged and asleep in my chair.

Faizuddin had asked me that night whether he could keep watch with me. I strongly disliked the idea. I wanted to be alone, except for Rashid. He must have seen my indecision, for he added: "There should be somebody of our family, too. We loved Sister."

What could I do? I scolded myself for my unkind attitude.

At last everybody had gone. Rashid, utterly exhausted, was asleep in the courtyard, with Waliuddin near him. I settled in a deep armchair near the bed. Faizuddin sat in the background, where I could not see him. The sandalwood Dr. Cama had sent at my request to keep away the flies burned steadily, filling the room with austere fragrance. It was just what I had hoped for—no heavy scent like *loban*, the incense so often used in India.

The very moment I was alone and undisturbed, I felt Mary Ann's presence. "Be calm," she seemed to say, "all is well."

It was not the first time I had had such experience. I remembered waiting in a foreign town for the traffic signal, in order to cross to a travel agency. I had just had the wire announcing Richard's passing. Suddenly in the middle of the street, he seemed to speak to me. "Do not worry. Be full of peace."

Now, as then, I took the words to heart. What struck me more than the loving concern for the one left behind was the ever-known and ever-forgotten truth that one cannot follow in thoughts the departed soul into realms above with a mind troubled and upset.

"I promise," I answered within my heart.

Then I began to meditate. But soon I felt my thoughts getting confused. Why had the air become so suffocating? Suddenly I perceived that Faizuddin was burning *loban*, several sticks at a time.

Forgetting my promise—such is the frailty of human nature—I grew cold with opposition. I had wanted to pray and meditate the whole night. Now Faizuddin was spoiling it all.

Resolutely I got up. "Please stop the *loban*, Faizuddin. I can't breathe."

"Mother, *loban* has to burn. If not, the flies——"

"But we have the sandalwood!"

"Sandalwood is used by Parsis, and I don't know its qualities. In a Muslim house, *loban* must be burned."

Communalism even in this! "Why, Faizuddin?"

"Because it keeps the evil spirits away."

"There are no evil spirits near Mary Ann; and if there were, prayers would keep them away better than *loban*. Please stop it, Faizuddin."

"But she is now a lady of our family, Mother! There must be *loban* to keep off the evil spirits. That is proper for a Muslim house. Brother is a Muslim. Sister was his wife, and we must do our best for her."

I gave in, trying to feel as if Faizuddin and *loban* didn't exist—a difficult aim, since the room was filled with blue clouds of heavy incense. Desperately I strove for peace of mind. And then I slept.

The funeral was to be at ten. Over breakfast—tea prepared by means of electricity to circumvent fire—Rashid said: "Will you get me some black band for my sleeve, Mother?"

"But Muslims don't wear mourning."

"You wear mourning, so I want to do it, too. But not just now, because I can't wear a suit today. The proper dress is black *chervani* and *pyjamas*. And I'm not allowed to shave. You know that custom, don't you?"

"Yes. There should be no vanity in externals on such day. Isn't that the reason?"

"I believe so. Mother, will you feel like driving out to the burial-ground, and meet me there? I don't want to be without you at the graveside."

"What do you mean? Are we not going together?"

"In this country, ladies never attend funerals. We'll take at least an hour and a half, if not longer, to walk to the burial ground in procession."

106

"I'm sorry, dear, but I shall also walk in the procession. We do, you know, in Europe."

"Will you be able to? After this terrific strain——"

"Somehow I'll manage. I brought Mary Ann into life; it is for me to—" I couldn't finish.

For a few moments we just sat there. Then Waliuddin joined us. They talked in Urdu for a while before Rashid turned to me. "I just told Waliuddin that nothing is to be arranged without your approval. I know how hard it must be for you among us here, far away from your own relatives and friends."

"I don't feel alone with you. Everybody else, too, is very kind. Don't worry, dear."

Two hours later, however, I did cry out—though wordlessly—for western customs, and my own kind.

In strictest intimacy the Christian service had taken place. Now the room was thronged with women. Apart from a small group of Hindu ladies, many veiled Muslim ladies, unknown to us, had come. Later I was told that the Hindus had come out of love for Mary Ann and myself, knowing full well that the Muslims would resent their presence. I have no judgment on the matter; but I remember that there was tangible tension while both groups were facing each other. I should have understood that the unrestrained talk and moving about, shocking as it was to me, did not signify lack of respect in the East. But I was past folk psychology.

My face must have betrayed my feelings. "What is it, Mother?"

"Dr. Cama, can't you tell the ladies to be more quiet? This is a funeral, after all."

"Do bear with them, Mother. They don't mean any harm."

"Why don't you tell them?"

"I, as a Parsi, cannot lay down the law in a Muslim house. Nor should you, if I may say so. Just let them be."

It was then I was suddenly filled with wild longing for my own people. I pictured the room as it would have been at home. Not a sound. Mourners who came to mourn—not to make noise, or introduce communal antipathies in the presence of death. I felt utterly homesick. How on earth had we got here?

But there was no time for thought. Some of the ladies approached the bed, talking all the time. I thought they were about to lift Mary Ann into the coffin. I ran to the door. "Rashid, Rashid!" He came in at once. Activity had perforce to cease. All Muslim ladies and some Hindus stood motionless, their veiled faces turned toward the walls. For the first and only time, I blessed the institution of purdah.

"Rashid, let us lift Mary Ann. It is time." We had arranged beforehand that none but the two of us should touch her.

"Mother, look, the smile has gone! I so wanted to see my darling's smile once more. What has happened?"

"I don't know, dear."

No longer did I think of irreverence, noise and tension. I only knew I had to lay my child into her coffin, at twenty-three.

Waliuddin, Faizuddin and two of Auntie's relatives had come to carry the coffin. Rashid was taken away by others. I picked up my black hat and followed—the only woman in Akbarabad ever to accompany a funeral. Dr. Cama had explained that even she, though not observing purdah, could not attend, on account of public censure.

But the two little nurses suddenly detached themselves from the Hindu group.

"You will walk all the way, Mother? We will go with you."

"They are of low caste, it doesn't matter to them," Dr. Cama murmured, while I stood still for a moment, amazed by their courage.

The procession did not form in any orderly way. Behind the coffin people walked in irregular rows of about fifteen or twenty, accompanied by vast congregations to right and left. As we moved into the street, more joined. Later I heard that there must have been at least two thousand mourners. Men of every description crowded forward to carry Mary Ann.

I have always been impressed by Muslim funerals. Coffins consist of unpolished boards, without even a lid. One and all, rich and poor, are buried with the simplicity characteristic of Islam's democracy. There are no horses or cars, however many the family may possess. Relatives and friends carry the body in turn. Even passers-by join in, for it is considered a good and pious act to carry a dead body to its last resting-place.

Towards funerals in India, Mary Ann and I had always adopted a special attitude. Whenever our car passed a Muslim funeral, we stopped, in order to enable our Muslim driver to get down and carry the coffin if he so wished. In the case of Hindu funerals, we just stopped the car in token of respect; for Hindus are carried to the funeral pyre by members of their own caste only.

While we were walking, men came out from shops and houses to carry Mary Ann. "There never was a better funeral," Faizuddin commented afterwards. "Barely had a man taken the coffin on his shoulder when another clamored for his place." And Seth Chandralal explained: "All these people came for memsahib's sake, Mother. Though not knowing her personally, the whole town approved of her. Do you know that lots of millhands went? My secretary told me that they said: 'Memsahib has stopped her car for our funerals; so we carry her on hers.' In this town nobody will ever forget her, be sure of it."

When we had marched what to me seemed eternities I realized with a shock that we were still quite near home. Accustomed to going to town by car or *tonga*, I was unaware how long it took to reach the main bazaar on foot. Everywhere the streets were lined with people. Bank clerks came out of their offices. In front of the Police Headquarters, there was a guard, saluting.

At last we reached the main bazaar. Through the narrow street of the cloth merchants we went on towards the market place. There was the shop in which we had bought saris and curtains, on our first morning in town; there another, in which we had purchased the gold gauze sari. How long ago was it? It seemed to have been in another life.

As all the cloth merchants and their friends joined, the narrow street could not hold the procession any longer. Some people had to take to sidestreets.

The biggest crowd was awaiting us in the market place. The inhabitants of the city proper had assembled here, together with the market people. All were ready to join the procession and carry Mary Ann. Strangely enough, in contrast to what had happened in our own house, now there was no sound to be heard but the marching of many feet.

Down the steps of the Town Hall came the municipal councillors, led by the mayor and the collector. They took Rashid in their midst, and the procession reformed.

I walked on, too tired to feel tired, in a haze of utter unreality, as though all this were not happening to me, as though I read it in a book, or saw it on the screen. Deep down, I knew it had everything to do with me; for there was intolerable pain and loneliness waiting somewhere. But what could these surroundings have to do with me? Wouldn't I soon wake from my dream? There was the street of brass-smiths, their wares gaily shimmering in the sun. The shopkeepers, Muslim Bohras with sharp-cut features and long beards, looked every inch like patriarchs stepping out of the Old Testament. For a moment I lost account of time and space. It seemed to me I was walking through the streets of old Jerusalem. I was about to turn with some remark to Mary Ann, when I awoke to the stabbing pain of reality. I was not traveling with her through the Holy Land. I was in India, walking behind her coffin.

The brass display had given way to groceries. Often had we shopped here always in a hurry, for the street was so narrow our car had prevented others from passing by. Here the people had seen most of Mary Ann. Many had been the laughs exchanged between shopkeepers and us over her struggle with Hindustani. Shops were kept both by Hindus and Bohras. I knew many of them. No longer was I in a dream. I realized that never again would I be among them with my child.

It was then I began to cry, for the first time since Mary Ann had made me sing to her. With closed eyes I went on, guided by the nurses. Somebody passed a handkerchief over my face. Later I learned that a shopkeeper—we had reached the street of haberdashers—had run to his shop, and returned with six of his best. Others were doing the same, so that the nurses had to reject innumerable handkerchiefs thrust upon us. I don't remember anything but my grief—and the murmur which arose from right and left, as we went on: "*Ma-ji, rona nahin hai!*" "Don't cry, Mother! Mother, don't cry."

When the funeral was over, we remained with a party of friends and officials, to make sure that the masons began their work at once, lest wild animals disinter the body.

Rashid and I stood together. Ever since he had nearly fallen at the graveside, his arm had been in mine. Now he wanted to walk back all the way, as Muslim mourners should.

I looked round for help, and encountered Seth Chandralal's kind eyes. "I can't argue any more, Sethsahib. Please make Rashid go by car. Otherwise I'll walk, too."

Seth Chandralal promised to bring Rashid in his own car, and I went off in ours, which had followed us, taking the faithful nurses with me.

For some reason or other, Ismail Khan stopped in the market-place for a minute on our way home. Looking idly round, I saw the fruit-stalls. Remembering that we were not allowed to cook, and thinking that bananas would solve the food problem, I called for some. It was a foolish thing to do, for I should have realized that cook or Faizuddin would see to everything.

The fruitwallah brought three dozen, and refused payment. "Mother's food for, I no money take." More fruitwallahs came up, some with bananas, others with oranges, peaches, grapes or pomegranates.

"Mine take, mother!"

"Mine too!"

"My fruit today do eat!"

"Pomegranate juice mother for good is."

The spare front seat was soon covered with gifts, and they opened the door to pile fruit at our feet.

I protested. "Many many salaams! But how can sahib and I eat all this? Please—please—no more!"

"Tomorrow mine, mother!"

"Fruit, thee for, we shall bring."

Meantime the Hindu vegetable sellers had arrived from their distant stalls. Cauliflowers, cucumbers, pumpkin, above all spinach, consumed in great quantities by Mary Ann and myself, were being thrust into the car.

But Ismail Khan interfered. "Do not you know that whole week cook we may not? Mourning is. What use vegetables are?"

Everybody understood. Reluctantly the vegetable vendors took themselves off with their gifts.

"One week after, food we bring will."

"Mother's food son's work is. Mother many sons has."

I drove away, deeply touched. These market people are very poor, especially the vegetable sellers. I wished that those who describe Indians as *bakshish*-hunters had been present.

At home there was but a bare minute before Rashid and the officials arrived.

Mr. Quraishi, one of the Muslim mill owners, brought two chairs to the small table standing in the cloister. "Sit down, Mother! Sit down, Rashid sahib! You will both do me the honor to eat my food today."

Signaling to two of his servants who carried trays fully laden, Mr. Quraishi began to set a substantial meal before us with his own hands.

I could eat but curds and sweets, but I made the pretense of taking up food with my *chappati*, lest the host realize that I was not eating anything. In reality, I ate only the bread.

But Seth Chandralal's sharp eyes were on me. I saw him scrutinize me closely.

"For a whole week you cannot use your kitchen?" he asked. Like the other Hindus present, he did not seem to have known before about this Muslim custom. "Must the food sent to you be of Muslim origin?"

"No, it needn't be. The point is to avoid lighting the fire."

"I see." Without saying more, Seth Chandralal took his leave. But I knew he'd take things in hand in his own way.

At four o'clock, Rashid came into my room, which was still in a chaotic condition. For a whole week nobody had seen to things.

"The collector sahib is here, Mother. He wants to say something to you specially."

The collector was waiting for me in the drawing room. He was dressed in immaculate white.

This is what he, who had hitherto always addressed me by my name, who was by far my senior in age, and the first citizen of town and district, said to me:

"Mother, your son has come to state that the whole town are your sons and daughters. You have lost your child, but we all have become your children. We know you must feel alone, without any of your own relatives, but you are not alone. Together with you we shall cherish your daughter's memory. You are standing by one of us in a way we should never have believed possible, had we not seen it before our very eyes. Rashid sahib might have lost his reason but for the help you gave him. We shall never forget what you did for him. Here is your home, here your family. Every house in town is yours. Command us, and we shall always do your bidding."

"Rashid is Mary Ann's husband. Is it not natural I should look after him?"

"Not many ladies would have behaved as you did, Mother. You think only of his grief, not of yours. But we are now thinking of you. There is nothing anybody here will ever refuse you."

The stranger, the Westerner, had been adopted by Indian hearts.

The week after the funeral seems in my recollection one big stream of visitors. There were so many visitors that I forget names and faces. Townspeople; schoolfellows of Rashid's; State officials; chemists of renown; relatives from Auntie's village; former personnel of the Laboratory; friends of mine from Delhi and Madras who wanted to take me away; and many others.

Auntie came, with her whole *zenana* and many more Muslim ladies into the bargain. The whole house had to be made purdah. Rashid and the servants ejected, which was both a nuisance, and a complication. There were many tears. I had to produce Mary Ann's photos, her saris and sandals. Many, too many, questions were asked of me; I was not up to the strain of answering them, but I appreciated the genuine kindness and interest behind it all. Sakri had not come.

His Highness, being in camp not far away from Akbarabad, drove into town to visit me. I liked him. His attitude was very different from that of most people here who want to make Rashid and me "forget" our loss as quickly as possible. At first he spoke of a son of his he had lost through typhus at the age of nineteen. Though he has six more sons, he has never got over that loss. Then he spoke of Mary Ann's qualities; how he had looked forward to all the help and stimulus she would give his subjects; and how not only Rashid and I were mourning her. When I mentioned the pet scheme we used to discuss together of having milk provided for every child and mother in need of it, His Highness said that I should go ahead with plans; he would help me. Looking back, it seems to me that his was the most comforting visit of all, because he understood so well.

What I liked best during that week was the large gathering in our garden after sunset. Chairs and benches had been arranged in an ellipse, fully the breadth of the bungalow. Beyond them were others, each and all occupied. There was the whole crowd who usually took their recreation at the Club after sunset; the employees of the Laboratory; and many more. What impressed me was the prevailing silence. A new arrival salaamed before both of us and the

113

collector, while somebody else vacated his seat for him, likewise salaaming before taking himself off. Nobody spoke. I was reminded of a Quaker Meeting, a very unusual experience in the East, where silence and privacy are given less value than in the West. I thought this nightly all-silent gathering more comforting than any words that had been spoken after our bereavement. Words jarred. People meant so well, but with very few exceptions they said the contrary of what I felt appropriate; they always emphasized somehow the finality of what had taken place: "You must try to forget." "You can still begin your life anew." "What has gone has gone; look into the future, not into the past!" Much better than these "modern" well meant words was the blessed silence of the nightly gatherings. Friends came and sat by you; they knew you were sad beyond words and, wordlessly, they were sad with you. There was beauty and dignity in those gatherings. I shall never forget them.

Maharaj looked the shadow of his former self. After the funeral I suggested he should go on a three-day leave, but he refused. On the third day, however, he developed brain fever and was taken to Hospital. I could do nothing about it. It was utterly impossible even to suggest nursing a first-class Brahman in our house; for he could not have taken water or food; nobody could have touched him.

So, though I made what arrangements I could for him and had fruit sent every day, I didn't see maharaj during his illness. I also refrained from sending any message. Forgetfulness about Mary Ann and me for the present seemed best for his recovery.

But will a Westerner ever be able to fathom eastern reactions?

About two weeks after the funeral Ram Pershad turned up with a heavy garland of jasmine, interspersed with roses, announcing that he would bring a similar one every day. As soon as maharaj had regained full consciousness, he had asked Ram Pershad to do this in his name, and had handed him a rupee on account. It was left to Mother to decide whether the garland was daily to adorn Mem-sahib's photo, or whether it was to be taken to her grave. In view of the fact that the Hindus, who cremate their dead, regard grave-yards and interment as an abomination, maharaj must have thought that to me a tomb means very much.

I didn't know what to do. Maharaj's pay is only eleven rupees per month. On this he has to support himself and to send as big a per-centage as he can manage to his father for the joint household where his wife and baby live. Much as I pondered, I didn't see a way out. Refuse? Impossible. Let him have money under some pretext or other? Supply the jasmine, in order to reduce expenditure? Equally impossible. Maharaj would have been hurt to the core.

So I ordered Ram Pershad to take a daily garland—on purpose smaller than maharaj's—and a coconut to the Hospital temple as offerings for the patient's speedy recovery.

It was in this way that maharaj and I, high-class servant and untouchable mistress, communicated with each other. I wonder whether such a thing would have happened in any other country than India!

As long as Rashid was on leave, we drove daily to the grave, sometimes even twice a day. These daily visits gave us the much desired opportunity of being alone with each other.

I always thought how the acts at Mary Ann's graveside corresponded to her all-embracing character. While I laid roses in cross-form on the stone surface—I had declined marble—Rashid burned *loban* with Ismail Khan to assist him. Usually one or two Hindu employees or senior servants from the compound had asked to be taken along, in order to *pranam* to Mary Ann; they brought a garland, and laid it at the lower end of the stone. All these activities ended, the others helped me to scatter the remaining flowers all over the place, and then everybody prayed; Rashid and Ismail Khan Muslim fashion with upturned palms, the Hindus joining their hands in *pranam*, I in our usual way. There was nothing planned about it; nobody had intended that the three religions should join in prayer for Mary Ann. It just happened.

Prayers over, Ismail Khan and the others retired to the car, there to await our return.

"Long after we and our children have gone, people will visit this tomb," some Club members said to me the other day. "There will be the lore of a beautiful maiden from across the Black Waters, whose heart was as white as her face; who was beloved by high and low, because, in spite of her youth, there was none to equal her in kindness, wisdom and piety. She will be cited as an example of perfect womanhood. Her intercession will be invoked in prayer. Flowers and incense will never be lacking. The East doesn't forget those who bring love and kindness."

I wonder.

Immediately after the funeral, we had to think of feeding the poor. This is a very beautiful custom, in India as well as in other oriental lands. Whether funeral or wedding, funeral pyre or birth, one feeds the poor; according to wealth and status one does so in tens, hundreds or thousands.

The first I knew about it was when, the morning after the funeral, Rashid and Waliuddin called me into the courtyard. An old dignified Muslim, in elaborate green turban, motioned six servants to step forward. Each carried a tray on which lay two legs of mutton, of superior size and quality. When I had duly inspected and approved of the superb meat, I was shown the rice, *ghi*, onions, garlic, spices, salt, raisins and sugar that would be used. Then the old man, who was the caterer, had his staff set up mighty cauldrons between our bungalow and the servants' quarters. Food for the multitude was to be ready by five P.M.

"Who prepares vegetarian food for Hindus? And where?"

"We only feed Muslims, Mother."

"But to bring in communalism even into such matters——"

"Mother darling, please, consider for a minute. Suppose we had a Brahman caterer to prepare a meal for Hindus. What would happen? He wouldn't be able to put up cauldrons in the vicinity of others containing meat. Hindus couldn't take their meals on the same strip of grass on which Muslims do. There'd be no end of quarrels and complications. Most probably we'd have a riot before we knew where we were."

"I certainly don't want to provoke a riot. But how can I participate in a thing done in Mary Ann's honor of which I know she'd thoroughly disapprove? I admit that, as a Muslim, you must go by the usual standards. But I needn't. Just do all you think fit, but leave me out of it. Say I'm too tired, or something like that."

"Mother! I'd never dream of doing anything without you being present. Couldn't we dine the Hindu poor some other day? Would that make things all right?"

Waliuddin, silent until now, intervened. "This has never been done so far in town, Brother. Muslims feed Muslims."

"Why shouldn't we be the first to start a good thing? But which Hindus shall we feed, Mother?"

"Why not feed both Hindus and Muslims together—the poorest of the poor. Why not go out to the Leper Asylum?"

116

Waliuddin cleared his throat. "You must settle first about today's arrangements. Muslims know that a meal will be provided, but we must go and invite them. All the inmates of institutions like the Orphanage, the Old People's Home, the——"

Rashid shook his head. "No, Waliuddin. I'm through with always the wrong people being fed. The institutions are not poor. Some are well endowed; all get plenty of food sent in on many occasions, and special treats at festivals. What of the really poor, those nobody takes care of? It is they I want to feed."

Nine sorties Rashid made during the day. Again and again he thought of some beggar or cripple he had forgotten to invite. Had I not loved him before, I should have loved him then. His sense of social responsibility is very strong, a remarkable feature in a country in which the Hindu law of *karma* colors the outlook of Hindus and non-Hindus alike. True, Islam instills the sense of social obligations into Muslims; but I know so many who live by Hindu class—or rather caste—standards. They give, but they don't want contact with the poor (which reminds me of home in many instances). Rashid, on the other hand, may at times be careless about paying calls or writing letters; but wherever the underdog is concerned, no trouble will be too great for him to go to. I'm proud of him.

About five P.M. the dignified old Muslim caterer led me from cauldron to cauldron, letting me taste of the contents at exactly the spot I chose, to prove to me that everything was prepared equally well. I started on sweet rice, thick with raisins and *ghi*, yellow with saffron, the dish of welcome with which ceremonial Muslim meals in India begin; burned my mouth with excellent vegetable curry, soothed it with curds; and ended with the best mutton *pilau* I have ever eaten. Not a single cauldron was I allowed to pass by. I was deeply impressed both by efficiency and quality.

"It's grand that you give poor people better food than anything we get in your or our house. I've never seen such meat in my life! Where can one get it, Waliuddin?"

"You cannot get it in the ordinary way, Mother. The best animals are reserved for such occasions. Why do you voice astonishment? Was not 'grand' the word you used? What is grand in it? Do not guests always get the best, especially guests on such occasions?"

I thought of a castle in Pomerania, where I had had the shock of my life. Driving over with the friends we were staying with in the neighborhood we found three different kinds of coffee, and three different hierarchies of cakes being served at the selfsame long table: the best for hosts and guests (our party); the second-best in central regions, for the titled agricultural apprentices staying in the house; and the third for the untitled ones, who led an unnoticed existence in the lower regions of the table, though they paid the same fees as their betters. Richard and I had just returned from the U.S.A., where high and low compete in genuine and delightful hospitality. We felt as though we'd just landed from the moon. "I thought that sort of thing happened only in books," said Richard.

I also thought of the grading of menus and drinks according to status and utility of guests I had known in many a western country; and that in the West I had never seen the poorest of the poor being served with food superior in quality to that of the donors.

Meanwhile Rashid had returned. "I've brought our first guests, Mother. Will you now welcome them? It's your show. I said to all: 'Mother asks you to dinner.'"

There were *talis*—round metal trays—in what to me seemed hundreds. The caterer asked me to indicate the size of each helping. The quantity standard thus set, I took the first tray and carried it to the first arrival.

"But *you* needn't carry the trays, Mother! Your presence is more than enough."

"I won't carry all of them. It's just a matter of principle, I don't want them to think Westerners stand-offish. And don't you think Mary Ann would have served the guests herself?"

During some minutes Rashid and I carried trays or tumblers of water. Then the influx of guests became too big for us to cope with. We greeted them, saw, together with Faizuddin, that they were seated on the grass in little groups of six or seven. Already before they approached, water had been poured over their hands. The caterer's six servants carried out the trays; Ismail Khan, his son and Ghafur took charge of the water-tumblers; some people I had not noticed before did the washing-up at the tap outside Ismail Khan's quarters. Waliuddin handed *pan* to departing diners.

Meanwhile the nightly gathering of officials and others had assembled in our front-garden, Rashid traveling between the two sets of guests.

"Why don't they all come here?" I asked, "Wouldn't they like to help?"

"With one or two exceptions they are Hindus, Mother. They would not want to disturb Muslim diners, even if they were interested in attending. You always forget."

He was right. I'm hopeless in the matter. I always forget communalism.

Immediately after the funeral Rashid said that he could no longer bear to be in Mary Ann's room. So we made it the drawing room, and Rashid's things were moved to the old drawing room.

The day Waliuddin, the kind, unobtrusive and faithful helper, left us for his home and family, Rashid said: "It will be lonely for me all by myself."

I know that, compared to Westerners, Orientals don't like to be alone. They always move about in batches, don't long for privacy, don't mind noise, prefer talk to books, except the modern westernized types, to whom Rashid belongs, or scholars. But it seemed to me that, just as Mary Ann returned to her roots after her accident and forgot her English, Rashid after her death returned to his, and forgot part of his westernization. Shocks like the one he had sustained, alter one's whole life.

7

IT took not two but four days to prepare the dinner at the Leper Asylum. Since this was not a Muslim enterprise, we did not feel we ought to ask Waliuddin's help, which had seen us through everything else quietly and efficiently. We called in Dr. Ram Chandra, who is the officer in charge of Leper Asylum and Jail as well as of the Hospital. The Asylum is much on his heart, but it is so out of the world, and he so overworked, that he can visit it only every three or four months. He says he is afraid the man in charge of the place beats the lepers; but he has not been able to get evidence reliable enough to act upon.

We engaged a Hindu caterer, ordering four vegetable dishes apart from rice, *chappatis*, curds, sweets and, of course, the ceremonial *pan*. The few Muslims would eat the same thing. We said we would be on the spot at four P.M., to taste everything. Dr. Ram Chandra promised to go with us.

I don't know how the caterer managed to get staff and provisions on to the spot; that was his lookout, not ours. Our party set out by car at two-thirty, taking along water and food, as one usually does in India. After a drive of about fifteen miles we changed over to a waiting bullock-cart, duly garlanded in our honor. The rugs and cushions we had brought were spread over its straw. Two other carts carried *chaprassis* and other staff. High officials cannot travel unattended.

Joggling along the rough trek, I looked to right and left into the jungle, its bare, yet impressive hills, its brushwood and its loneliness. I remembered how amazed and disappointed Mary Ann and I had been on our first journey to learn that such ordinary landscape was the jungle we had had romantic notions about.

We couldn't understand. Morning and afternoon we had driven out into the country, but we had never been able to discover any jungle. Finally, one day when we were driving with a party of old-timers, one of them spoke of the medley of meadows, hills and brushwood as "jungle."

"Where *is* the jungle?" we asked in despair.

"Well, we are in the midst of it, aren't we?"

Life always holds some such major disappointment as that. We couldn't place the Jungle Book any more. Visually, that is to say. For the jungle inmates belong definitely to long-cherished jungle dreams. There are jackals and hyenas galore; panthers in plenty; tigers occasionally; and any amount and variety of snakes, from cobra and Russel's viper, to the deadly *krait*, against whose bite no serum is available.

Now, peering from the bullock-cart into the jungle, I thought of the dramatic qualities of its inmates, and how truly deceptive appearances can be.

"What about proceedings?" said Rashid, the kind-hearted. "If we don't ourselves see to the distribution, who knows whether everybody will get his full due."

"But we shall see to things ourselves, shan't we?"

"We must ask Dr. Ram Chandra first, Mother dear. Can we go near the lepers, doctor sahib?"

"Of course you can. I've disinfectant in my kit for us to wash our hands in afterwards. But the lepers should not go near the cauldrons."

"Do they use the caterer's trays?"

"Not the metal ones. There'll be big trays made of leaves. Today it's an easy job to see that every one gets plenty, with the three of us and our *chaprassis* about. But I worry about the usual practice. I see to the weekly rations, but if I look at faces and bodies, I can but assume that they do not get their due properly. Where is the hitch? I can't get at the bottom of things. They are too frightened to give evidence."

"Such strange things do happen," said I, thinking of our first journey. "I remember a State Leper Asylum which was ideal, as far as building and endowment went. The lepers could have had a happy life, and every necessary medical treatment. But they didn't have. The people who were in charge had their own fish to fry. Not only were the inmates insufficiently fed and clothed, but they were actually sent out to beg their livelihood during the day, a constant menace to other citizens. At long last the Committee was dismissed, and the Municipality took over. Since then everything is as it should be."

"Well, such a thing would never have happened in British India!" said Dr. Ram Chandra. "Why do you smile, Mother?"

"About that remark of yours. I've heard it so often. Even fierce nationalists—I know you aren't—who declaim against the *raj* at every occasion, will suddenly utter it quite unashamedly."

"Yes, it's illogical on their part, I agree. Well, here we are. Has the bullock-cart tired you, Mother?"

"Not half as much as I thought it would. Is this house part of the Asylum?"

"It's the doctor's house, outside the Asylum compound."

We were ten minutes ahead of schedule, but the food was ready to be tasted. Using our own spoons, I burned my mouth several times, in the tasting, since all the curries and vegetables were of course highly spiced. Everything seemed good; Dr. Ram Chandra and Rashid, more competent judges than I, confirmed my opinion. Knowing that Hindus honor their guests specially by putting lots of *ghi* on the food at the last minute, I ordered more *ghi* to be added to the already very good *dhal*.

"Can we start, doctor sahib?"

"Yes, Mother. Look, they are all assembled down there."

Everything went like clockwork, with the three of us about. After the food had been ladeled on to the trays neatly made of big leaves I put the sweets on the heaped trays, thus inspecting them before departure. Rashid and Dr. Ram Chandra stood near the lepers, to see that everybody got his due. The last tray dispatched, I joined the two others. It was a joy to see our guests eat. Rashid had the same thought, for he said: "Isn't this a hundred times better than to entertain people who have good meals every day of their life?"

The lepers looked pathetic in their thinness, a fact which impressed me much more than missing noses or sores, to which one gets, alas, accustomed in the East. In reply to our questions Dr. Ram Chandra told us that their rations included no milk and almost no *ghi*.

Meanwhile the resident doctor approached us. "Whose name am I to give the people to cheer?"

"None at all. We don't want any praise."

"But it is always done! I told them their meal was in honor of somebody, but I didn't know his name."

Rashid and I remained silent. Dr. Ram Chandra said finally: "This meal is given them in honor of a very great Lady, Mary Ann Begum Rashid Ali."

And to that name three cheers went up, in the feeble, quavering voices of the lepers.

Rashid took my arm. "Just imagine Mary Ann were here with us, Mother. Full of thoughts about how to help these people! Let's do something she would have done!"

"Let's supply sufficient *ghi* and oil every month, so they won't lack fats as they do now."

"That's a very good plan. Doctor sahib, if Mother and I should send enough *ghi* and oil, could you insure that it reached the lepers?"

While the two men were discussing technicalities, I pressed Rashid's arm. I don't think I had ever loved him so much as in that moment, in which he had decided to go on helping these poorest of the poor, whose majority were not his own people.

It began to rain, and we hurried to the bullock-carts. There was no place for us to stay inside the Asylum. Tarpaulins spread on bamboo roofing covered our cart. Nevertheless we were soon soaked. Monsoon rains are no joke The bullocks were made to march as fast as they could, for the bridge we had to cross by car would already be well under water by now.

At the *nullah,* or river, Ismail Khan, the *chaprassi* we had squeezed in, Rashid and the doctor linked hands and advanced to probe the water's depth, Ismail Khan being the outpost. The water reached well to his thigh.

"We can make it," said Rashid.

Slowly the car moved along on the submerged bridge. Sometimes it had to stop. What had been a small river a few hours ago was now a wide, dangerous-looking expanse of swirling water.

"If the worst comes to the worst, we can always swim," I said.

"I'm afraid not, Dr. Ram Chandra and I don't know how to swim, Mother."

"How on earth——"

"You see, we've always been upcountry. I wanted to take up swimming when in England, but with one exam or other I never did."

"Listen, you two," I said. "I think I'll be able to manage both of you. Only don't take me round my neck. Hold on to my belt, one from each side. That'll leave my arms and legs free. But I can't manage Ismail Khan and the *chaprassi* as well."

"Ismail Khan knows how to swim. Besides——"

"Besides what?"

"I'm afraid you won't be able to get us out, Mother."

Naturally! How could a mere woman be able to do anything useful? Even in danger, they couldn't get over their Indian male superiority complex.

When the car at last again reached the road, all of us began to talk excitedly. "Promise to learn to swim!" I said.

Just on the outskirts of Akbarabad a sudden thought occurred to me. "Was this the *nullah* containing alligators?"

Both men laughed. "Every *nullah* is full of them, Mother. That is why you couldn't have pulled out the three of us intact."

123

"I see," I said, feeling thoroughly ashamed of myself.

It was just a week after the funeral. I was visiting Mrs. Lavanyia, who was down with flu, when Ghafur brought me a note from Rashid: "Please come home, Mother dear. There is a visitor for you."

"Who has come?" I asked Ghafur.

"Very burra sahib! Lahore *wallah!*"

Lahore? I didn't know anybody there.

I went in my room first, and in a few minutes Rashid came in. "So sorry to have disturbed you, Mother! But you will see for yourself; this visitor came for you, not for me."

"Who is it?"

"Khan Bahadur Mohammed Husain Khan. He is a big landowner in the Punjab, and a late member of Government."

"But I don't know him!"

"Of course not. I said to him: 'Don't talk any further, please, until my mother returns. It is to her decision I leave everything. I have no say in the matter.'"

"What are you talking about? *What* am I to decide? I don't understand a word."

"He'll explain it best himself."

With a queer feeling I entered the drawing room. What could it be? Did the Punjab offer a better job to Rashid, and was I to decide acceptance or refusal? What utter foolishness! I've never interfered with other people's decisions, even not my own child's. I wouldn't start now. Strange, how de-westernized Rashid was becoming! It is an entirely oriental conception to let parents decide major matters.

The Khan Bahadur was a clean-shaven man in the fifties, in a white silk suit of superior cut. After having condoled with me in suitable words, he talked of the Forum Romanum and Einstein, Ascot and the London School of Economics. No danger that *he* would mistake Austria for Australia! He has often attended the Salzburg festivals or been to Viennese specialists. All in all, not exactly the kind of person you expect a Punjabi landowner to be! What did he want? What was he driving at?

As though he read my thoughts, he drew himself up. "You may be wondering why I asked for the honor of your acquaintance, madam. Rashid sahib has pointed out to me that he regards and reveres you not only as his lamented wife's mother, but as his own. Without you he would not have been able to survive the cruel blow he has just sustained. Let me thank you from the bottom of my heart, madam, for what you did for one of ours. If a western mother behaves to an Indian as you do, all Indians have to be grateful."

"Let us hope for a time in which we forget to think in East-West terms, Khan Bahadur."

"This remark of yours renders my task more easy, madam. You understand our way of thought."

"What is it you call your task, Khan Bahadur?"

"Briefly, this, madam: both you and Rashid sahib have suffered irreparable loss. Never can you or Rashid sahib be as happy as you were. The past cannot come back, alas."

What was this? Utter tactlessness, or what?

"Once we are aware of that sad fact, we can look into the future. Though the past cannot come back, the future can hold new and different happiness. Can it not, madam?"

"It can," I replied, feeling a strange chill in my heart.

"I have, therefore, traveled here in order to offer in marriage to Rashid sahib a very delightful young lady. She is Akhtari Begum, the eldest daughter of my good friend and neighbor Saheb Zada Mumtaz Sultan Khan. I admit that her family, though a ruling one before the British took the Punjab, cannot compare with Rashid sahib's in pedigree. But after all, it is the girl that matters, not the pedigree. Akhtari Begum is everything that could be desired: beautiful, distinguished, cultured. I should consider the marriage a very advantageous one for both parties. Every detail as to family and so on are at your disposal, of course. I have also brought the girl's horoscope, so that it may be compared with Rashid sahib's. Since he says that he leaves the decision to his revered mother, it is in your hands, madam, I have the honor to place it." He put a bulky envelope in front of me.

I don't think I can adequately describe what I felt during the Khan Bahadur's discourse. Though life seemed to have ebbed from me, I was strangely awake, with a kind of triple consciousness. Above all, I wanted to leave. Not only the room and house—but India. I didn't want to have anything to do with a country in which such happenings were possible. The indecency of it! One week, one bare week after Mary Ann's death! Here that man sat, obviously thoroughly pleased with himself. The brute! But what did he matter? What had I to do with him? It was Rashid that mattered, Rashid's incredible, incomprehensible behavior. He had known the go-between's message before sending for me. Why had he not thrown him out of the house at once? Or, more politely, told him he was not in the position to listen to a proposal of remarriage a week after his wife's death? Was his love just make-believe? But that could not be. I *did* know he had loved Mary Ann, loved her still, would always love her. Who knew better than I, to whom he unburdened his heart, on whose shoulder he wept during many a bitter hour? But how could the two be reconciled—his love for Mary Ann, his decency, his goodness on the one hand, and condoning so outrageous a step? They couldn't be. Rashid was either genuine, or he wasn't. And his action—his action—! Not only had he not forbidden the Khan Bahadur his house on first hearing of his errand, but he had in cool blood recalled me; he had wanted my help in this outrageous affair. Even now he had not silenced the interloper, but sat there, waiting for me to speak. Oh Rashid, Rashid—that you should behave in such a way!

But beneath my outraged feelings there was a voice which kept on saying: "Be cautious. Don't show your feelings. Don't commit yourself. Wait until you understand." And underneath there was still another voice ringing in my heart. It was Mary Ann's. "Remain calm, dear one. Don't run away. Bear with them—for my sake."

In reality there can have been only seconds between the Khan Bahadur's proposal that Rashid should remarry at once and my reply. I felt frozen. But my voice rang composed. "It is not for me to decide this matter, Khan Bahadur. It is for my son-in-law, and for him alone."

"But Rashid sahib said that he left every decision to you, madam."

"That was kind of him, but I can't fulfill his expectations." How strange to talk to Rashid via an outsider! "You see, I am too much of a Westerner for that. We don't want to interfere with other people's right of decision."

"But it is my own decision to put everything into your hands, Mother. Who is better qualified to take the responsibility? Who knows me better than you do?"

Did I? Did I know him at all?

"May I, then, take it that you will consider my friend's daughter, madam? I shall proceed to Bombay now. On my way back in about a fortnight's time I shall take the liberty to call again."

"Thank you, Khan Bahadur. As I said before, the matter rests entirely with Rashid."

As soon as the two men had left—Rashid was to show the visitor to his car—I slipped into my room. I simply couldn't face having to talk to Rashid before I could be surer of my self-control. But my room wasn't a safe hiding place; he would proceed there, directly he found the drawing room deserted. Was there no place to be by myself? Mary Ann's grave? But how could I get there without half the town knowing my whereabouts? The neighbor bungalows? How to explain such a queer demand? And the last thing I'd find in an Indian house was privacy. Suddenly I knew my way. Hurrying through bathroom and courtyard I ran up the stairs, reaching the comparative security of the roof just in time to hear Rashid call for me downstairs.

"I'm sorry you had to hunt for me. I wanted some air, so I went up."

I had not remained in my refuge long, for I felt it had been undignified and foolish to run away. Face Rashid I had to; I also knew I had to try to understand what was going on in his mind before condemning him. "Remain calm!" Again and again I failed.

"I've looked for you everywhere, Mother dear. Please don't ever go away without letting me know where you are. I get so frightened. You are all I've got. You do know that, don't you?"

He was as genuine as ever. How to understand him?

"What do you think of the Khan Bahadur's proposal, Mother?"

This time I was so amazed at the candidness of the question that my face gave me away.

"What is it, Mother? Did you dislike something? Tell me exactly what you feel."

"You mustn't forget that I am, after all, from the West. To propose remarriage to a man who lost his wife just a week ago is so incredible a notion to the average Westerner that you must understand my utter amazement, or worse."

"I understand—but only partly. What does the time factor matter? After all, I've lost Mary Ann. Do you think that in twenty

127

years I shall love her less than I do now? Apart from Mary Ann no woman will ever exist for me."

"If so, why remarriage? Would you even be able to bear it?"

"Having to bear the loss of Mary Ann, everything else seems utterly unimportant and, hence, easy to bear. What does anything matter now? I shall be unhappy all my life. In this country, and in my community, a man is expected to be married. But, to be perfectly frank, that would not determine me. What I want is children. I've always longed for them. Had I a child by Mary Ann—never, never would I dream of remarriage! Her child and you to bring it up, as you did her: that would be all I want. But I have no child. So I must marry, knowing all the time I shall be unhappy for the remainder of my life."

"You mustn't think like that, dear, really you mustn't! You will not have the kind of happiness you knew with Mary Ann; but you may find another kind. And are you not terribly unfair to a girl if you'd marry her only to have children? You wouldn't make her happy either, that way."

"I'm not out to. Why should I make some other girl happy? Children are all I now want in life. That's not much, is it, for a man in the thirties?"

"I won't have you talk in such bitter way, forswearing all happiness forever. And I won't allow you to make a girl unhappy by marrying her in such a frame of mind! Indian girls' lives are sad enough, as it is. I won't have you make one of them unhappy in the name of your love for Mary Ann!"

Without noticing it at the time, I had taken up the cause of the Indian girl Rashid would some day marry. I would see that she got her due.

The old western craze for "right as such" had made me slip into the role of an eastern mother, who takes a hand in, or even arranges, her children's matrimonial affairs. But I was not aware of this.

Rashid, however, was.

Next day we took up the same talk. On his repeating: "It is for you to decide, not for me" I reiterated that I would not dream of interfering with his decisions. It was his life, not mine.

"But didn't you say yesterday 'I won't allow you to make a girl unhappy'? That means you don't wash your hands of me altogether, doesn't it?"

I couldn't help smiling. "I don't want to, if you behave yourself. But can't you see that I can't fit myself into the place of an oriental parent, whose word is law? Love is one thing, interference another. Everybody must be free to make his own decisions."

"Not here in India! Do you realize that a man can do nothing for himself in such matters; it is always a member of his family who has to act for him. If you refuse to act for me, people will approach the uncles or Auntie or Waliuddin. Then where shall I be? Please, Mother dear, do stand by me. You are nearer to me than anybody else. Therefore I repeat: my mother decides, not I."

"But if that Mother remains incorrigibly a Westerner?"

"Does she? She suits the East very well."

"Shall we meet between East and West? Fifty-fifty?"

"Thank you, Mother."

Together we decided that, on the Khan Bahadur's return, Rashid would tell him that remarriage was not yet contemplated. But when Rashid asked me whether I could, now, understand his position on remarriage I replied: "No, I can't understand it, but I shall help you nevertheless. You can rely on that."

Uncle Fakhruddin arrived ten days after the funeral, unannounced as usual. He said he had "traveled day and night, overcoming many obstacles," to join in the mourning for his beloved niece Mary Ann; and he felt it to be his duty to stay with the bereaved for the whole period of mourning, that is, the forty days of Muslim observance. Nevertheless he departed in a week, having proposed first one, then another of his nieces in marriage—and not without having spread more or less dark allusions as to the western mother who held Rashid in her grip and would prevent him from marrying a true believer.

I have already related how the market people did not want to accept payment for my food. After the first week, when we began again to use our own kitchen, baskets or handfuls of vegetables and fruit were brought to the bungalow, invariably with the remark: "Mother's food for." At first I didn't pay any attention to that formula; or, if I did, I explained it away with the special respect shown everywhere to a mother who has lost her only child, and with the particularly kind feelings expressed by the collector on behalf of the citizens of Akbarabad.

Soon I was startled by the daily arrival of dishes of food from people all over the place, again with the remark: "Mother's food for." This seemed all the more curious as our kitchen was again functioning normally, and there was no reason whatever to send me cooked food.

The remarks of the donors were startling, too.

"Only my food eat, masahib, or my sister's!"

"Only Hindu food eat do!"

"Food only Mother for is, not sahib for."

"Sahib and I always eat the same food," I said a little curtly. "We share everything."

"That not good is, Mother! My food only eat, not sahib's!"

I could not understand what it was all about. But other things seemed more important, so I forgot to investigate.

During Uncle Fakhruddin's stay I was increasingly overwhelmed with cooked food. After his departure remarks became such that I could no longer overlook them. This time they came from educated people.

"Do you always carry enough money on you, Mother, to be able to leave by the next train?"

"Why should I want to leave at a moment's notice?"

No reply.

"If any time you need anything, Mother, I am entirely at your disposal." A man, that was.

"What should I need which I haven't got?"

No reply, but a telling look.

"If you want some help, Mother, my house is open to you at any time, don't forget it."

"Mine too!" Two men had spoken. What was this?

"What help or house do I need as long as I have my son's?"

No reply. Then, after a while: "One day you will understand, Mother. I pray it may not then be too late."

By then I had become seriously alarmed. I had to find out what it was all about. Some instinct prevented me from informing Rashid; I felt I ought to find out for myself, since all the presents of foods and messages had deliberately left him out of the picture.

This time I did not go to Mrs. Lavanyia, but to the Ram Chandras. I wanted a man in it all.

When I had explained my errand both husband and wife looked at each other.

"I'm not quite the right person for this, Mother," the doctor observed at last. "You see, I don't believe in these things as much as others do, in fact I don't believe in them at all. But it is certain that many people think you are in danger."

"In danger? I? How can I be? I don't go to the jungle by myself! In fact I'm always home, either with Rashid or waiting for him."

Dr. Ram Chandra smiled. "How western you still are, Mother! Can't you see? People think it is just at home you are in danger."

Though I had repeatedly thought that nothing that happened in India would ever again astonish me, I was dumfounded.

"Don't you see, Mother? People say that the Muslims had already been very angry at Rashid sahib's marriage to a Christian. Now they absolutely want him to take a Muslim wife, but they think you will not allow it. They—the Muslims—are supposed to say that you have already cabled for a western bride. Some say it's another daughter of yours. So people say—our people, Hindus, that is—that the Muslims will do away with you, if you don't go in time yourself."

"I see." But I didn't. Implications were so many that I had to sort them out one after the other. Yes, all people who offered me refuge or sent food had been Hindus. "But why did they send so much food? Did they think I'd be made to starve? It's too ridiculous for words, really!"

"Mother, listen! Your cook is a Muslim. Your boy, who serves at table, is. Both can easily get at your food. So can the driver, who often shops for you. Do you now understand?" Mrs. Ram Chandra was much more outspoken than her husband.

"But this is preposterous!" said I, thinking of the devotion the Muslim servants had given alongside their Hindu colleagues during our trials.

"This is India, Mother. Things may happen here which don't in Europe. And Muslims are so fanatical. You don't know them."

Dr. Ram Chandra stopped his wife's frankness. "We have said enough now. Mother knows all she needs to." But later she and Mrs. Lavanyia and others talked to me even more freely.

"Before he left, Fakhruddin sahib said that Mother would not be in the house for long to prevent a Muslim marriage."

"He has gone round the town to enlist the help of every Muslim.

He said your feeding the Hindu lepers proved that you hated Muslims. Don't buy anything from Muslim shops, don't accept Muslim food, don't eat what your cook prepares, Mother!"

"It is very kind of you to tell me all this. But do believe me, the Muslims are very good to me here, and have been so everywhere. You mustn't judge by Fakhruddin sahib. Such people exist in every community."

Condescending smiles as to my western innocence were the only answer I got. Tell a Muslim good things about Hindus, or vice versa: if he is not very modern and broad-minded, or has not risen to spiritual heights transcending the confines of creed, caste and background, he won't believe you. It is useless even to try. Yet, with truly western stubbornness, I did.

"Apart from the uncles, all Muslims have treated me with very great kindness," I continued.

"Was it kindness, too, to kill memsahib?"

"What?"

"How was it that the car's door was not shut as it should have been? Did not your driver grumble a lot when Rashid sahib came back with a Christian bride? Is he not a Muslim? I told you, Mother, there are more ways than poison to get rid of a person."

"Really, I don't allow you to talk like that. Ismail Khan didn't shut the door. My daughter did herself. I bear witness to that."

"And why didn't the door shut properly? Can't a driver tamper with the handle?"

I was getting fed up. Argument was useless. I had to take action.

At home I laid my plans.

I would not talk to Rashid about all this, until the storm had blown over. Nor to Auntie and her sons, who had given me nothing but love.

"We're not seeing enough of Auntie," I said at dinner. "Let's find out whether we may dine with her tomorrow and, after that, something like once a week."

And next day in the car I set out on a carefully planned shopping campaign, going to Muslim shops only; buying sugar in one, semolina in another, raisins and almonds in the third. I only went in for eatables; my point not being to patronize Muslim shops, but to prove to the town *ad oculos* that no wares of Muslim origin did me any harm. I wound up by buying lots of sweets in three different shops, taking good care to spread the word that they were for Auntie's household, and that I would take them myself at night. By noon the whole town would know that I was dining at Auntie's.

During the next few days I made many calls, to all those who had warned me, to the collector's house, to the Sethani. I put on a bit of rouge, which I usually don't do, just enough to make people say, "How well you look, Mother!" The word "Muslim" was not so much as mentioned; I simply paraded my well-being all over the place.

After a week of such object lessons the storm subsided. Nobody has dared to mention such a thing to me again.

"Here is my son, masahib. He is yours."

"What a lovely little boy!" I caressed him, without paying much attention. This was a few days after the funeral; Uncle Fakhruddin was staying in the house; I was dead tired, and took the expression "he is yours" as one of the many politenesses bestowed on me.

"Do all that Mother commands thee to! Thou art lucky to grow up under the care of so great a lady! Here are his things, masahib."

"But—why? Doesn't he need them at home?"

"You have lost your daughter, masahib. My wife and I have decided to let you have one of our children for your own. A mother should not be without child. So we give you our third-born."

This was the first of six offers made to me of a "child of my own." In India such adoptions do frequently take place. To have no children is regarded as the very greatest of misfortunes. True, some of the offers were certainly made from semi-selfish motives. Parents thought it would be a great gain for their child to get the education I might give—and said so. But in the majority of cases the offer of a child was a kind action only. I had lost mine, and I was to be comforted. For that kindness I was, and ever shall be, grateful. But my reply was invariably the same. "A child should grow up with his own parents, brothers and sisters. He is born into his own surroundings."

Actually I never feel lonely, even if by myself for days and weeks. And, above all, I don't feel I've "lost" Mary Ann, or my other dear ones. But how to explain all this here in India, where blood relations count for so much, and where people get frantic if alone even for five minutes, being used to clan, caste and community collectivity in nearly everything? I couldn't. I had to keep all this entirely to myself.

Rashid solved the problem of adoption by saying that I had already adopted him, and hadn't I my hands full anyhow?

I had.

Some years earlier Rashid had stood security for a friend of his. The sum involved was very considerable. Now, about three weeks after Mary Ann's passing, news came that, for various reasons connected with ill health and misfortune, the friend could not meet his obligations, and Rashid's security was being called in. There was nothing to do but to comply. And illness, death and charities had used up a good deal of money. We resolved to retrench sharply wherever we could. We would do without Ghafur, our personal boy.

So it came about that I had, and still have, much more to do with the household than before. We manage with the government servants attached to the bungalow, keeping besides only cook and Ismail Khan.

If this tale should ever reach my friends at home—I dare say it will some day—they may wonder why on earth I should have to do any work at all if a household of only two adults commands the services of a cook, *chaprassi*, *chowkidar*, driver, sweeper and gardener. How true this is—for the West!

Things are different here. A cook is a cook, and does only cooking —and shopping in case you entrust him with it! *Chowkidar* is nightwatchman; he may do a room or two in the early morning, or move your bed late at night to where you want it to be, but that is all. The government *chaprassi* has to take care of the front veranda and the "Foreign Affairs" department during the daytime.

On the other hand, there is much work unnecessary in the West. The continual moving of sitting accommodation and beds in pursuit of some breeze; the sandstorms which transform a clean house into a filthy one within half a minute; the monsoon rains in their vehemence, getting in somehow, somewhere, however well you kept walls and roof in repair; the black and white ants which may, all of a sudden, cluster in hundred-thousands on your ceilings or walls; the battle against mosquitoes, including the spraying of every room's every corner; the constant vigilance against snakes and, last but not least, the perpetual flow of *unannounced* visitors.

It is easy to cope with guests if you know beforehand they're coming. But here you don't. Modern-minded and educated people announce their arrival; old-fashioned people don't. They are the great majority. At all hours they arrive, for an hour or a month. If you don't provide them with proper meals you fail in hospitality. Under such conditions it is very difficult to keep up a regular routine and free hours for servants; this may be one of the reasons for which many servants are needed. Indians expect service at all hours. Even Rashid can't quite understand why, if he comes home about midnight from some inspection tour, I've sent cook home and am serving his dinner myself. "Why should I have a cook if not to give me my meals when I need them?" is a typical eastern way of thought. That the self-same cook needs half an hour to tramp home, and to work again early in the morning doesn't enter anybody's head. True, if Indians don't get their hot *chappatis* with each meal—the cook has to finish preparing them while his masters are already eating—they are not happy. If I send cook home, Rashid has to eat European bread which, to Indians, is no bread. That is a catastrophe, though he takes it very nicely.

To tell the truth, we have not had any guests falling unannounced into the house for a prolonged stay, apart from the uncles and an occasional friends or two of Rashid's. His westernization and my presence prevent surprise visits of any duration. But there are lots of visitors coming in for a chat and a meal, or for calls of ceremony. Rashid being one of the senior government officials and a light of science, all notables passing through the town do call.

So there's a lot of impromptu entertaining to do. If it could be informal, as at home, it'd be easy. But it can't. Every act of hospitality has to be formal and official, lest it be said that the host is not doing his duty. At times I have found myself longing for western formality in announcing visits, and western informality in entertaining.

On the other hand, I've always been deeply impressed with the overwhelming and dignified courtesy of oriental hospitality. Just picture a hostess in Vienna, Leeds or Boston, presiding over a dinner table extended to capacity; she has planned the party with great care; there is enough lobster salad or asparagus for a second helping; there are enough plates—just enough—to last through the dinner without need for washing up. There are enough wine and champagne. Picture her, over the soup, beholding the work of her brain, if not of her hands, the perfect dinner party, with just the right mixture to give prominence to *the* guest of honor. Picture the door opening; four or five former school friends of her husband's tramping in unexpectedly, obviously expecting a dinner *en famille*. They are good souls, but not presentable; never would she have dreamed of including them in this select gathering. There they stand, waiting sheepishly to be made welcome. She knows that the table can't be extended; that there are no spare chairs and plates; not enough food and wines; she knows that they are spoiling her party, and that she hates them. How will she rise to the occasion? What will she do?

The East is different. Hospitality comes first. I remember a young official in a certain State. He had invited Mary Ann and me to meet his Minister at dinner. From a friend of his we learned how much care and thought he gave to the arrangement. His wife was away, staying with her parents; she would not have come out anyhow, since she refused steadfastly to leave purdah. It was the first European dinner party he had ever given; being related to the Royal family, he was allowed to borrow china, crystal, cook and bearers from the State Guest House. It was a great occasion, and everything was perfect. We were a party of eight, four Europeans, four Indians; the latter—apart from our host—all of ministerial rank. We had finished the third course when four friends of the host came in. They couldn't have known of the party, for they had just arrived from their village to ask for dinner and bed.

The young host behaved magnificently. He welcomed them with the same courtesy and warmth which he had bestowed on us; ordered the servants to lay four more places; sent back the fourth course they were about to serve to us, in order that the late arrivals might catch up. He was not a shade more polite to the Ministers and ourselves than to the rather coarse, intruding youngsters. I admired him. Had I been the hostess—would I have risen to the occasion as he did?

Every Oriental I have met would behave like that. Hospitality first. The guest is sacred. Rashid, tired and wanting to rest, will smile at visitors at every time of day or night, minister to their comforts, take them about, and so on. Mrs. Ram Chandra, Lavanyia or any other lady will cheerfully prepare a full meal for an unexpected visitor exactly thirty minutes after the family meal is over, even if she wants to go out or to rest. And an Indian meal is not a western one! To begin with, there are no leftovers in the house, owing to the tropical climate and Hindu fastidiousness. When the family and servants have eaten, what remains goes to the sweeper. The next meal must be prepared anew. In addition to this, our makeshifts of cold luncheons would never satisfy either Indian guest or host. Cold food is no food at all—or good only for Westerners, who are crazy anyway, poor things!

So the unexpected guest, loved or unloved, much thought of or despised, is served a complete meal, the preparation of which takes hours. Suppose an hour after he leaves there is another unexpected guest? Another meal is prepared, uncomplainingly, cheerfully.

Whatever our western hospitality, it cannot compare with this in unselfishness and self-sacrifice. Indian devotion to guests impresses me ever anew. On the other hand, hospitality in the East is a religious duty, and counts among the good actions which bring salvation. So, in the end, the host benefits more than the guest. Perhaps that is why he thanks the visitor.

Maharaj came back in mid-September. After his illness he had recuperated in the house of an uncle some hundred miles away, where his wife and baby had gone to await him. Our floral conversation had ceased on his leaving the Hospital; trying to find out from Ram Pershad whether maharaj had got into debt over it, I could not get a conclusive answer.

I therefore felt I ought to take the initiative. "Much money thy illness cost must have, maharaj. For it this money take do!"

"For son mother's money to take bad is! Thy son I am."

"Good. Thy baby for this money is. Baby girl is. All right is?"

He laughed. "Mother knows, son not knows." I noticed that he had dropped the "masahib."

Not finding Ghafur, and his own work having been rather neglected by the *chaprassi* who had replaced him, maharaj developed great activity. He came at six A.M. to prepare early tea, taking even the untouchable tray to Rashid, the equally untouchable; he and

137

chowkidar cleaned the house satisfactorily between them; if we had guests for tea, he carried in the things except cakes or sweets containing eggs. But since most guests were Hindus, sandwiches were in any case vegetarian and sweets eggless. If there were eggs I told him so. One should be scrupulous about such matters.

Whenever I go to the tomb, maharaj wants to come with me. But if I take him always, the others get jealous. So I'm taking them in turn, which doesn't prevent all of them from turning up if I go. When I found the same kind of garland each time at the tomb's lower end, I inquired from maharaj whether he was going there on his own, too. It must take more than two hours' walk, both ways.

"Work after I go," he said simply.

Before ending this narrative, and taking up again my day-to-day diary, I want to say a few words about my staying on here after the Khan Bahadur's proposal. I don't think I'll ever be able to explain this satisfactorily to friends at home—one more reason why I can't bring myself to write letters. At times even I myself can't understand why I did not leave at once. So how can I explain it to others?

I have not recovered from the shock then received, and since repeated many times. I don't think I ever shall. The eastern attitude towards death hurts me ever anew. Since after death there can be no tangibility and tangible satisfaction in a bond between two partners, the whole thing is over, and therefore nonexistent. So why not remarry at once, to enjoy again tangible relationship, by which means one's grief can be forgotten in the quickest of manners? Many a former widower, Hindu and Muslim alike, gave me exactly this reason for advocating immediate remarriage for Rashid. "I too lost my wife," said one of them. "I know what Rashid sahib must suffer. I could not sleep, not eat, not breathe after having lost her. So I remarried at once, in order to be helped to forget."

In general, this strange materialistic attitude of the so-called spiritual East is an ever-recurring phenomenon. The so-called "materialistic" West knows of a higher kind of love. Dante did not lose Beatrice through her death. Faithfulness beyond death, in thought and action, is a frequent happening in the West, while in the East it is known to a few only.

On the other hand we should not forget that the premises for

138

love and marriage are different in East and West. In Islam a wedding is no sacrament, but a social contract only; consequently, once the material presence and tangibility is removed, nothing remains. Hindu marriage is a sacrament; but in Hindu conception the departed soul proceeds according to the laws of reincarnation and transmigration to a new life in new surroundings. The bereaved should not even by thoughts chain it to its former existence.

This being so, I felt I had no right to reproach people for their "materialistic" outlook on marriage. That it made me suffer was nobody's concern but my own. Generally speaking, and without making any exception, the West has so often misunderstood the East, that I willingly sink any wrong I may have to suffer in the East into the balancing of these accounts.

But generalizations are always unsatisfactory. I know of a number of cases in which Westerners have remarried very quickly, sometimes almost at once, even though their marriages had been happy. I also know of Indians whose faithfulness to their loved ones is beyond comparison.

I remember a boy who met a girl at some western spa. Both were modern Indians, both belonged to ancient Rajput families of very high standing. At home they would never have had the opportunity of meeting and free choice; the West gave it to them. They became engaged, and were to marry on their return to India. But, just before sailing, the girl died of pneumonia. This was fourteen years ago. The man is now thirty-eight, good-looking, rich, in high position. He has never been interested in another woman during all that time.

I know of a similar case, a Muslim, of exceptional culture and sensibility. Though holding many foreign distinctions, he is first and foremost an orthodox Muslim, believing in purdah for religious reasons. When he was twenty-eight, he met a French girl, deeply interested in Islam. They fell in love and became engaged. A few weeks before the wedding day the girl died of typhoid. He is now thirty-six. His family, one of the oldest in Islam, has repeatedly insisted on his getting married. He has always refused. "I shall never marry," he said. "Yvonne is my bride forever."

Unlike the two men just described, the Bengali hero of the following touching story is not personally known to me. I owe it to a friend, who assures me, however, that every detail of the story is true.

A mathematical genius and deeply religious in his feelings, this young man was the eldest son of his family, who were constantly trying to push him into marriage. He had no inclination to marry, until he saw a little girl of twelve, who was already accustomed to spend several hours in meditation every day. He was attracted to her for her spiritual qualities, and said that if he married at all he would marry only that little girl. Their horoscopes corresponded, and their marriage took place, but it was not consummated for six years, though they slept side by side in the same room every night. Then they had two children. When the second child was about a year old, the wife one day remarked to her husband that the child would not live, and that she herself would die one month from that day! It seemed absurd, since both of them were quite well. The husband did not even remember her prophecy when, a month later, he went to a neighboring town to attend to some business. On his return, as he was walking to his house from the station, he heard a strange sound of wood-chopping, and it flashed into his mind that some one had died, and the funeral pyre was being made ready. When he got back to the house he found his wife dead. The baby died soon after. He took the vow never to sleep in a room with any other human being, and to observe the widow's fast for the rest of his life. It is now about twenty years since his wife's death, and in all this time he has lived on only milk and fruit. He also took the vow that he would not take spiritual initiation from any one who could not make him see his wife sitting beside him, so that the two of them together might be initiated at the same time. With this fixed object in view, he went up and down India, searching for a *guru* who could initiate them, his wife sitting by his side. At last he found that *guru* living in a tiny hut with three stones near the entrance. The *guru* sat on one, the man on the other, and, when he turned his head, his dead wife was at his side!

People in India differ just like people anywhere. There are those who go in only for tangible things, and those who care for higher values. As everywhere else, the second group is in the minority. The people I know in Akbarabad are not interested in philosophy and the Sublime *Gita;* it is but natural that to them tangible things mean everything. But I know that there are Indians who think and act otherwise. I wish I had been among that sort of people during the past few months, everything would have been so much easier for me. However, one learns more if things are difficult—more tolerance, more patience, more courage.

Rashid's love for Mary Ann is above any doubt. Whatever I don't understand in his outlook has to do with his "blood and soil," as Mary Ann put it, not with his individuality. That is why I am still here. I shall remain until he does not need me any more.

~ 8 ~

November 15

$\mathcal{T}$HE weather is glorious just now, cool, yet not cold. Everything is in full bloom, but one gets so used to having flowers and blooming trees all the year around that the color symphony is not so impressive as the sudden emerald green of garden and jungle, that precious short-lived gift of the post-monsoon season. At home we take lawns for granted but consider flowers and fragrance all the year round a blessing beyond imagination. In the tropics flowers are daily fare; but one takes no end of trouble over a bit of shabby lawn—usually without result. Perhaps we feel subconsciously that flowers are cake, and grass is bread. It is a feast to see the meadows and hills richly green, not gray and brown as during eight parched months.

November 16

Rashid comes home unexpectedly in the middle of the morning and finds me washing some of his things.

"Really, Mother! Why do you go among the *dhobis*? People'll say I'm making a slave of you!"

"Is washing a few things 'slaving'?"

"*My* things, yes. I resent your working for me."

"But I don't want bills to run up."

"You fret far too much over money. When I go to Bombay next month to attend the Science Congress, you'll come with me. That'll teach you to worry over expenses! Besides, I don't like you to be so useful."

"Why?"

"Because I've had enough of people telling me about it. They seem to think I keep you here to run my house, not because I love you. That is what I dislike. Please be less useful!"

"And if the house suffers?"

"Let it. What is a house, after all?"

"Very well. You won't get your meals in time."

"You won't catch me like that, Mother. Now let's plan Bombay!"

"It's impossible. Think of the expense: fares, hotels——"

"Only the fare! I'll stay with Hamidullah, my London pal; your hotel bill will be lower than mine would be, because you don't go in for drinks. You'll also prevent me from buying all sorts of extravagant things. We'll economize by your going, you'll see."

I can't help laughing. "What about the drinks I'll have to offer you? I dare say you'll visit me."

"Of course. What else am I taking you for? Really, if we deny ourselves things all the year round, we can well afford a fling in Bombay. And"—in changed tone—"I don't want to go without you. It'll be terribly hard anyway. Bombay without our darling! Do you remember, Mother?"

I do.

November 22

At last I've seen Sakri. She has been absent for some months—to learn embroidery, I was told.

Whenever we come to Auntie's there is some treat for me. Either Hamid has composed another poem along Persian lines, or Faizuddin's eldest has some drawing ready. True to the eastern conviction that a woman's happiness lies in children and grandchildren, some child or other is deposited in my arms the moment I sit down. Usually it is Akbar, looking as cherubic as ever. Twice he has been offered to me, not for adoption but as a companion; as usual, I refused firmly. But I like him very much.

Today there is a floral sketch by Faizuddin's eldest, and a pillow case embroidered by Sakri, which she is almost too shy to present.

"Show Mother what you worked for her!" says Waliuddin, motioning her forward. "It is good embroidery."

The pillow case is covered with brown, black, bottle-green and

142

pillar-box-red stem-stitch in a pseudo-naturalistic pattern. At the mere thought of having to rest my head on such a chaotic thing, it begins to turn. But I thank her warmly. It is not her fault that she is being made to embroider ugly designs.

My words of thanks make Sakri look at me with so loving and sweet an expression that it is now for me to lower my gaze. Is it—does she think she can become Rashid's? What a hopeless affair! She stands no earthly chance with him, and I can't blame him. She's the submissive, old-fashioned type of girl, outstandingly pretty, sweet of character, looking up adoringly to a future husband's superior wisdom. Even if I had her educated, he'd always look down on her. And how could I? The very moment I were to show any interest in her, false hopes would soar. It is a pity. She is so sweet, and I like her.

At home I sit down by Rashid. "Listen, dear, something must be done about Sakri. Did you see how moved she was when handing me her present?"

Rashid yawns. "Sorry, mother, I didn't look particularly."

"I'm afraid she thinks—or her people think—I'll arrange a match between you two."

"Well, let them think! I told them long ago that the idea was crazy."

"But they still believe there's a chance. We must undeceive them once and for all."

"Nothing of the kind. To take notice of such preposterous foolishness makes it worse, Mother. Believe me, I know my people."

"If Sakri knew there's no hope, she might settle on some other man."

"They have known for ages there's no hope, but they simply won't believe it. It's ridiculous."

That's that.

November 25

As usual I am out in the garden just before sunrise, ever anew delighted at the fragrance of jasmine and roses. Several Hindus have asked us for permission to pluck our jasmine every morning. At first Mary Ann and I couldn't understand this rather bewildering request. We learned, however, that dew-fresh jasmine flowers are offered first thing in the morning at Hindu household shrines. Our house being Muslm-Christian, Hindus think we have no use for all the jasmine growing in our garden. To their mind flowers belong to worship. Only after sufficient floral offerings have been made, may the remaining flowers be used for adornment.

Today, while I am watching the three women who, in eager competition, gather our jasmine, I see an early *ghi-wallah* approach the house. Cook has not yet arrived. So I call *chowkidar* to taste the *ghi* for me. I know how to buy butter; but *ghi* still baffles me. To me it has always an acid taste and smell; and, being unable to distinguish between adulterated and unadulterated *ghi*, I have always to rely on expert help. *Ghi* being the most important item of Indian cooking, everybody is an expert.

After having compared the loose stones which constitute the vendor's weights with our kitchen weights, *chowkidar* tastes the *ghi*, and pronounces it unadulterated.

"Good is, *chowkidar?*"

"Good is, masahib."

"Good thy house for, or only me for?" I want to make sure. It often happens that high-caste Hindus think Christians and Muslims so unclean in their habits, that it doesn't matter anyhow if what they eat is dirty or not.

Chowkidar looks up. "My house in *ghi* not is, masahib. Too expensive is."

"Never *ghi* is, *chowkidar?*" I am shocked. I know he has two children. He himself is very tall, though of delicate build, and should have plenty of good food.

"Four or five years since *ghi* not is, masahib. That time before *ghi* cheaper was."

"Thy meals what are?"

"One meal only is, masahib."

"When?"

"Night at."

"Not eat thou doest whole day? Night from to night from, no meal thou hast?"

"No, masahib."

"And thy children?"

"No, masahib."

I swallow. "What night meal made of is?"

"*Dhal chappati*—pulse and bread."

"Chillies and?"

144

"Sometimes only."

"Never *dhal ghi* in is?"

"*Dasera* at only." He smiles wistfully. *Dasera* is the greatest Rajput festival, in remembrance of Rama's victory over Ravana in the battle of Lanka (Ceylon) and his subsequent journey to Ayodhya. It is a festival observed all over India, but on the most magnificent scale by maharajas and princes, who all belong to the warrior caste —today called Rajputs—as does *chowkidar*.

Ghi only at *Dasera!* No fats all the year round!

"Thy pay what is, Tejsingh?"

"Ten rupees, masahib. Parents and father's brother with me live."

I see. That makes seven people, all in all. No wonder they can afford only one meal. No wonder *chowkidar* is so thin. I dare say the three elders are served first, then the children, then he and, finally, his wife. I wonder how she is.

"Thy wife I call. Here bring her children with. This *ghi* take do. Now, at once."

He understands. The other servants are not to know.

"Sahib what say will, masahib?"

I smile. "This my work is. Now go thou do."

Very quickly he transfers the *ghi* into a vessel, covering it with newspaper. I remain with much food for self-reproach. How thoughtless of me not to have inquired before! Letting *chowkidar* work for us in the morning, carry our food, while he has to go without until night! I'll see to things now, though. But what about others? If he, a much-envied Government servant has only one meal a day—what about others?

November 27

My old publisher friend in England makes an interesting suggestion.

"You will remember that, before your first journey to India, I had already suggested you should write on India. I repeated my suggestion on your return and, once again, when you left last March. On all three occasions you gave the same reply: that you did not think you would ever know enough about India to write on the subject.

"Having heard from Frank and Kay" [mutual friends of ours in Madras, who had visited me after Mary Ann's death] "that you contemplate staying for an indefinite period, I am renewing my suggestion. After your close association with Indian life during the past year you are certainly in a better position to write on India than before—though I maintain that you would have written well even then.

"What about it? Do make up your mind and let me know by air mail. The world wants to hear about India. There are so many interesting topics, especially the application of high philosophical ideals to everyday life. How does the seclusion of women fit in, how the poverty of the masses? In your experience is 'Mother India' wrong or right? What about communalism? Does it really exist? What about Indian mysticism? What about labor conditions? And so on.

"You are the person to write about all this. For decades you have studied eastern philosophies. On your first journey you got to know India as a traveler; the little—too little—you told us afterwards was thrilling. Now you share the life of Indians. Surely you can no longer escape into saying that you 'don't know enough about India to write on the subject'!

"I'm eagerly looking forward to your 'yes.' A book on India by you would be sure of success. Look after yourself.

"Yours sincerely,
"Peter."

What food for thoughts this letter brings!

November 30

"You would be astonished to see her hands, her feet! They are tiny as a child's."

I remain silent.

"And her eyes! Pure almond shape. 'The Well of Delight,' as the poets say!"

My silence reaches home; the visitor proceeds to depict more material splendors to catch my fancy.

"She must have well over a hundred different outfits. Her saris are bordered in gold and silver, some of them so heavily embroidered that one can't lift them with one hand. Even her *diburthas*—veils—for the night are bordered in real gold."

"Lucky girl," I comment politely.

"Lucky groom!"

Dr. Miss Fathma Sharif has come from one of the smaller States of the Central Provinces to propose a bride for Rashid. She seems to be *zenana* doctor in the girl's house, and takes her task much to heart.

At lunch time I can't help asking Rashid: "Why are people so after you? Are you so great a catch? You are, of course, being such a dear; but that's just what strangers don't know. Financially you can't mean very much to such a rich girl. I'd be astonished to hear that your science is the attraction—these people most likely don't care about it. So what? Why do you get so many proposals?"

Rashid laughs. "Mother, you're still so delightfully naive! How do you know the girl is rich?"

"Well, that doctor woman says so."

"Words are cheap, as the saying goes. She may have nothing at all, and my salary may seem a big amount to her people."

"But how can they say she's rich if she isn't?"

"Why shouldn't they? Didn't you read the other day about that case in Calcutta? Just before the wedding the groom found the dowry was less than half of what had been promised; so he refused to be married until the rest was produced. The bride's parents were quite small people, so the groom could act like that. Better-class people can't. They grind their teeth, and submit to getting cheated. I know lots of such cases."

"But even that doesn't explain why they consider you such a catch?"

"Now you are getting offensive, Mother! Firstly, any man as such is a catch; it's very difficult to get a son-in-law nowadays. Secondly I have quite a good job and reputation. Anyhow, I'm considered safe. Thirdly, there's my pedigree. Personally I don't care a brass farthing for such things, but others do. Fourthly I have a darling mother. After that, no fifth point is needed."

"I thought a European mother-in-law was rather a drawback."

"On the contrary, whatever faults Westerners may have, they are much more reliable than we are. That's why we trust them individually, however much we may grouse otherwise. A father wanting to marry his girl to me, knows you will not make her unhappy, as many a mother-in-law would out of sheer jealousy."

I ponder over this novel point of view. "It is all so strange. I would never be able to explain to people at home the smallest bit of it." How even to explain the remarriage problem as such?

I'm thinking of this lunch-time conversation, while my visitor's voice is droning on. The enumeration sounds like an auctioneer's haranguing.

"You would not believe the amount of jewels she has. Three strings of pearls, a dozen or more gold bangles, emeralds, diamonds, rubies——"

I don't reply or comment.

"In spite of her riches she is modest and well-mannered. She will live to love and honor you, Mother, knowing she owes her happiness to you. As long as you live you would have no troubles to fear. Ample provision would be made——"

Well, well! Bribery? I begin to see Rashid's point concerning Westerners.

"When does your train leave, Dr. Sharif? It is time I saw about tea. Excuse me, please."

She leaves with an unhappy face. I'm afraid she won't cut a good figure on her return home.

December 2

Am I the person to write on India? I certainly don't feel it. The more I learn of conditions, the more I realize that whatever one says remains one-sided and, therefore, misleading. There is such an intricate complexity of problems and divisions! You relate something about say, a Brahman; the reader in the West, unable to see for himself, concludes that Brahmans behave in the way you described. But what you say of a Travancore Brahman is not done by a Kashmiri or a Deccani "twice-born." I know too much to write in blissful ignorance of the facts, a thing I would never do anyhow. And I haven't spent a lifetime in India. There are so many things I don't know.

December 3

"Evening out thou goest, masahib?"

"In I am, *chowkidar*."

"My wife and children I bring will."

Now I am waiting, a parcel ready for them to take away. At first I didn't know what to prepare. One or two of Mary Ann's cotton saris? Many Indians would not like such gift, thinking it unlucky. Flour? They might not think ours milled correctly. Grain? That wouldn't be out of the ordinary—they eat *chappati* daily, though certainly not enough. Finally I decide for sugar. I'm sure they never can buy any. I wonder how they all look. Starved, I dare say. As the little procession arrives, I sit in the courtyard. Both *chowkidar* and his wife are carrying brass trays. She is nearly as tall and fair as he, with proud bearing and features as well-defined as a Rajput painting. The little girl of about eight, looking charming in crimson bodice and long crimson skirt, carries her baby brother on her hip, a perfect little mother.

While I am greeting them and asking the children's names, *chowkidar* places his tray on one of the benches and, being an intimate of the house, proceeds to the dining room, whence he returns with a small table covered with my best tea-cloth. He lifts the snowy cloth off his tray, which I had thought to contain a garland or two. There are about eight highly polished brass vessels. "Rajput food is, masahib," says *chowkidar* with satisfaction while pouring water over my hands. Then he begins to set out a meal before me, closely and proudly watched by his family.

"These biscuits thee for my wife prepare did," he concludes, taking and unveiling the second tray. There are about three dozen, the size of a palm. Even from afar I can see that they are heavy with *ghi*. So is my food. The Hindu code of hospitality says that the more you want to honor your guest, the more *ghi* you put into his food. In addition to the dishes on my tray there is a little vessel containing nothing but melted *ghi*; *chowkidar* pours of its contents in each dish, just to prove in my presence there's enough *ghi* and honor. I've always been bad at arithmetic. But even so I can guess that nearly all the *ghi* I've given to *chowkidar* comes back to me. In addition they must have spent much on the other ingredients. And I who had thought to give them help! For a moment I reconsider my reply about the book. Wouldn't it be a glorious thing to dispel the wrong conception of India as a *bakshish*-hunting land? True, the Westerner knowing but Bombay or other big towns has every excuse to think so, for he is surrounded by professional beggars wherever he goes; but the pity is that he thinks "So this is India." It isn't. Professional beggars beg; that is their particular and often unsavory job. But average Indians are proud, though none can equal the pride of the Rajputs, the best fighters and friends, the most courageous and generous of people. I wish I could tell the whole world of the dinner *chowkidar* brought me, he who has to keep a family of seven on a salary of ten rupees a month!

Rajabai is coughing, a hollow sound, and at one moment she puts her hand to her side, as though in pain. Is she getting T. B.? Somehow I must find means of helping her.

Now they garland me, each of them—four garlands in all.

"Many salaams, *chowkidar* and Rajabai! Very good food was! Very beautiful flowers are!"

"Our mother thou art."

"If mother I am, Rajabai and children for medicine I send can?"

"What mother sends medicine is."

"Very good. Every morning medicine home thou take wilt, Tejsingh, one goblet each child for, two goblets Rajabai for."

"Hospital medicine?" *Chowkidar* sounds doubtful. Only western-ized Indians like western remedies, as a rule. The bulk of the people prefer the Ayur-Vedic system if they are Hindus, and the Unani system if they are Muslims.. The first is of purely Indian, the second of Arab-Indian origin. Both have great medical merits. Many of their followers have recourse to western medicine only in surgical cases—if then. On the other hand, for the improvement in health conditions and the battle against epidemics credit goes to medical men trained on western lines.

"No, hospital medicine not. Jug full prepare I shall every morning."

"Mother's medicine!" Remembering how often people think I must be a better healer than any doctor, simply because I am a mother—they turn up, bare the ailing part of their anatomy, put my hand to it, and confidently expect I can cure them—I understand why *chowkidar* is so delighted.

"Wilt thou wife and children give?" I want to make sure that my "medicine" will not go to parents and uncle.

"Mother's word son hears."

Now *chowkidar* takes daily a jug holding one and one-half pounds of milk. (In India liquids are dealt out in pounds, not in pints.) Since people here take milk always sweetened, I have the longed-for opportunity of getting rid of my sugar. At present, I put three yolks into my "medicine" and shall go up to six. One must go slow with stomachs not accustomed to good food. It's a blessing that Rajputs can eat eggs. The first day I started on skimmed milk; today it's already creamy in quality. What if, after my "medicine" is a success, the whole town clamors for it? Perhaps His Highness will help me with the milk scheme when I tell him!

Would anybody in the West believe that it takes such amount of thought and scheming to get a man on whose income of three and one-third dollars per month seven people must exist to accept some little help from a memsahib who, like every Westerner, is considered fabulously rich?

Well, *chowkidar* is a Rajput. *Noblesse oblige.*

December 6

Tidying my cupboard before leaving I am faced with an insoluble problem. I've lots of magazines, both from England and the United States, most of them sent by friends. And now I don't know how to dispose of them. For most of our western picture publications bring the photographs of women not sufficiently dressed for the strictness of oriental standards. It doesn't matter whether it's a strip-tease photograph or the portrait of a dowager in decorous evening dress: maharaj, *chowkidar*, Ismail Khan and all the others would be horrified to discover a respectable woman—meaning me— in possession of pictures revealing such disgraceful want of modesty. Here in India even dancing-girls of doubtful morals are covered from head to foot. The usual western magazine, with the usual nude or decolleté illustrations shocks the average Easterner to a degree no Westerner has ever troubled to investigate. This is a purdah country; for a woman to allow her face to be gazed upon by men is considered shameless. Is it any wonder that the average Oriental considers evening dress and modern bathing suits an abomination, and their wearers as steeped in sin and shame?

However that may be, I'm not willing to lose our staff's—and the town's—esteem over those magazines. When they arrive, I carry them to my room and lock them up. Funny to think that at home, they are among the most respectable magazines; here I can't have them lying about. I take them out to read at night or in the early morning, when the servants don't pop in every minute. I don't trust Rashid with them, unless I'm near. He might forget to lock them up.

It's not only that *I* don't want to lose face—I don't want the West to lose face. People here don't know anything about the West from personal experience; whatever they get hold of they generalize about. So what am I to do with my copies? I can't burn them without cook knowing about it. Suppose I staged a secret cremation during the night, *chowkidar* or Ismail Khan would find out at once, and rush to my aid. Take the lot to the jungle or the river? How? The driver of both car or *tonga* would know. The more I would wrap up the parcel, the keener would he be to know its mysterious contents. Gossip, being just as potent as in Gopher Prairie, with the added flavor of domestic oriental imagination, would probably waver between declaring the parcel's contents as a baby of mine or of a mistress' of Rashid's. Or, if discovered, the sinful photos might be said to pollute the holy river. Anything might happen.

And I could never get to the jungle by myself. People would certainly accompany me to see what crazy thing I was bent on—walking all alone with a huge parcel, an utterly undecorous undertaking. So what? I really don't know. That magazines considered highly respectable in the West—*Life, Time, Saturday Evening Post, Punch, Picture Post, Graphic, Tatler*, etc.—should create such an insoluble problem is a joke of first order. Yet, at the same time, it is a very serious object lesson.

December 8

"Hill House, Madras

"December 3

"Dear Hilda:

"We are very glad to hear that you will leave your seclusion and spend some time in Bombay. Can you come to Madras on your way home, though I admit that, geographically, this would be a roundabout way. Do try. We'd love to have you with us. Madras is very interesting for a writer and research-student of your type.

"If you can't come here—if really you can't—Frank and I will try to meet you in Bombay for a few days. There's so much to talk over, last not least Peter's fond hope of your writing about India. Will you?

"Yes, there are good libraries in Bombay. I can imagine how you'll plunge into them.

"Write you are coming.

"With love from both of us,

"Yours always,

"Kay."

Frank and Kay are the friends from home I like best. We have known each other for about fifteen years. Richard and I often spent our holidays motoring with them all over Europe. Frank is high up in the I.C.S. (Indian Civil Service), but that is not all there is to it. He is extremely well read, with a passion for anthropology. He and Peter, my publisher, were together at Baliol and correspond regularly. That's how he and Kay know about Peter's request.

I wish I could see them. They are such dears, and were devoted to Mary Ann.

December 11

"What is the girl's name, masahib?"

"Which girl?"

"She whom to inspect you travel all the way to Bombay."

"Inspect? A girl?"

"Oh, masahib, don't always try to hide things! The whole town know you have settled on a Bombay bride for Rashid sahib. Now you go to inspect her. What is more natural? You are a good mother."

"I'm afraid I'm not, from your point of view. There is no girl in Bombay I know about."

"So I was right! I said to Mrs. Lavanyia: 'You will see, masahib will make secrets. She will not tell us. She does not trust us.' But we know all the same."

"I'm afraid you'll be disappointed, then. I go to Bombay to meet friends, to study, and to keep my son company."

"Now I see you are joking, masahib. How can a lady of your age talk of studies? Is she beautiful? Rich? Do tell me!"

It is useless to protest. Whatever I may say, people here will think I am setting out on a matrimonial expedition. Strange, how utterly tactless they can be at times. Mrs. Sharma means so well, but she doesn't realize a bit how repelling her words might be to me—did I not know the background from which they spring.

December 13

Not finding another way out I've packed the magazines into a suitcase to send them on arrival to Bombay hospitals. They represent a formidable weight. But the suitcase will be useful for taking back all the books I want to get in Bombay.

"Thou comest back, Sister?"

"Of course. Why dost thou ask?"

"Last night, when I could not sleep, I suddenly was full of fear. I said to myself: Mother will not come back from Bombay. There she will meet her own people, all of them white like Mary Ann and herself, all of them learned and able to read and write books. She will say: 'Why should I go back to a place where all people are brown and nobody is as learned as I am? I shall stay in Bombay or cross the Black Waters to rejoin my own people in lands in which everybody is white and learned.' My fear became ever greater, and there was nothing to ease it. Only thou canst do so, it is my house that is thy home forever."

Auntie cries, while she holds me close to her, my head on her shoulder. Her attachment is so touching. What have I done to deserve it? Were I not here, she might have more say with Rashid, act for him, perhaps even influence him. But she never thinks of such things. She and her sons also never mention the vexed problem of Rashid's remarriage, though there must be no end of tentative suggestions made to them. They don't even talk about Sakri. Auntie's tact is exquisite.

While I reflect, she is stroking my hand. Hers is soft as a rose petal, a strange thing for a woman who has cooked many meals all her life.

"If thou art here with us, Sister, it is as though Mary Ann had not gone for good. It is so hard without her. She was so—so—." Auntie fumbles for words. "She was so good. She was so clever. It was the happiness of New Moon and Full Moon all in one when she entered the house in all her sweetness. I look around me, and there are my children and grandchildren and, *inshallah*, there will be many great-grandchildren—but there never will be anybody like Mary Ann. And I cry. Do not leave us too, Sister, for thy white people. They don't love Mary Ann and thee as we do. If they did, they had not let you depart. Do come back!"

"Of course I will!" My tears come more easily than they ever did. "I shall come back to thee and Rashid. Why dost thou doubt it?"

For a long time we sit hand in hand, without talking. Strange to say, it is in that fantastic house full of unbelievable people, methods, animals and smell that I feel most at home. Suddenly I remember Rashid's words, uttered in a different connection: "What does a house matter, after all?"

What does a house matter, if in it lives a soul like Auntie's?

"Maharaj does some other work at the Laboratory while sahib and I are away. So I give thee the key to the small provisions. [The 'big' provisions are in chests, stored in a separate go-down.] Don't forget to look out for ants and rats. Don't let anybody have the key. Thou art responsible. Dost thou understand?"

"Yes, masahib." Cook seems proud that I trust him.

"If somebody asks thee to let him have of the provisions do not give any. Say 'Masahib said I am not to take anything while she is away.' [It suddenly occurs to me that the uncles or somebody resembling them might turn up.] Dost thou understand? To nobody thou art to give anything, if I don't tell thee to."

"I understand, masahib."

But maharaj, superior as befits his Brahman rank, talks to me when we are alone.

"I every day go will. No harm I shall let come, Mother."

"Not every day! Way too long is."

"Every day, until mother to son back comes." For a moment he is silent. Then, looking fully into my eyes: "Back thou comest, masahib?"

"Back I come, maharaj."

"Good is, Mother."

9

*W*E are alone in our compartment, thank heaven. Though it is mid-morning Rashid pretends to sleep, and I pretend to read. Both of us, presumably, do so for each other's sake, but we are not successful in pretending.

It started as soon as we left on this journey to Bombay. Neither

of us had traveled by train from the time of our arrival in Akbarabad with Mary Ann last April. There were the fields about whose
crops Mary Ann had inquired; Bunagar, the last station before Akbarabad, at the sight of which we had started to get ready for
arrival, Mary Ann vowing that she was wearing a hat for the last
time, because she intended to adopt saris at once; the groups of *nim*
and *banyan* trees we had admired together; and so on. Rashid must
have his own memories of the journey; I had left them to themselves. They were so happy.

I've never seen Rashid's face immobilized by sleep—or pretended
sleep—as I do now. Now only do I realize how the five months since
Mary Ann's death have aged him. Deep lines from nose to mouth,
from mouth down to chin. I must make him talk on the Science
Congress or something of the kind, when he opens his eyes; something that holds his interest.

But when, after two further hours of pretending, Rashid gets up
and settles himself in the corner opposite to mine, he waves away
my question as to his forthcoming lectures.

"Mother dear, neither you nor I are interested in cellulosis at the
moment. We think of our darling. Pretending is no good."

What am I to say?

After a while Rashid changes seats. Wordlessly we sit near each
other, my hand in his. Incapable of any talk, we continue to sit in
silence.

That is the story of our journey to Bombay.

Bombay, Savoy Hotel
December 21

So many things have been crammed into the past twenty-four
hours that I don't see how I can describe everything.

Arrival at Central Station, with Rashid's friend Hamidullah, D.Sc.
(London), Ph.D., F.I.C., awaiting us on the platform. He is the overworked secretary of the Science Congress and it says much for his
friendship for Rashid that he found time to receive him. They kiss
each other on both cheeks, as Muslim men often do.

"This is Mother, Hamid."

"Welcome to Bombay, Mother! At last I get to know you personally, though I know you well from Rashid's letters. But why
have you decided to stay in a hotel? My house is yours. My mother

and my wife ask you to stay with us. We can ring up the hotel and cancel your reservation."

"Thanks very much, brother," says Rashid. "But one of us is quite enough. You and I will be in and out all day on business, meeting pals, visiting laboratories and so on. You'll have to entertain lots of colleagues. Your ladies'll have their hands only too full as it is. I want Mother to feel free and have a good time while she is in Bombay, undisturbed by the Science Congress."

"Don't believe him, Hamidullah sahib. I certainly expect to attend the Congress, at least those lectures I think I'll be able to understand. Will yours be very difficult?"

"Not at all, Mother, above all not for a lady as learned as you are. But don't call me sahib. Just say Hamid, as Rashid does. I'm one of his oldest friends."

Hamid beams down on me, as we enter his car. For a moment I don't know what to do; sit near him in the front seat, or inside the car with Rashid? Western fashion, the lady sitting with the man who drives? Or eastern fashion, which means she doesn't sit near a man who is a stranger? Funny, how purdah-minded I've become, all cooped up in Akbarabad. A year ago such a question would have never entered my head. But Bombay is neither East nor West, and certainly not India. That's why I lost my bearings for a moment, before sitting down decorously in the back seat. You never can tell. Hamid, a tall slim Punjabi, clean-shaven, wearing rimless glasses, looks every inch a modern man; yet he might not be. Appearances are often deceptive as in the Lahore Khan Bahadur's case. Better be on the safe side. Had I sat down near Hamid, he might have made a mental note of my disreputable western manners!

Later both come up to my sitting room in the Savoy, to see me safely settled.

"What are you taking, Hamid? Soft drinks or——"

Rashid laughs. "Don't be afraid, Mother! Hamid likes his peg just as much as I do, even more, I dare say. Many are the bottles we have shared over exams in London, first in the certitude that we wouldn't pass, later to celebrate the fact that we did."

"Two whiskey and soda, one orangeade," I order. Then, turning to Rashid and Hamid: "I'm afraid I'm the only good Muslim of the party. I never drink."

"That I will tell my mother at once," says Hamid, thus disclosing unconsciously that there must have been some previous domestic discussion as to the likely depths of my western depravity.

Before the two depart, Rashid and I accept an invitation to dine at Hamid's next day.

"What about your lunch, Mother?" Rashid comes back again, just as I was thinking that both had departed for good. "Will you be all right all alone here in the hotel?"

"Don't worry, dear! I'll ring up some people, read the letters I found waiting and have a jolly good time."

"Will you be in all day? I'll call some time this afternoon, but I don't know when I'll be free."

"In all day?"

Rashid laughs. "Don't look so disappointed, Mother dear. You needn't be. Have as good a time as you can. Only phone me at Hamid's whether you're in or not."

Now I am alone. There are about half a dozen letters waiting for me, and several phone calls I've promised on arrival. But the lure of the all white and chromium bathroom is too great! I haven't had a real bath, a tub bath, I mean, since last April.

How illogical and unfair human nature can be! If people are sneering at the little zinc tubs we use upcountry, I protest. I say—it is my honest opinion—that Indians are right to prefer their bathing methods to ours; that it is cleaner to perform one's ablutions under the running water of a shower or tap, as they do, than to sit in the stagnant water of a bathtub, as Westerners do; that I too now prefer showers to soaking. Yet, in spite of this conviction, the first European porcelain tub I see after eight months so delights me that I'm delaying everything else in order to luxuriate at last in a full-length tub. I won't tell anybody. People might say "How like a woman!"

I take a whole hour over my bath, enjoying its comfort and luxury, soaking, refreshed in every pore, both physical and mental, so to say. Then, ashamed of myself, I set out to deal with correspondence and calls. There's a phone in the sitting room, thank heaven.

One letter says that All-India Radio would like me to broadcast; another that Joan and her Bengali boy, who has now become her husband, are in Bombay, en route to Bengal; a third is an invitation to dinner with friends from Inverness, two other invitations are for lunch, one with Brenda O'Connor, the niece of a London friend, the second with Lady Ardeshir Jehanbhoy, one of the leading Parsi women of Bombay, socialite and social worker all in one. And there is one more letter, the last, which interests me most.

"Queen Mary College for Women
"Malabar Hill
"*December 20*

"Dear Hilda:

"I'm so glad you've come at last, though far too late for all the chats I wanted to have with you. Since I am leaving the morning of the 23rd to spend Christmas with friends in Poona, please keep the afternoon and evening of the 22nd for me. I'll call for you at 4:30 P.M. We can have a good chat over tea. Then, I'm afraid, I'll have to whisk you out to my College, where there's a big Social on, which I simply *have* to attend. I think you'll enjoy it. After that I'm free, and we can dine wherever you like. It's a shame I have to leave next morning, when you've just come, but it's too late now to alter arrangements. So be a good girl, and say you're free.

"Affectionately yours,
"Aileen"

Aileen Fitz-Carruthers is one of the most brilliant women I know, but she's much more than that: really good and helpful to anybody and anything. She is about thirty-five, not beautiful but very charming, a well-known archeologist who, on her own, excavated with interesting results west of Leh. After an exhausting spell of archeological work, she has now agreed to take over History at Queen Mary's, while the regular historian is on leave. It'll be good to see her.

When I'm ready I take my courage in both hands and sit down on the veranda. There is the sea which I saw last with Mary Ann, which we had crossed and recrossed with joyful expectations—the sea she loved far beyond mountains. Here it is, a shimmering blue-green expanse. Why am I here to enjoy it and not she? I've had my life—she hasn't had hers. But these are foolish thoughts, I know. She wouldn't like me to think them. Mary Ann lives. And she does not want me to be negative, to shut myself off.

159

After having duly reached Rashid on the phone to tell him about my program, and having enjoyed a preliminary talk with Aileen—we have lots of mutual friends—I find myself in the crowded Gymkhana of Queen Mary's College. Band and gramophone alternate in providing dance music. There are more boys than girls, a rare feature in a woman's college. Nothing could make me more aware of the contrast between Akbarabad—"upcountry" in general—and Bombay. There purdah, seclusion, strictest restraint wherever the opposite sex is concerned; here unconstrained meeting.

"You can't imagine, Aileen, what it means to me to see these girls so free and happy," I say. "Upcountry it's heart-breaking."

"I know. You must come up against pretty old-fashioned cases."

"Yes," I reply, thinking of the Rani of Sangwar and our womenless club.

Later, over dinner at Green's, Aileen tells me that she begins to regard me as a pretty bad case myself when, upon her ordering a sophisticated dinner, I disclose that since I left the boat eight months ago I've never tasted ham or bacon.

"Why on earth not?"

"Because my son-in-law is a Muslim."

"Well, what of it? You needn't eat ham in his presence, if he resents your doing so. But surely there is no reason why you shouldn't if by yourself!"

"He doesn't resent anything. But it's somehow not feasible in a Muslim house."

"Why?"

I feel I don't want to explain, and switch over to another subject. How to report the many deliberations Mary Ann and I had had about ham! Rashid, considerate as usual, had said we could eat whatever we pleased. But we knew that the Muslim servants and Auntie would be scandalized; cook would not want to touch a plate polluted by ham and so on. We forgot all about it until Mary Ann's hungry period began. Then she craved familiar food, especially ham and eggs. Somehow I have no heart to tell all this to Aileen, sitting at Green's. I cannot find my way as yet to speak about Mary Ann. It'll be bad enough when meeting Joan, who'll want me to do so. Instead, I make Aileen tell me about archeology. It's marvelous how the latest excavations and discoveries are throwing light on the common background of mankind!

At home, again a very prolonged lazing in my dazzling white bathtub. The first day in Bombay is over.

December 24

Today is Christmas Eve. I'll stay by myself, together with Mary Ann, Richard and all my dear ones, and celebrate Christmas in my own way. But first I must write up yesterday in my diary, lest I forget. There are so many things happening every day.

Lunch with young Brenda, whose husband is in the P.W.D. (Public Works Department) and just now on tour. Brenda is glad to unburden her heart after two years out in India.

"In a way it's dreadful, being here. Oh yes, I know I'm fortunate and all that. Servants galore, nothing to do, going out every night. But at times I wish Bob and I were at home in a Sussex cottage, with me doing the housework and he trimming the lawn on Saturday afternoons."

"Why, Brenda dear?" I want to understand. This girl comes from thinking stock, and she thinks for herself. No herd instinct about her and her people!

"Because it's not real life out here. It's like being in a conservatory, sheltered but without fresh air. Sorry for talking like a sentimental book, but I feel like it. So does Bob, but he thinks it's unmanly to say so. At least that's what most of his colleagues would like him to think. But I suppose things are better for him than for me, because he has his work. I've nothing. Just fool around, between Turf Club, Willingdon Club, Taj and dinners, wearing nice frocks and getting used to drinks. There must be lots of things going on, real life, but we don't know about it. And I'm lonely. The other women don't feel like that. Either they are forever sailing home to their children, or thoroughly enjoying themselves with being great ladies, having lots of servants, horses and everything, while at home they'd live in suburbia where most of them belong, with a charwoman in the morning, if that. Why, in our previous station —it's only four months that we are here in Bombay—ten or twelve servants for an average household was the usual thing. A *syce* to each horse, the rest for the house. Horses, dogs, dancing, drinks, club. Always the same people. It's not life, is it?"

She is visibly in earnest, though an onlooker might think that this charming young women, perfect in every detail from curls to lacquered fingernails, would enjoy just that kind of life.

"Have you met Indians?"

"Met, yes; properly talked to, no. One meets them at the Willingdon, and, as upcountry, at official functions, but it's always a world apart."

"What a pity to be in India and not know Indians!"

"Yes, isn't it? When I came out I was eager to. I said so to the wife of Bob's boss. Her reply was that during the thirty years of her stay she had never met Indians apart from official functions, and I shouldn't either. I was dumfounded at such a thing being possible."

"But there are lots of things to do, Brenda. Here in Bombay you have every chance to learn about India in an easier, that is more westernized, way than, for instance, in the part of the country where I'm now staying. You're interested in social work, aren't you? I remember you worked in the slums at home. There's excellent social work being done in Bombay. I'll get you in touch with my Parsi friend, Lady Jehanbhoy. She'll be delighted to have you as a fellow worker, I'm sure."

Brenda is enthusiastic. Afterward I reflect on the strange fact that I, the provincial, am the one to tell her about activities in Bombay. In the four months of her stay nobody, apparently, has encouraged her to do anything serious or worth-while.

Later

I skip the description of my tea with Joan and young Chatterji, or rather I leave it for a later date.

As I was waiting in the hall of the Taj for a taxi, who should come up to me but the Khan Bahadur, whom I had imagined safely tucked away in Lahore!

"You are in Bombay, madam? How delightful! And Rashid sahib?"

"He is here for the Science Congress."

"Of course! I should have thought of it. How long will you stay here, madam?"

"We have not yet decided, Khan Bahadur. Oh here is my taxi!"

I drive away, leaving him to gaze after me. I'm glad I didn't give

162

him our address. He's sure to evolve some scheme or other in pursuit of his goal of getting Rashid as a husband for Akhtari Begum.

At the Savoy there is just time to dress for the dinner at Hamid's before Rashid turns up.

"There's lots to tell you. First, I've been asked to tour for a fortnight in company with about a dozen others. We are to be shown all sorts of laboratories and plants. I'd have to wire to His Highness for leave. Do you think I should go? And what'll you do if I go off for two weeks?"

"Don't worry about me. I can stay on in Bombay, though not in this palatial abode. You know I've a number of invitations. Or I can visit Her Highness of Raipuri. She has asked me so often. Or I can go off to the aborigines."

"What?"

"You must resign yourself to all sorts of things where I'm concerned, poor dear. You see, I'm very deeply interested in the primitive tribes—Bhils, Gonds and the others."

"Why on earth are you interested in such backward people? Haven't you enough filth in Akbarabad?"

"But don't you see that from them we can learn about mankind's past? They're the remains of the Proto-Indians and the Dravidians—those people who lived here long before the Aryans entered India from the north. And they still exist! They are still keeping their old customs and traditions! Can't you see how breathtakingly thrilling it is to learn something about them?"

"Sorry, Mother, I can't. Give me real progress in science, medicine, sanitation! Make the house clean! Do away with malaria, T.B. and typhoid, above all with malnutrition! That's what would thrill me. But study backward diseased people, just because they happen to have a longer history to their backwardness? India'll never progress with all that retrospection. That's a national illness, and a Westerner like you should know better than to get infected with it."

"But—!" On second thought I decide to drop the subject. I'll never get Rashid to see my point of view. The young scientifically minded generation of India are pioneers of something entirely new as far as their country is concerned. Pioneers can never afford to mellow down. Instead I ask "What else did you want to tell me?"

"I've had two offers: one from a big sugar concern in the south of the Bombay Presidency, and the other from Jehangirabad State."

"I say! You *are* sought after, the very moment you appear. Congratulations!"

"Nothing to congratulate me about. Thanks all the same. You know I'm out for scientific research. The sugar-concern people would allow research work only in the very limited degree of their own interests. And Jehangirabad? I wouldn't have better opportunities for research than I have now, probably less. So why bother?"

"You want to stay in your present job? Always?"

"I didn't say that. If I'm offered a chair, and a good laboratory to experiment in—did I ever tell you that I've always wanted to teach students?"

"No, you didn't. If this is your aim, you should certainly stick by it."

"It's sweet of you to encourage me like that, instead of inquiring after the very substantial salary the sugar people have offered, and urging me to accept it so we should have plenty of money. For a moment I was tempted to accept without even consulting you —just to make sure, once and for all, that I'd never again find you washing my underwear!"

"Rashid, you mustn't even for a moment dream of going into industry while your heart is in an academic career."

"Then do you promise not to do *dhobi's* work?"

"Isn't that what is called 'taking unfair advantage'? I—yes, I promise!"

"Splendid. I'm sorry we can't celebrate this victory of mine by ourselves. I'd have taken you to some nice place. But we must be off to Hamid's, I'm afraid."

Hamid's mother and his wife, Sultana, are very modern compared to Akbarabad ladies. We all sit together at dinner. The dining room is furnished on western lines, the curtained-off drawing room, too (in Bombay flats one big room usually serves for both purposes). But when, after dinner, I retire with the ladies to their sanctum, we sit down on the floor, propped up against pillows, as though we were upcountry. Hamid's mother rules the house, there can be no doubt as to that. She calls a spade a spade, and does so also where Rashid and I are concerned.

"I never thought that memsahibs were much good, Mother; but

you seem an exception as your daughter has been. We've heard nothing but good about both of you."

Sultana, visibly embarrassed about the old lady's frankness, says that there are many good and delightful memsahibs, but her elder doesn't pay any heed to her remark.

"Let us talk about the errand which took you to Bombay, Mother. Have you got the right kind of girl for Rashid?"

"Both he and I do not yet think about his remarriage, I'm afraid."

"Then it's high time you did. A man cannot be for so long without a wife. How many months has he been a widower?"

"Nearly five." The tactless remarks are well meant, and after a moment my resentment dies down.

"Five months! But it is impossible! I said so to my son. We must do something about it! You, a foreigner, are perhaps not able to look after such things as Muslims would."

"Thanks very much, but there is no need for you to worry. A man of Rashid's family is always besieged by proposals. We have many, but we refuse them all; such is his wish." With these words I get up, fully conscious of having been almost as tactless as the old lady, by thus rubbing in Rashid's pedigree, which happens to be superior to hers.

She looks at me with a wistful smile. "So many proposals? Yes, his pedigree is very ancient. But there *are* brides in Bombay good enough even for him!"

Rashid takes me back to the Savoy. We walk along Marine Drive, listening to the gentle sound of the waves, looking at the brilliant stars, happy to be together in that big town which both of us would have been afraid to face separately. The air is mid-summery, by western standards, yet it is Christmas time.

December 25

Yesterday I stayed at home all day, except for getting some red roses. Rashid lunched with me, and came back for a quiet dinner. At about half past eight he left to attend a preliminary party in honor of some scientists, himself included. This engagement of his was a great relief to me. Without it I'd have had to tell him that I wanted to be alone this Christmas Eve.

To the three of us—Richard, Mary Ann and myself—Christmas Eve was always the center of the year. It had been so even in my parents' house. There we had the traditional Christmas tree full of apples and gilded nuts, little stars and animals in silver and gold, cotton-wool to suggest snow, and pink candles, the whole enmeshed by silver "angels hair"; we entered the room, dark except for the tree, singing "Silent Night"—children, servants, guests. Everything was perfect, and in due course each was conducted to his lovingly prepared place and shown his presents, after which the servants departed to get dinner ready, while the others remained in the beatific atmosphere of the Christmas tree.

But when I had my own home, and Richard and I learned to understand the background of the Christmas tree, our celebration was altered considerably. From Mary Ann's sixth year onwards, she never knew the tree decorated with anything but red roses, white candles and silver thread.

Why?

Perhaps now, while I am celebrating my first solitary Christmas without my child, while I am fastening red roses on to the cypress branches carefully brought from Akbarabad at the bottom of my trunk—one can't get Christmas trees in Bombay—is the right moment to remember: why? Why did Richard and I give up the fully laden tree of our childhood for the simplicity of red roses and white candles?

Christian tradition knows of *two* trees: The Tree of Paradise and the Tree of Life. In the Middle Ages—which knew far more about these things than we usually do—two pine or fir trees were used for the religious Christmas plays handed down from one generation to the next. One of them was hung with apples for the Paradise play (*Dramatis personae:* God the Father, Gabriel, Adam, Eve, the Devil) ending in man's fall and expulsion from Paradise. The other was hung with red roses for the Nativity play (*Dramatis personae:* Gabriel, Mary, Joseph, the innkeeper, the shepherds, the Magi).

Deep wisdom lies behind this differentiation, but we have nearly lost it. In our ignorance we mix up the ideas of both trees, hanging apples, toffee, chocolates and all manner of things together with candles on our Christmas tree, if we have one. This is a great error. The apples are symbol of man's fall into sin and loss of Paradise, the candles symbol of man's re-ascent to Paradise in the footsteps of Christ. Therefore the two should never adorn the same tree.

In accordance with ancient Christian tradition, a Christmas tree

166

should bear nothing but white candles and red roses; later times have reverently added silver threads. The tree is crowned by the five-pointed star of Bethlehem which, from the very moment of the Nativity, replaces the older six-pointed star of David. The five-pointed star alone can be the herald of the Son of Man since it symbolizes the human figure, head, arms, and feet planted firmly on the ground. Silver threads flow down from the Star to remind us of the flow of Divine Light which came to earth with the Nativity. The white candles burning upwards symbolize the human response to Divine Grace: prayers and gratitude offered by man to God. There is a tradition that the number of white candles should be thirty-three, to commemorate the years of our Savior's earthly pilgrimage. Likewise the number of red roses distributed over the branches should be thirty-three.

Why red roses on the Tree of Life, the true Christmas tree? Because they mean a very definite thing. In Christian tradition and lore, red roses growing out of the most desiccated and mineralized of trees, or out of a barren staff, are always meant to remind us of the new life and hope which Christ brought to a spiritually desiccated and barren humanity. The fir tree—and next to it the pine—have more silica in their leaves than any other. It is for this reason that these trees have been chosen for many centuries to represent the Tree of Life. The radiance of Heaven comes to earth in the Nativity—and out of the deadest of living matter there blossom forth the red roses which God alone can call into existence.

Many traditions and legends speak of this miracle. According to one old legend we are told that, as the Child was born, the snow disappeared everywhere and needle trees covered with fragrant red roses sprang from the winter-bound earth. On the night of the Holy Birth the Rose of Jericho sprang up in the footprints of Mary. When Joseph of Arimathæa landed at the south coast of Somerset on his road to Glastonbury (supposed to be King Arthur's Avalon) he stopped at Weary Hill in order to gather fresh strength. Leaning on his long staff he stood amidst the snow and ice of a cold Christmas night. But when people passed the place soon after midnight they saw that the barren staff had grown into a bush covered with red roses. From that day, concludes this legend, the bloom of red roses can be seen on Weary Hill every Christmas night by him whose heart is pure.

So each year we kept Christmas Eve with red roses and white candles only. Presents were looked at only after some hours. "It is the tree that matters," said Mary Ann once, after she had been watching it in silence all evening.

Looking at the red roses on the cypresses—my tree here in the tropics—I remember two other occasions when I celebrated Christmas in the same way. Last time it was on our first Indian journey. We were staying in a Hindu State Guest House, and our hosts had kindly arranged for crackers and bunting to be provided for the 25th, thinking that this was our way to celebrate Christmas. They were much astonished when we asked for cypress branches and began to fabricate red roses from crêpe paper we had brought for the purpose, a timely thought, since red roses were not obtainable in that particular place and season. Mary Ann claimed the right to get everything ready by herself. "Maybe I'll marry and have children soon—it's high time I learned how to prepare Christmas. Moreover, I want you to feel a child for a change. I'll be the mother today."

The first time was in Jerusalem. Richard and I had arrived that same morning, to spend Christmas in the Holy Land. Very tired, we slept all day. While Richard slept on, I went out, accompanied by our dragoman, to get red roses for the pine branches brought from Switzerland. It was already dark, and a sharp wind was blowing across the Judean hills. The dragoman began to explain all sorts of things, but I asked him not to talk. I wanted to think of Christmas only and the fact that, at last, we were celebrating it in Palestine.

After an early dinner, we sat in our room, the pine branches standing on the table against the wall. We had brought beeswax candles, and their sweet scent now mingled with the resinous fragrance of the pine. The room was long and narrow; our two armchairs had to be placed side by side. We sat wordlessly, looking at each other, supremely happy. At last it was time to set out for Bethlehem. Again the poor dragoman was requested not to interrupt the blessed peace of that silent night. Past the Shepherds' Field we drove up to Bethlehem. We were too early and stood at the rampart, looking over the soft hill curves of Bethlehem towards the right, where under the starlit sky the ragged forbidding beauty of the desert of Judea was faintly discernible. It was cold, as it must have been on that other night two thousand years ago.

And then the bells of Bethlehem began to ring, and we went to the manger.

Now I am far away in Asia, quite by myself. Never again shall I be anything but alone for my Christmas celebration. But I am not lonely. My dear ones are with me—and He. The three of us felt never closer, never happier in each other than when we were nearest to Him. Nothing has happened to alter this bond between us. Death is but a transition.

December 26

"If you say I must, then I must, Mother. But I'm sure your friends would prefer you without me."

"Nonsense. The Careys are very nice people. You will like them. And they understood at once that I'd accept an invitation for Christmas dinner only if you were to come too."

"Yes, but they'd prefer it differently. Westerners want to remain among themselves, especially at Christmas. Knowing that, I'll feel uncomfortable myself."

"You'll be wrong, then. That I've been staying on in Akbarabad after Mary Ann left us clearly indicates the bond between you and me. All my friends will respect it."

"Don't forget that I am an Indian, Mother. That's what they may dislike."

"For goodness' sake, don't start on inferiority complexes, dear! What do such things matter to thinking people!"

"It's not an inferiority complex. If we are at it, let's have things out, Mother dear. I don't quite know what it is, but here in Bombay I feel as if you belonged to another world, as if you were being taken away from me. You have so many friends—you go to so many places—you don't seem to need me at all! Somehow I'm getting afraid that your friends will persuade you to—! You *do* belong to their way of life, after all, not to a small upcountry town with no Europeans about. I can't help feeling that something may happen to take you away from me. Don't let it happen, Mother. Our darling has left me; don't leave me, too."

"Rashid, how can you think of such a thing! Is it not our joint and free decision that has kept us together? Why should a stay in Bombay alter my feelings for you? I'm not a child, am I?" But I can't prevent my voice from trembling.

"Don't cry, Mother! I know I've been a fool. Here we've been together so little. If we had, I'd not have gone so morbid."

"You've been very naughty," I say, taking up a lighter note in order to stop crying. "Fancy taking me to Bombay, putting me up in a palatial hotel and then imagining that that selfsame trip will cause me to desert you. You have a nice opinion of me, I must say!"

"That's better. Do scold me. I deserve it. And I like it, too."

"All right. I'll scold you every day from now on. There'll be always some reason, I'm sure. As to the dinner at the Careys to-night: we go together, or I don't attend at all."

"We go, and I'll don a boiled shirt so as not to disgrace you."

"Nothing of the kind. I'd hate to know you're uncomfortable. Moreover, everybody wears soft shirts nowadays."

After lunch, Rashid departs. I have to prepare a broadcast. But his words do not leave me. *Why* did he feel like this? Is it imagination, or did I give him any reason for it?

December 27

This morning I went to the opening of the Science Congress. It was very interesting, and the speakers excellent. I wish I knew more about science than I do, which is very little. As it is, I'll attend the anthropological section, to learn all I can, especially about the Gonds.

Rashid sat among the elect on the platform. I was very proud of him and his fine bearing. Afterwards he and Hamid chatted with me in the lounge before they joined a committee and I departed to meet the Chatterjis, who were having lunch with me.

On the way to the Savoy something strange happened. I was looking idly out of the bus window when, driving along Church-gate Street, we passed a girl who reminded me so much of Mary Ann that I caught my breath. She was sitting in a big car drawn up outside the Asiatic Stores. For a moment I thought it was Mary Ann. The way she talked to the lady beside her, the tilt of her head, the movement of her hand were instantly familiar. I got up to leave the bus at once. Unfortunately the next stop is a good way off. When I had raced back to the Asiatic Stores, I saw the car departing.

I wonder who the girl is? She had her head covered, so she may be either Muslim or Hindu. The young generation among Parsi women—the Parsi community are very strongly represented in Bombay—generally leave their heads uncovered. It was a strange experience. Somehow I cannot forget that girl.

December 28

The Hamidullah ladies have sent word asking me to attend a women's party in their house on January 4. No excuse will be accepted, for the guests are eager to meet me. Well, so be it. I'm quite looking forward to a purdah party after all this "western" life of Bombay. But I'm still western enough to rejoice that the Khan Bahadur has not put in an appearance, as I had dreaded he would. Perhaps he has dropped his plan, or the girl found another husband. At least I hope so.

December 29

I've been thinking all these days about East-West problems in general and in particular, especially the latter. Has the contact with western life affected me, as Rashid implied it had? Do I feel happier in the free and natural give and take of western social contacts, unhampered by all the restrictions and inhibitions of Indian traditions? In one word, do I want to escape the East?

To the best of my knowledge, it is not so. I stick to Rashid and life in Akbarabad not only from a sense of duty. I love the people. That is the answer to the unspoken questions of my western friends: "How can you stand it?" If I had the choice—and, all things told, I *have* the choice—I would without hesitation return to Akbarabad to stay until I am no more needed.

On the other hand, I do realize that this stay in Bombay has complicated matters for Rashid and me. Christmas dinner *à deux* with him would have been as delightful as *à trois* with the Careys. As it was, Rashid was not at ease, thus not setting our hosts at theirs. Both parties did their best to make the evening a success, for my sake. The result was, of course, to the contrary, since social intercourse can only thrive if effortless. On our way home, Rashid said: "Didn't I tell you, Mother?"

I couldn't truthfully deny he had. But that is not the last word in the matter. If both parties knew each other as well as I know

171

them, they would be at their ease at once. It is a matter of time: East and West must know each other better than they do.

Rashid's lecture was a big success, and I received lots of congratulations with maternal pride. I had picked him up at Hamid's, approved of his suit and tie, at the same time exhibiting a new dress which I had donned in his honor for the first time. Afterwards he was very mysterious about not being free to lunch with me. At 2:30 he turned up at the Savoy, beaming and carrying a big parcel.

"Only when I saw you so smart in your new dress this morning did I realize that you haven't enough to wear, Mother. So I went and bought four dress-lengths."

"So many! You shouldn't! One or two, yes,—but four! Why didn't you take me?"

"That's just what I didn't want. You would have said, 'Only one!' or 'This pattern is for younger women only.' I want my mother to look nice. So I went by myself."

Out of the parcel there emerge four pastel georgettes. One has a pattern of pansies on mauve ground, and is wholly delightful; the three others, however, would have suited Mary Ann, not me. Feeling that it doesn't matter if I look ridiculous as long as Rashid is pleased, I promise to see the tailor at once and pretend to like his choice very much.

"I shall now always buy your materials for you, Mother! You don't spend enough on yourself, and always choose dark colors!"

Bless him!

Now I shall set my teeth, and don a pink chiffon sprigged with lilies-of-the-valley, as though I were seventeen. Rashid matters, not my being dressed appropriately.

"My dear Hilda,

"I don't want the old year to close without writing to you about a matter much on my mind since I left you.

"You have told me but little about your life in Akbarabad. I've tried to visualize all you left unsaid. I know of your son-in-law's

172

deep attachment to you, and yours to him. But even allowing in the fullest measure for this mutual love, I cannot see why you should give your whole time to him. Your gifts and yourself are wasted in such up-country small-town life, too conservative for any progress. Fancy what you could do somewhere else for India so dear to your heart!

"Your son-in-law will build up a new life and marry. You told me so yourself. Whether this'll happen now or later, it *will* happen. Why should you, under the circumstances, lose touch with so much and bury yourself in a place where people, however kind they are, cannot possibly appreciate you? It is all very well for you to look after the house, but there are more important things you can do. Many people can keep house well; few have your gifts.

"I can, to a certain extent, understand your loyalty to Mary Ann's husband and don't therefore advocate travels around India to collect book material or return to Europe. But there is something else you could easily do.

"I met two people of All-India Radio during the last days, and heard from them that, though agreeing to one broadcast, you had turned down everything else. Why? They were delighted when I outlined a possible program of regular talks for you. You could come to Bombay every two or three months, give a few talks, and go back to your son-in-law. If you prefer you could broadcast from Delhi, but I'm selfish enough not to want you to. I suggested you should talk about the different peoples of this earth, whom you know so well: the peoples, mind, not the governments. How the different peoples think, feel, work, pray, play, hope, etc., etc. Wouldn't that tempt you? But if you suggested something else, I'm sure they'd accept it.

"I'm sorry to have been what you would call 'un-English' and to have interfered in your personal affairs. It was difficult. That's presumably why I am writing instead of waiting for my return to town.

"I've been having a lovely holiday, full of peace and nature.

"God bless you,

"With love,

"Aileen."

Of course I'm tempted. There are so many misunderstandings in this country where other peoples are concerned (and vice versa).

173

I'd love to give that series of talks. It wouldn't be difficult either; perhaps my absence could be worked in with Rashid's inspection tours. He is away so often, and there seems no reason for me to stay in the house all by myself. And I could reach libraries and bookshops every few months. That would be marvelous. Yes, Aileen's plan is excellent, from all points of view.

From all?

What about Rashid's imaginings? Will my going to Bombay or Delhi give fuel to them? Will he not say: "Did I not tell you, Mother—your Bombay friends are taking you away from me?"

Distrust is always lurking in this country. Will Rashid understand that I don't love him less if I occasionally leave Akbarabad? Will he mind? What ought I to do?

~ IO ~

*A*LL over India New Year is celebrated at different times. The two factions of Parsis have their celebrations on separate dates in September; not all Hindu castes begin the year on the identical day; Muslims follow the Moon Year. So do Hindus, for religious observances. The first of January, however, is celebrated by each and all. So is Christmas, to a certain extent. We've had lots of Christmas and New Year congratulations from Akbarabad, some addressed to both of us, some only to Rashid, the noteworthy point being that Hindus and Muslims often exchange Christmas and New Year greetings among themselves. Conservative or anti-Christian people choose cards bearing the words "With the Compliments of the Season," but the majority exchange Christmas cards pure and simple.

I have lots of cards from people to whom I didn't send any. As usual I'm aware of the fact that others are nicer to me than I am to them. In a way it's a pity we've not been at home for the holidays; I could have returned some of the many courtesies received during various festivals by sending out "Christian sweets" at Christmas.

Hindus couldn't have eaten them, though. So it is better to stick to our usual way of sending choice fruit. Everybody can eat that.

Frank and Kay can't come, after all. They'd have had only three days in Bombay, which isn't enough for a twenty-eight hours' journey both ways. They say I should come to Madras instead, but I've already arranged to go to Raipuri. Our meeting'll have to wait for a later date. It's a pity; they are such dears.

On the other hand, it's perhaps just as well. They'd try to persuade me to write on India. I won't. I know too little.

January 3

"And so you went slumming?"

"I did, at twenty."

"As early as that?"

"For me it wasn't early. By then I had had enough of dancing and racing. That's four years ago. I haven't regretted it yet. My work is much more interesting than dancing, especially helping to organize Trade Unions."

The girl who calmly says these words over tea is of striking appearance. Her sophisticated green-and-gold sari enhances the fairness of her skin, her curls betray superior cut and handling, her jewelry is exquisite. To look at her nobody would associate her with slums and T.U. Yet I've heard a lot about her excellent and courageous work.

"Please tell me more. It's disgraceful, but the purdah of Akbarabad has made me, too, somewhat purdah-minded. Meeting you is like a breath of fresh air."

"Tell that to certain aunts of mine! They call me a hurricane, if not an earthquake."

"How do your people take it? Even to modernists of their type your doings must seem strange."

Humayum belongs to a great Muslim family, renowned for having educated its girls before any other did. Both her father and grandfather have held very high office, including that of Prime Minister.

"I can't say they were delighted at first, but what could they do? My grandfather had advocated education and freedom for women, irrespective of caste and creed. So, once they saw I was determined, they actually helped me."

175

"How grand of them! What did they do?"

"I was allowed to set up my establishment in Jehanabad exactly as I chose. So I took my own ayah and three old family servants. I knew they'd stick by me through everything, and they do, though they're bewildered, at times, if I bring in as guests people they'd never have allowed to enter the front door in my parents' house."

"You have only the servants to help you?"

"No. Two former fellow students of mine live with me. So we are three, really. But that's far too few. There's no end of slums, both huts and so-called "modern" flats. In a way there's always more to do in the flats than in huts."

"How so?"

"Disgraceful as a hut is, it does nevertheless represent a kind of home. Somehow it reminds its inhabitants of home and village, gives them a feeling of dignity and independence. But those foul one-room tenements built for the mill hands! Two or three families live in a single room, exactly as in the huts—but no feeling of home about it! You hear what goes on in the neighbors' rooms, right and left, above and below. There's no end of quarreling. Having no home brings out the worst in everybody."

"That's understandable. Indians are rooted in village life. Moreover, their wives and families can't accompany them to town, usually. Wages are not high enough for that. In Bombay and Calcutta there are about two men to one woman. How is this in Jehanabad?"

"Pretty much the same. Yes, men without their families constitute a problem in itself. Let's put it to one side for the present. There's enough else to get angry about in those one-room tenements. Water-supply and sanitary facilities leave much to be desired—if not everything. If three families live in a room, there are three charcoal stoves. If ten or fifteen single men share it, there may be as many as ten stoves, since most of the men prepare their own food."

"And you move among it all?"

"Of course. Afterwards I return to my nice house where my ayah has an elaborate bath waiting for me. Sometimes I feel ashamed about it, sometimes I don't. Such is human nature."

"I don't think you need feel ashamed in the least. You should have the comforts you are used to, provided they are kept within reasonable limits and you are not dependent on them."

"How do you mean?"

"I mean that you'll be able to work better if you lead the life you've been used to. Why shouldn't you enjoy a good bath with all the paraphernalia? Only, if you can't have it, don't grouse. Don't even pay attention. Be independent of things."

"If I adopted that point of view, I'd certainly be better balanced than I am now. I do enjoy lovely things, but often with a bad conscience."

"Don't have it. The chief thing is that you should give all your energy to work."

"I do."

"Now tell me more about that work, please. Does communalism come in at all? Did you start work among Muslims?"

"Certainly not. Our country must get rid of divisions. I want all Indians to have better living conditions. It doesn't matter to me whether they are Hindus or Muslims."

"Are you not more or less alone in this point of view? Few people seem to have freed themselves from communalism to such an extent."

"You are right, unfortunately. That cursed communalism stands in the way of everything. If I'd work only among Muslims I'd have more support from my own people, including the socially minded."

"I expect they say there's enough social work to do among purdah-women."

"So there is. But if nobody ever begins to work for Indians as such, we'll never get anywhere."

"How does it work the other way round? Do the non-Muslims resent your interference?"

"Not really. There were a few cases of hostility before they knew me properly. But that's over. I'm part of the Jehanabad slums by now. People take me for granted."

"Don't some think you crazy to forego your own home for slumming?"

"Yes, some of them think me an utter fool, but others don't bother about it. They are desperately poor and exploited. I try to help them. That's all there is in it to them."

"It's marvelous that such work is being done, especially by a Muslim girl. It sounds too good to be true."

"There are a few more like me coming on. But on the whole social work, when not confined to Muslims, is mostly carried out by Hindus, Parsis and, of course, Westerners. Most Muslims stick to Muslim welfare work, if they do anything at all."

"By the way, I have a young woman friend, Brenda O'Connor, whom I'd like you to take up. She has done social work in England, I dare say she'd make a good worker."

"I'll love to meet her, and pass her on to social workers in Bombay. But now it's your turn. What about conditions in the Akbarabad mills?"

"Pretty bad. Contractors supply the labor, with whom the management never deals directly. Not only do millhands have to pay the contractor a monthly percentage of their wages for an indefinite period, but they are entirely at his mercy. He can dismiss and replace them at his own sweet will."

"No T.U., I dare say."

"Good heavens, no!"

"Wages?"

"Five to six rupees for child labor. Nine to twelve rupees for adults. Highly skilled people draw somewhat more."

"Much child labor?"

"Lots. They're cheaper, that's what matters."

"No schooling for them?"

"Of course not!" Strange, that I have to be the one to give these replies, revealing conditions every Westerner would regard as disgraceful. Not that I am dewesternized; but, knowing conditions in Akbarabad and elsewhere as I do, it comes quite naturally to my lips to say, "Of course not."

"Crêches?"

"No. Mothers deposit babies where they work. None has been injured so far as I know, but it's awful, all the same. I did try to persuade the people concerned that crêches were necessary. But they said other mills hadn't any, either, and how could they compete if they had to raise prices?"

"The usual reply."

"I, as a foreigner, can't insist. Indians must take up these things. If the mill owners themselves realized how terrible conditions are, things would be better."

"They don't want to. Hence the necessity of Trade Unions."

"Do come to Akbarabad. I'd love to have you."

"I'd love to come, as soon as I've time, which won't be before spring. Why do you laugh?"

"I picture the disappointment of Akbarabad, if not its horror. There's a charming, elegant girl—and she talks about T.U.!"

"It's people like me who should. The ordinary type of 'agitator,' as social workers are called, is easily shut out of Indian States, sometimes even jailed. I can't be, because of my family. Mill owners have to entertain me and be polite, poor things. But they deserve the worst. Conditions in British India are bad enough; but in most of the States they are infinitely worse."

"Yes, so they are. Do come and help."

Trade Unions can be many things. I remember the militant ones of the twenties in Europe; old Samuel Gompers explaining to Richard and me the milder form and aims of the movement in the United States; and many others. India has about two hundred and forty Trade Unions, nearly all of them in British India. In the States—except the few progressive ones—they would mean something very tame: some kind of initial labor legislation for children and women, some alteration of the contractor system, some kind of protection against injury sustained while working. Today a man loses his arm or leg through no fault of his while in the mill, and doesn't get an anna's worth of indemnity.

But it wouldn't be right to view this appalling state of affairs from the western angle only. Hinduism bases its outlook mostly on the law of predestination and *karma*. If a man is born an untouchable, this is the result of former lives. If a man is poor or loses a limb, it is destiny, with whose working no outsider can interfere. Many Muslims profess fatalism. Both philosophies account, to a very great extent, for what Westerners call the "lack of social responsibility" in India. Noninterference with the destiny of others is a chief tenet of orthodox Hinduism. Only modernists break it, do social work and try to bring about better conditions for untouchables, bless them.

January 4

"We leave on the sixth, Mother. First by car, to view some plants in the vicinity. In the evening we catch the Frontier Mail in Kalyan. I'll be home on the twentieth or twenty-first. Shall I find you?"

"Of course. I'll arrange to be there a day before you."

"I'm so glad. I didn't want to say anything, so as not to curtail your movements. But coming home without you there, isn't home. I hate it even on ordinary days, when you are out somewhere and I return earlier than expected."

That is decidedly not the moment to speak of the broadcasts, I'm afraid. I'll have to postpone the decision.

"When is that purdah party of yours over tonight, Mother? Let's dine together afterwards."

"Let's. I dare say I'll be free by 7:30. And you must tell me lots about the Congress. Are you satisfied on the whole?"

"Beyond expectation. There are some excellent men, doing excellent work. It's a good thing to be among one's fellows from time to time. It prevents vanity, and is most stimulating. There are intrigues and jealousies, of course—but not worse than among the medical or legal profession. One thing is certain: there is no communalism among scientists, praise be to God. Only the man counts."

"How marvelous!" Here it's the scientists. There Humayum, and friends of her type. Until, one day, surely, the whole of India will discard communalism!

January 5

When I enter the Hamid ladies' drawing room, the company is already assembled. Only Muslim ladies are present; but Bombay's modernism has made most of them forsake Muslim dress. There are three ladies wearing the wide Punjabi trousers, long shirt and veil worn by both Muslims and Hindus hailing from the Punjab, a delightful dress. Wide gold brocade trousers worn with a green gold-spangled shirt and gold gauze veil; silver combined with pink; mauve satin combined with purple and silver. All the other ladies wear the sari, an equally lovely sight.

While waiting for tea—why do we have to wait?—I make friends with a Mrs. Hassan Latif, the widow of a professor of Persian and Arabic. Her son and Rashid went to school together. They seem to have liked each other; later, however, the one went in for science and modernism, while the other graduated in Persian and Arabic. He seems to be his mother's all-in-all. Like Rashid he had been married; his wife died and left him with two little girls. Now his mother wants to find a good wife for him.

"But it is difficult, memsahib," she says. "I don't want a wife only;

she must be a good mother to the children, too. They are so sweet. As long as I'm here they have me. But what if I'm gone? It is not good for a daughter not to have a mother to arrange for her marriage, and afterwards to welcome her back home whenever she feels she wants to leave her husband's house for a while."

"But surely you can find Muslim girls with enough kindness and affection to make a good mother for the little girls, Mrs. Latif!"

"It is not easy. Besides, they are all so bold and modern these days, not as a proper Muslim maiden should be. My son would never take a wife not keeping strict purdah, nor would I. It is not easy to find a girl upholding our laws, good-looking, healthy and a good mother to stepchildren."

While I idly ponder over these requirements I suddenly see Sakri's sweet face before my mind's eye. Who could be more loving and good-looking? As for purdah—she'd rather die than give it up, I know. Orthodox Muslim routine among good people would be the very haven she needs. The Hassan Latifs are much above her social station, and she would lead the kind of life I've always wished for her. It seems a good thing. But first I must find out about the young widower. Rashid will know.

"I might be able to help you, Mrs. Latif." How funny for me to be among the matchmakers! "But I must first make sure that the girl is free. She's very sweet-tempered, more than pretty and brought up in strictest purdah. She's a distant relative of my son's."

"Praise be to Allah, the All-Merciful! Who would have believed that from a memsahib I should first hear about my future daughter! If you say she is good, she is good."

"Let me first find out how things stand. I shall talk to her people, and then let you know."

"When will I hear from you, memsahib?"

"After my return to Akbarabad. In about three or four weeks, I dare say." Perhaps I'll invite Mrs. Latif for a short visit.

Why are we still without tea? Really, there seems no need to wait for belated visitors. At last, on some murmured words of an ayah, both hostesses get up and leave the room. Soon they come back, escorting a lady and a girl, both very richly dressed. The elder Mrs. Hamidullah motions Mrs. Latif away from me. I find myself sitting between the two latecomers, whose name I didn't catch in the introductions.

"How do you like Bombay, memsahib?" asks the mother.

How does she know I come from upcountry?

"I like it better than I ever thought I should. At first I didn't much want to see it, because I thought it was neither East nor West."

"And now?"

"Now I've been to many places of 'real India' and I find that Bombay has a charm all its own. But I still prefer upcountry India."

"So do we. Have you ever been to Lahore? I hope you will visit us there some time."

Something in her smile makes me sit up. Is it possible——?

Just then the elder hostess hands me my tea. "Who are these two ladies, Mrs. Hamidullah?"

"Very big people indeed, memsahib. Sahebzadi Mumtaz Ali Khan from Lahore. This is her daughter, Akhtari Begum." She pats my shoulder none too gently. "And you wanted us to believe that you had nobody in view for Rashid sahib! But we never believed you."

Wedged between Akhtari and her mother, I try to collect my thoughts while busying myself over tea and cake. The Khan Bahadur hasn't left us in peace, after all, and I have been a fool ever to believe he would. After meeting me in the hall of the Taj he must have phoned or returned to Lahore, to arrange for the ladies to proceed to Bombay. The rest was still easier. Rashid is staying with Hamid, his old friend; there must have been hundreds of ways to approach the Hamidullah ladies about the tea party. Good Punjabi Muslim families are either inter-related or have relations of relatives who are. Though the victim, I can't help appreciating the smooth and efficient working of Muslim social structure. A very neat job indeed! to get me landed like that!

It's not the girl's fault, anyway. I must put her at ease by being as courteous as I can, short of holding out actual hopes.

"Do you visit Bombay frequently, Begum Saheba?"

"Very rarely, memsahib. The journey is too long. We stay at home, most of the time. We have lovely gardens."

"Ah! Is this, then, your daughter's first visit to the south?" Everything in life is relative. Upcountry people speak of Bombay as "south," while Madrasi and Travancoreans duly classify its position as "north."

"It is. Akhtari, tell memsahib how you like Bombay."

"It is very big," murmurs Akhtari, hanging her head as a maidenly damsel should. It is bad manners for a bride-to-be on view, to look up in front of prospective in-laws.

Akhtari is a good-looking girl, fairer than her mother, with very small hands and feet. To my astonishment she doesn't wear any jewelry except a very simple gold watch. According to usual custom among old-fashioned people she should wear dozens of things to impress me with her wealth. I dare say the Khan Bahadur advised her mother against it. "Westerners, fools that they are, are not fond of jewelry in daytime," he may have said.

"Bombay is a very interesting town," I continue, sticking to the one safe subject of conversation I can think of. "Museums, shops—there's lots to see."

"My daughter is very interested in books. She has read"—the Begum falters and addresses Akhtari in Urdu, getting a murmured reply. "She has ready 'Little Lord Fauntleroy' and 'The Taming of the Shrew' by Shakespeare. And many more books."

"Oh!" I comment politely. Then I call myself to order. It's unkind not to try putting the girl more at her ease. "I'm sure your daughter has read much Urdu and Persian."

"Not very much. She is more interested in western books." That's for my benefit, no doubt.

At this juncture some ladies rise to depart. There's general commotion. I'm not sorry. It was strenuous to maintain conversation. Had I only been alone with the girl! I like her in a way, but not for Rashid. There's something about her I can't fathom. What a strange day! I'm glad to go home.

But the strange experiences are not yet over. Sultana bai, who usually lets her mother-in-law do all the entertaining—what else can she do?—takes my hand just as I'm about to leave. "Will you step in for a minute? I want to show you my baby."

Inside her room she doesn't even pretend to do so. "Will you be kind enough to help Akhtari, Mother? She wants to talk to you."

What is this? Rebellion against age-old fetters? How amazing—and how marvelous!

"I'll be delighted to help if you tell me how."

"Akhtari was afraid to talk to you, but I said you would understand, and that you wanted to help Indian girls to be happy."

"If only I could!"

"In this case you can. Akhtari will tell you everything herself. Are you free tomorrow morning, Mother?"

"I can be, of course. Will she come to me?"

"I've planned it all. Her mother and my mother-in-law go visiting together. Akhtari will be left in my charge. Her ayah will remain with her, of course; that's all to the good since she takes her side. I'm borrowing a purdah car from a friend of mine, and will say that we are going for a drive. We'll be with you a little after eleven. We'll come up the purdah stairs, and go straight to your room."

"Has the Savoy a purdah staircase?"

"Of course. Besides, ayah has been there this morning to make sure. The number of your room is 26."

What is the Khan Bahadur's efficiency compared to that of purdah ladies!

Benumbed, I take my departure, and resolve not to tell Rashid about the meeting. Who knows what Akhtari will say?

Farewell dinner with Rashid. "I'm glad to get away from that fancy food, Mother!" meaning European fare. "And I'll be so glad to get back to work again. I wish it were two weeks later. I hate leaving you here all by yourself."

"Don't worry, dear. I'll manage."

"Take care of yourself, Mother. There'll be lots of things to talk over at home."

"Yes, lots." I am thinking of the broadcasts.

"You will be there when I come, won't you?"

"I promise."

January 6

"We've known and loved each other from childhood, memsahib. Being cousins, we were allowed to grow up together, until I entered purdah. Even afterwards we could see each other occasionally. We always knew we'd marry each other, and be happy." There are tears in Akhtari's eyes. In the sincerity and defense of her love, she is positively beautiful. I like her and her spirit.

"What happened then, Akhtari Begum?"

"About five months ago our fathers had some quarrel about politics and land. Asaph was forbidden our house, both by his father and mine. My people asked a friend of my father's, the Khan Bahadur Mohammed Husain Khan, to find a husband for me outside the

184

Punjab. He is also involved in the quarrel, and dislikes Asaph's father. So he went south and told my parents——"

"I understand. There is no need for the sequel."

"Thank you, memsahib. You are as kind as Sultana said you were. It is not that I have anything against your son-in-law Dr. Rashid Ali; on the contrary, I like what I heard of him, and I should love to be related to you. But there is Asaph. He and I are meant for each other. So please help toward our marriage by saying that Dr. Rashid Ali does not want to marry me."

"I've said so, in whatever way possible!"

"But the Khan Bahadur told my father you were most keen to see me!"

"Then he told him wrongly." I perceive the implications of my words, and want to explain things truthfully and satisfactorily. "You have given me your confidence, Akhtari Begum, now let me give you mine. It isn't that I didn't want to see *you;* I had nothing for or against you—while now I have much for you, if I may say so. But neither my son nor I is interested in his remarriage so soon after my daughter's death. That's why we said 'No' to the Khan Bahadur. Now that I've met you, I like you very much; but even this fact would not alter our decision. You can feel quite safe as far as we are concerned. The Khan Bahadur, apparently, gave your people a wrong impression for reasons of his own."

Akhtari's magnificent eyes light up dangerously. Obviously the Khan Bahadur is no special pet of hers.

"What can I do concretely to help you?" I continue. "I'd love to, but I can't see anything."

"You can, memsahib. The Khan Bahadur will soon travel to Akbarabad to ask you once more, now you've seen me. If you then say that you dislike me, my father will be disappointed in me. Perhaps I can get him to marry me to Asaph, after that. Meantime, Asaph's mother is laying siege to his father in our favor."

"But how can I say I dislike you! It wouldn't be true."

"Yet it's necessary. Please do. You see, if you simply said that it is too early for Dr. Rashid Ali to think of remarriage, my matrimonial value wouldn't be diminished, which is just the thing I need. You must explicitly say that you dislike me, please."

"Even if it were true, such outspokenness would be extremely rude on my part. Refusals are always couched in very polite terms, I know."

"But isn't it just the way of Westerners to be very—frank?"

I can't help laughing. "Well, I promise to compromise; I won't be quite as rude as you want me to, but I'll make it sufficiently clear that we are not interested in you at all."

"Please be as disapproving as you can, memsahib."

"I'll try my level best."

"Will you come to Asaph's and my wedding? I'll invite you myself."

"That would be a little difficult, wouldn't it? Your parents mightn't understand. But I certainly want to know whether things turn out all right. Perhaps Sultana bai will be good enough to let me have your news."

"Of course I will," replies this lady, heart and soul of the conspiracy.

When they've gone—they have to be at the flat before the return of the elder generation—I can't help feeling elated. If purdah ladies take their fate into their own hands so courageously, things must get better soon.

January 7

I've only three more days left in Bombay. It is time to be selfish, and spend as many hours as possible in the Royal Asiatic Society's library.

Bombay has other libraries, too, but only in these time-mellowed rooms does one find so great a collection on history and on India. And the many scientific magazines! I go from one table to the other, afraid to lose time by concentrating on one at the expense of the others, equally afraid of losing it by scanning headings only. I'm quite astonished at my being so greedy. I didn't use to be. Am I really so famished for realms intellectual? Or is it because, since Mary Ann left, I'm all alone with my thoughts and interests?

Later

"I'll write from Akbarabad, Aileen. I've not yet had the opportunity to talk things over with my son-in-law."

"But the broadcasting people want your answer."

"I'm sorry. I can't give it just now. I'll write between the twenty-fifth and the thirtieth. Is that in time?"

"It is, and it isn't. It's so complicated for both sides to explain everything by letter, complicated and unsatisfactory. Couldn't you decide to talk things over while you are in Bombay, letting All-India Radio know later the dates which are convenient?"

"It's no use, Aileen. The question is not 'when' but 'if it all.' I can't and don't want to decide without my son-in-law."

Aileen doesn't reply, but her expression conveys volumes. Only English discretion and breeding prevent her from saying exactly what she feels.

I regret having been so curt. Would I have been, though, had I not been tempted to accept?

January 8

"AKBARABAD
"Margshirsh Krishna
"Paksh Panchem
"*January 5*

"To Mother, greetings.

"With Mother and Sahib gone house empty is. Empty house good not is. I happy not am.

"Every day tomb to I go. Flowers are. Tomb's gardener not good is. Water enough not he brings. I him told.

"Burra sahib, Sahib's elder father's brother, come did. Cook said house empty is. Cook said food not is. Burra sahib said where keys are. Cook said Mother said no keys are, no food is. Burra sahib go did.

"Garden in many red roses are Mother's room for. With God's will Mother comes soon.

"Mother for and Sahib for greetings.

"Mother's son
"Jagdish."

When the *hamal*—cleaner—who does my room at the Savoy reads maharaj's letter to me—I can't read Hindi script—I nearly start to cry. It'll be good to get back to him and *chowkidar*.

What luck, by the way, to have missed Uncle Fakhruddin! Cook did very well. I must get somebody to write in Hindi to maharaj, and somebody else to write in Urdu to cook; once more I'll impress on him that nobody is to get the keys until my return.

Later

The telephone rings. A man's voice, unknown and yet reminding me of something.

"Who am I?"

"I'm afraid I don't know."

"But you should. Have you forgotten me entirely?"

"I'm afraid I have."

"That's not kind of you, dear lady. You were always so thoughtful. Has India changed you as much as that?"

"Better not blame India. It is difficult to be thoughtful, not knowing to whom I'm talking."

"Don't you, really?"

"Certainly not!"

"What a shock for my vanity!"

"Are you vain?"

"You always said so."

"Oh—can it be you, Arthur? How ever did you get here?"

"Speak of vanity, and she knows who I am! What a reputation to have!"

"How did you know I was here?"

"I arrived two days ago—if you read your newspapers properly, you might have found something about it—and ran into Aileen Fitz-Carruthers this morning. Now you know. When shall I see you?"

Arthur Ridgeway—Sir Lancelot Arthur Ridgeway, Bt., etc., etc.— has been a friend of mine for more than a decade. He is brilliant in every respect: politician, shot, wit, writer, squire. His farms are the *non plus ultra* of agriculture, his speeches in the House perfection, his after-dinner remarks just what they should be. All that, of course, doesn't account for our being friends. If he were only brilliant we wouldn't be; I dislike brilliancy both as means and as end. When I was about fifteen I discovered that I was in danger of becoming "brilliant" (a Vienna illness of that epoch); thereupon I deliberately crushed all signs of it I could lay hands on. If I had ready a clever repartee or comment, I left it unsaid; if I could have amused people, I didn't—with the happy result that I have never since been hampered by the burden of being thought too clever. Squashing brilliancy at any early age was, perhaps, the only really brilliant thing I ever did in my life.

In addition to being brilliant, Arthur Ridgeway is very much *homme à femmes*. Always within the limits of good taste and reputation he has innumerable woman friends, in whose friendship or admiration he basks. I've never been able to understand what draws him to me—I'm not at all his type. But there is something in him which does not fit into the picture of the perfect shot, wit, etc., etc. And that something is friends with me.

I'll dine with him tonight. After dinner we'll go for a drive and the movies. I only hope he will not talk of my life in Akbarabad. How to explain India to somebody like Arthur?

January 9

Nobody'll believe it if I say that I had not seen any western films since I left London. The five talkies we boast of in Akbarabad show Indian films only, to which we go regularly.

Modern Indian films are usually far too long. The story lags; the one-roomed village hut is as remote from reality as the glorified interiors of Hollywood films. Yet there is something to enjoy every time we go: village life, good songs, weddings, children. As for historical or religious films, some of them are superb. They relate the lives of great saints and men, sometimes of demi-gods. If Lord Shiva appears in the clouds to prevent the malefactor's victory, the whole house applauds. As far as pictures are concerned Indians want the triumph of virtue above anything else.

I remember a very interesting film I saw together with orthodox Brahman friends. In it a despised untouchable boy rose to the rank of a saint against every Brahman opposition. When the curtain fell over the last scene, in which his former enemies, overcome by his sanctity, bowed themselves down before him together with multitudes of other Brahmans, my friends cheered loudly. "But this is an untouchable!" I exclaimed. "How is it that you cheer?" "There is no untouchability where a saint is concerned," one of them retorted, while the other said enthusiastically, "It is time untouchability went."

I could not believe my ears. How marvelous, that a picture could transform their outlook to such extent! "Will you touch an untouchable tomorrow?" I asked to make sure.

Both laughed. "That is another matter, Mother. You see, in everyday life——"

Double morals. As everywhere.

When watching with Arthur my first western film in nearly a year, I remember that episode. We see the usual triangular comedy, with an unusual amount of pep, bathing belles and bedroom vistas. Soon I close my eyes for sheer annoyance. How utterly out of place such films are in the East!

"Why?" asks Arthur, when I say as much. "If Indians didn't like that sort of thing they wouldn't be here."

"You don't understand what I mean, I'm afraid. Easterners see our films and think, 'This is how Westerners live.' Hence their notions about everybody being divorced, immoral and so on. They take our films at their face value."

"If they do, it's high time they learned better. But I don't believe they do. You've grown morbid in your Akbarabad."

"Have I? Now listen to this, produced by a Bombay girl a few days ago. She's studying for her M.A. We were talking of women's problems in East and West. She said *en passant:* 'In the West, where everybody has so many servants, etc., etc.' 'Many servants?' I asked. 'Most women do their own housework, including those who are smartly dressed and go places. In the United States for instance, guests in evening dress may help their hostess after dinner to wash up. In England the work in many flats and houses is done by the mistress, more often than not with her husband lending a hand.' 'It can't be so,' she replied, 'I do know Westerners have lots of servants.' 'How do you know?' 'From the films, of course.' There I was. And remembering our western films, I couldn't even blame the girl."

"Don't take all this so much to heart, dear lady. We have more important things to discuss. You don't seem over-keen on this film. Let's get out, shall we? We can walk slowly to your hotel and talk."

When passing the Gateway of India, I stop. "Let's stay here for a few minutes, Arthur. Those islets look enchanting in the moonlight."

"As you say. The Gateway seems an appropriate place to ask you why you still stay out here?"

"It is difficult to explain. I dare say not one of my reasons would mean anything to you."

"Try, anyhow."

"There's my son-in-law. I feel I ought not to leave him yet. We've grown very fond of each other. Then I've not yet learned enough about India. Don't forget I came out to learn. Then——"

"Then?"

"I'm a coward in a way, I suppose. I can't yet face the journey home without Mary Ann. Aden, the Red Sea, Port Said where the vendors called her *'la petite madame'*—I simply can't. We were so happy coming out."

"Go on, Hilda."

"There's nothing more. These are my reasons for not having gone home." How am I to speak of maharaj and Auntie and *chowkidar*, of all the many ties of love and gratitude that bind me to India?

"I can understand about the journey. You should not travel by yourself. Why not come back with me? We could go via China and Japan—or via the Cape. There's no need for the Red Sea."

"How sweet of you, Arthur! But I don't want to run away. If home I go, it'll be via the Red Sea."

"What do you mean by 'if home I go'?"

"What it says. I haven't yet decided. There is my son-in-law to consider."

"Listen, Hilda. I don't profess to understand the reasons that bind you to him and India. But, even so, I know they must be good reasons, being yours."

"But don't you often disapprove of me? I'm sure you never call me a crank even in your thoughts but that's what it amounts to, doesn't it? You think it's foolish of me to stay out here?"

"I should think any other person foolish. But not you. You mustn't forget that hard-boiled materialists like myself have deep underneath a very soft spot for idealists of your type. You've gone against my better judgment countless times; yet, in the end, I always found you were right. But I want you to return home. Even without knowing anything, about your present life, I'm sure that you are being exploited."

"Exploited? Good heavens; if you knew how sweet and kind people are to me. It's I who exploit their kindness, not vice versa."

"You'll forgive me for sticking to my own opinion. You see, Hilda, I know you very well."

"But you don't know Indians at all, Arthur! You stay only in Government Houses and Residencies or in State Guest Houses.

What do you know of Indians as they really are? Moreover, you are a burra sahib *par excellence*. Everybody will treat you on an official footing, and not in a personal way."

"I'm not interested for the moment in India's attitude towards me. I want to talk about you. Must you really leave the day after tomorrow, now that we've just met after so long?"

"I'm afraid I must. From here I go to Her Highness of Raipuri, and I can't put that off."

"I see. Well, what about tomorrow?"

"No—yes—I'm free at night. There's a lunch with a Parsi lady, and teas both at 4 and 5:30. After that I'm free."

Arthur is very different from what he has been, much softer and mellowed down. I wonder why. But somehow, somewhere, I'm a little bit afraid of what he is going to say.

January 10

So far two wires and a letter from Rashid. He is well and busy, bless him.

Later

When I sit down to lunch with Lady Ardeshir, I find myself facing the girl resembling Mary Ann, while her mother is at my right hand.

For a moment I am unable to follow the general conversation. Such likeness! The small head, big eyes, the straight nose and especially the lips and smile could belong to a twin sister of Mary Ann's. I was not mistaken, then, when I saw her from the bus. Even the modulations of her voice are the same. How is such resemblance possible?

"Who is this young lady?" I whisper to our hostess, who sits at my left.

"A lovely girl, isn't she? From a good old Muslim family, too, but brought up along reasonable lines. No purdah, as far as I know. The family come from the Central Provinces, but the mother is Bombay-born, and saw to her daughter's having a good education. Why don't you talk to her? You met Mrs. Liaqatullah, didn't you?"

Thus apostrophized, my other neighbor and I begin to talk, she leading the conversation.

"How long have you been in India?"

"This time not more than eight months, I'm afraid." Yet wasn't a lifetime condensed into them?

"I hear you come from Vienna. What a delightful place! My husband and I liked it very much indeed."

"I'm glad you liked it. Have you been all over the continent, then?"

"Oh yes. Prague, Budapest, Salzburg, of course Paris and the Riviera."

"Not England?"

"We've been there three times. My husband studied for the bar in England, and it is there he took me first. Now he is a High Court Judge."

"Has your daughter been to Europe, too?"

"Not yet. But she wants to go very much. Her two brothers are there, one at Oxford, the other at the London School of Economics. How many children do you have, memsahib?"

"I have no child now. My only daughter died out here. She was only twenty-three."

"Oh! I'm sorry!"

"Thank you. It is very kind of you."

"And where are you staying now?"

"With my son-in-law in Akbarabad."

"But then he is not a European! You must be Dr. Rashid Ali's mother-in-law! I've often heard of you, memsahib."

"What made you think my son-in-law was European?"

"Because you are. It's the usual way, isn't it? And I don't much believe in mixed marriages myself. Indians should marry Indians. It's better for all concerned. But your case was very different. We all know that. It is rare that there is such a bond between a Christian mother and a Muslim son. Everybody praises you."

"There's nothing to praise. My daughter and he were very happy together. He is lovable in every respect."

"And a famous scientist into the bargain."

"I dare say he is. But I don't understand enough about chemistry to know. What I do know is himself. He is good and fair-minded."

"If a mother-in-law can say such things of a man, moreover a man not of her race, he must indeed be good."

"He is. He made my daughter very happy."

"Tell me about her. What was she like?"

193

"If I may say so, your daughter bears a striking resemblance to her. That's why I'm looking at her all the time."

"Really? My daughter and yours? Tell me in what you see the likeness?"

"In nearly everything. It's unbelievable. Please spare me details."

"I understand. Will you come and see us?"

"I'd love to. But I'm leaving tomorrow, I'm afraid."

"When does your train leave?"

"Late at night."

"Can't you dine with us? Or, if you prefer, come to luncheon? My husband is not at home at midday, though."

"You are very kind, Mrs. Liaqatullah. Unfortunately, I'm booked for both luncheon and dinner. But would you and your daughter give me the pleasure of having tea with me at the Savoy? What is her name, by the way?"

"Maryam. Yes, we will come. It may be less tiring for you before your journey."

"Maryam?"

"It's the Arabic form of Mary. Don't you know?"

"Yes, I know. It's only—you see, my daughter's name was Mary Ann. How very strange. Or perhaps not. There is likeness even in this."

"Yes, it does seem strange. We'll say no more now. Tomorrow at 4:30, memsahib?"

"Tomorrow at 4:30, Mrs. Liaqatullah."

~ II ~

*W*INTER travel is pleasant. There is not much dust yet, and the windows can remain open.

The weeks in Bombay have passed like a dream. When Rashid first spoke of taking me there, or even after I had planned my stay,

194

I never should have imagined that so many experiences and problems would result from that journey.

Akhtari—Humayum—Brenda—Joan—Aileen—Arthur—Maryam——

And not only they! Problems of a general nature, as bewildering as the personal problems represented by all those names. It was the first time I had been with my own kind after my life with Indians. This meeting has given me both joy and sadness—perhaps more sadness than anything else.

There is a kind of wholesale western attitude out here. In different shades, yet identical pattern, it applies to all Westerners, whether hailing from Britain, Denmark, the United States or Czechoslovakia. This attitude has become a tradition. It is passed on to every newcomer by word of mouth and implications. If he is not much of an independent thinker, he will believe every word the old-timers tell him, and conform to pattern during all of his stay in India. It's not the individual's doing: it's the species! Laws are laid down as to what comforts and mode of life a Westerner *must* enjoy, so as to be able to stand life out here at all! These laws have crystallized into superstitions and taboos. Few people dare to question them.

Westerners, for example, are supposed to travel only first class, whether they can afford it or not—the very limit they can go on the downward path is second class. If they were to sink as low as the Inter—meaning leather-cushioned Intermediate class—they'd never stand the strain, quite apart from the other unspecified horrors and dangers.

That's sheer nonsense, of course. As everywhere else, expensive travel is naturally more comfortable than cheap travel. But it's not true that first or second is *necessary* for Westerners to travel in, if they can ill afford it. Inter, comparable to American tourist and English third class, is good enough. Since it is without fan, a second-class compartment with revolving fans is certainly preferable during the hot season. If, however, the intended journey takes place between 7 P.M. and 11 A.M., one can manage all right in the Inter class, even in the brunt of the hot season except in a sandstorm when windows have to be closed. There is a basin and tap in the washroom attached to each compartment; India being a country of many infectious diseases, a seasoned traveler perhaps carries his own rubber or enamel basin (together with his own boiled water, for rinsing his teeth), by means of which he washes equally well or badly in Inter and second class.

We are now in the middle of the cold season. I travel second, because it is more agreeable, and because to arrive otherwise as Her Highness' guest would not look well. But, suppose I couldn't afford it, I'd certainly be none the worse for traveling Inter.

Ramnagar
January 13

Since Her Highness has no A.D.C. at present, the little Maharaja's English nannie comes to meet me at the station, which is a nice unofficial touch. The Dewan lives in Raipuri proper, where a big and rather somber palace stands awaiting the end of His Highness' minority and his accession to the Throne. Once a week, the Dewan drives to Ramnagar, a neighbor State, in whose capital the young Maharaja, his mother and their staff occupy a sunny modern bungalow; he acts as liaison officer between the little ruler and the Raipuri State Council which is governing the State during the minority period.

Her Highness receives me in the big drawing room full of chintzes and formal photographs in silver frames, representing her late husband in many kinds of uniform or sport clothes. She herself takes me up to my room, and I can't help meditating on how different and formal my arrival in Raipuri Palace would have been.

"Yes, it's a country-house existence," agrees the Maharani, when I say as much. "Nannie and I agree that Jai should have as simple and happy a childhood as possible. In Raipuri there'd be no end of ceremonial for him. Here he is a child like any other, running about the garden without any guards behind him. It was hard to get it through; the State Council thought it their duty to insist on guards. In the end we compromised: there are guards posted at every garden-entrance, but not near the house. Jai loves to take the salute when driving out. That is his only official duty so far, I'm glad to say."

"Is the lack of ceremonial here Your Highness' reason for not staying in Raipuri?"

"Partly, yes. Ramnagar has a better climate, too. The palace in Raipuri is very damp."

Nannie, however, is more outspoken. She hails from Selly Oak,

Birmingham, where I have a number of friends. So there are lots of subjects to chat about.

"Poor little fellow, how could we make sure of his life in Raipuri?"

"Do you mean that——"

"Of course I mean it! You cannot have traveled all over India without knowing that it is the custom to educate rulers who are minors out of their own State—and a very good custom it is!"

"Yes, of course, I do know these things. I suppose I had just forgotten. Is there somebody to covet the Throne of Raipuri?"

"Isn't there always somebody, in this country? Her Highness was the Senior Maharani, though she is barely twenty-six. There is a Junior Maharani with a son and a daughter. Moreover, there is His late Highness' younger brother, with four sons of his own. He is one of the Executive Council. So the Throne would come in usefully for quite a number of people. Jai is never allowed to go to Raipuri, of course. Here we can make pretty sure of his safety. But there? However vigilant I might be, there are always ways and means to get rid of him for those who want to. There are sweets—or an inexplicable snake in the bathroom—or some inexplicable fire—! Well, we are taking no chances. Jai remains here."

"Who is 'we'? Her Highness and you?"

"No. I take my orders from the 'Great Father' as the British Resident is called by the princely families he has to look after, and I send him my monthly reports. He is responsible for Jai's safety and education. He and Mrs. Thurston come to tea every few months to see Jai in his own environment. It was his predecessor who engaged me, and gave me full responsibility. I'm in charge until Jai reaches his eighth year, when a tutor'll take over."

"Does Her Highness not resent this interference? I mean, you being in charge, and not she?"

"Oh no, she's far too intelligent for that. She knows that without the Residency, and me as the Residency's watchdog, Jai's safety could never be safeguarded as it is now. If His late Highness' relations come to visit Jai or take him out, how could she refuse them permission? I can, and I do, if I think it necessary. Since I'm English, it doesn't matter if people talk badly about me."

"She is very charming, isn't she? I know her parents, and I marvel ever anew how the daughter could turn out as she has. The Rani of Sangwar is very old-fashioned."

"Don't I know! But the daughter is really a darling. It's a pleasure to work in her house. She never goes against me. I'm very fortunate in that. Quite a number of nurses or governesses I know of have to fight in the nursery every day of their life. However vigilant they may be, there's always a mother or grandmother or aunt who stuffs the children secretly with heavy curries or greasy sweets, and upsets their little digestions. Horrid!"

"Her Highness would never do that. She's far too straightforward and sensible."

"Bless her, she is! What a rotten shame she has to remain a widow all her life! Though, if you come to think of it—what good is a husband like hers, taking a second wife at fancy! Heathen remain heathen, if you ask me. I'll be jolly glad to have seen the last of this country some day."

Intolerant, narrow, yet delightful nannie! There are many like her, steady and reliable as rocks. In the eyes of Indian servants, especially of the offended elder *zenana*-ladies whom they superseded in attending the children, they are disgraceful and ridiculous at the some time. Always asking for some foolish thing or other! Toast it must be, and not bread! The room must be sprayed with Flit instead of sweet scents! Under their Spartan regime the royal infants are deprived of even the comforts most Indian children enjoy, not to mention those belonging to Royalty. No trusted lady chews their food for them before putting it into their mouth; they have to chew for themselves! Nor are they allowed to wear the soft silks against their skin that are their due, reds and pinks, greens and royal blue; instead of putting them to bed in gold-bordered silks, as befits their rank, those wretched western nannies put them into mere cottons! Even gold-bordered veils which cover babies' faces during sleep against the evils of the night, are not allowed. Nor is that all. Who has ever heard of royal children going to sleep by themselves? They need their attendants on both sides of the bed, lest they feel lonely; soft massaging of feet and legs to help them fall to sleep; servants to lie all through the night across the threshold, so as to guard their sleep. Above all they need charms hung round their neck, sacred signs painted on their forehead, *kohl* to encircle their eyes, both for health and to ward off evil spirits. All of which is denied to the poor princeling handed over to a western nanny!

Rashid writes that he'll be home on the 20th. That means I should be there on the 19th, leaving here on the previous day. Only four more days! I must make the most of them, talking to the Maharani, seeing what there is to see in Ramnagar and, above all, making up my mind to tell Rashid about the A.I.R. talks.

From a western point of view, I am an utter fool to dread telling him. What could be more natural than some activity on my part? But there is an eastern point of view, too, which is much more personal. He may think—I'm afraid he *will* think—that he was right, and my Bombay friends have taken me away from him. Auntie and maharaj will be of the same opinion. I know it so well. That is what scares me. The last thing on earth I want is to hurt them. Should I bury the A.I.R. talks silently, without even mentioning them?

January 15

"I shall never forget your daughter."

"Thank you. She liked Your Highness very much."

"That just such people have to go! She could have done so much for India! We do not always like to accept the collaboration of foreigners—to put it mildly—but she was different, just as you are. She could have stimulated women into action. She could have got them out of purdah, lots of them."

"That is what she always wanted. I can remember the day when that wish of hers became a firm resolution."

"Do tell me, please."

"On our first journey we went to the Convocation at Bancore University. Unfortunately we were considered such distinguished visitors that we found ourselves seated on the platform, just behind the Rajkumar, or Crown Prince, of Bancore and the Chancellor. The whole hall was full of officials and students, with a handful of western wives between. But you don't notice five or six women among hundreds of men facing you solemnly. We felt extremely uncomfortable in our august situation. Mary Ann was in a short dress; and she kept tugging all the time, so it should cover her knees."

"I can well picture her. She must have looked charming. What color did she wear?"

"Yellow, and a simple large hat with yellow ribbons. We couldn't understand where the girl students and the *zenana* College staff were tucked away. A number of girls and women of our acquaintance were to get their M.A. and B.A. degrees that day. Though we should have known better by then, we had naively expected to see them at their own Convocation ceremony."

"Except in British India, you won't find that so easily."

"Yes, but we hadn't realized it. At last we detected some signs of life behind the trellis screens on the gallery. 'How will they manage to come down and onto the platform, when their turn comes?' we asked each other in whispers."

"How did they come down? Or didn't they?"

"Of course they didn't! When a girl's name was called, the Principal of the *zenana* College, an Englishwoman in her full dress of *magistra oxoniensis*, came forward from the academic fold and took over the girl's diploma. 'I can't tell you how I hate to do it,' she told us later. 'The boys come forward, get a royal nod, a Chancellor's handshake and lots of applause into the bargain. The girls, having the same or greater merits, remain invisible. Hours later I hand them their diplomas. It's disgraceful, really.' Twenty-two times we saw the Principal come forward and take over diplomas which belonged to those to whom even the reception of their academic honors was denied. Twenty-two times we saw red."

"Was it then that your daughter formed the resolution of helping girls out of purdah?"

"Partly only. For us the climax came next day. We went to a purdah party. 'We saw you sitting on the platform yesterday,' some of our friends told us. 'We were in the gallery. You couldn't see us, of course.' 'We didn't realize where we were being taken,' we replied. 'When we did, it was too late. We felt awful, sitting there by ourselves, the only women among all those men. Next time they won't trap us like that. We'll ask on arrival to be conducted to the Ladies' Gallery.' 'You certainly should not do that!' retorted a spirited girl. 'Get us down on to the platform and into the hall! That's what you should do. Help us down!' In that moment Mary Ann decided what her chief work would be."

"I'm glad she did. You must try to take it up in her stead."

"I'd love to. But, as you say, it was she who would have achieved so much. I wish Your Highness could take it up."

"I wish I could. As you realize, I can't. Perhaps when His Highness—Jai—rules Raipuri, I'll be able to do something. By then times will have changed. And as an elderly lady I'll be allowed to do things which I can't do now."

And maybe the Rani of Sangwar will be dead by then! Aloud, I say: "How is it that Your Highness is so modern-minded? This is so rare in a Rajput princess. I know you had an English governess. But it's astounding that in a few years she taught you so much."

"Ah, but you don't know her! You don't know my Miss Jones! She is everything that is kind and dear. I wanted to become like her, I wanted it more than anything else. I asked her innumerable questions; I read more than she wanted me to. I've kept up my reading since she left me on my marriage. You must see my little library."

"I'd love to. Where is Miss Jones now? Still in India?"

"Yes. Meantimes she has brought up two Dharpur princesses. When the third is married—in about two years from now, I hope—Miss Jones will come to me as my companion and stay with me forever. I want her to be well looked after in her old age. All her people have somehow died. She doesn't want to return to Europe. She says she'd be too cold there, for one thing."

The Maharani is laughing. "I adore the cold. I haven't been in Europe, alas, but three times in Kashmir with His Highness. There was snow every time we arrived. I couldn't see enough of it. And once we went on a pilgrimage along the Tibetan frontier. His Highness bade everybody march on. Then I left my sedan, all muffled up in things I'd bought in Srinagar. I walked with him through the snow and we looked at the Himalayas." A far-away look is in her eyes. This one outing of her life must mean a tremendous amount to her. When will she and her like be allowed real freedom? When will Rajput princes and nobles let their widows remarry? They'll be the last to set women free, if ever. Brahmans are more progressive, in certain sections, very much so.

January 16

A letter from Waliuddin. Rashid having spoken very highly of Maulvi Professor Abdul Latif, I'd written to Akbarabad about my talk with his mother, and had inquired whether I was to invite her or not. This is the reply to my letter, a very dignified reply indeed. "Mother, Auntie and I are full of gratitude that you have remembered us and Sakri while staying in Bombay which is so big a town. You are full of goodness to have done so. The All-Merciful be your rewarder. We are eagerly waiting for your return and Brother's return. Insh'allah, you will be back within a week. The children are inquiring after you very much, especially Akbar. It will be an honor and joy for us to welcome any visitor to your and Brother's house. So we shall also welcome Mrs. Hassan Latif."

Nothing about their disappointment! Yet don't I know how they wanted Rashid to marry Sakri! But they are far too dignified to breathe a word. Gratitude for my arranging this match is all I'll ever hear from them about this affair. If only things turn out well! I've never yet taken such responsibility on myself. I've never interfered with other people's matrimonial affairs. In one word, I've been hitherto but a mere Westerner.

If Sakri were now married off in the ordinary way, however, it would be much worse. Perhaps she'd marry below herself, perhaps her surroundings would be coarse. She does so need gentleness and refinement! No, all told, I am acting for the best. The Latifs will be good to her, perhaps even love her—who could help loving Sakri save Rashid, that modernist?—and she'll worship them in return.

Strange, how many girls' fates I take to heart. I don't worry about Akhtari and Humayum, though; they can ably fence for themselves. But Sakri; Joan, who'll find life in a smallish Bengali town much more difficult than she thinks; and that lovely sweet-tempered girl here who is "Her Highness" and shut up for life.

Later

The Maharani's library is astonishingly good. From Shakespeare to Proust, from Tolstoi to Thomas Mann and Lin Yutang there is nearly everything one can think of, especially lots of travel books and memoirs.

"They constitute my journeys into time and space!" comments Her Highness. "Memoirs are practically never disappointing. They give readers an understanding of the epoch described, and that's why I like them. It's the same with travel books, except that you can't always rely on what their level is going to be. As for travel books dealing with my country, the less said the better."

"I know. But you mustn't forget one thing; the western writers describing India after a stay of only a few months have no opportunity to know it at all. They travel officially, so to say. You people are very polite to them, but you more or less keep the shutters down. So how can they learn to know India?"

"If they don't know India, why do they write about India? How can they have the cheek to write at all, after a stay of mere months or even weeks? Do you think the rubbish they produce, the lies they spread about my country out of sheer ignorance, a triumph of western civilization?" The Maharani has risen and paces the room, sometimes standing in front of me, sometimes looking out to the veranda, as though to ask heaven and earth to second her. With flushed cheeks and flashing eyes she presents a new aspect of her usually ivorine tranquil beauty.

"No western man can write on India, because he doesn't get to know Indian life from the inside. And that he can't."

"What about western women?"

"They could—if they would! I've read some good, really good books on India by Englishwomen, though, in general, like their male colleagues, they are far too much after glamor, princely India, elephants, jewels and show. Why are Westerners only out for externals, do tell me?"

"They don't know any better. Like all good democrats, as Sinclair Lewis would say, they are thrilled by ceremonial and display, not realizing the Hindu religion that stands behind them. That's why they describe India 'from outside,' so to say. Elephants, but not what the elephant means. At home they are different. You have read far too much not to realize that the western mind searches far deeper than externals."

"You are right, though others might at this juncture remind you of strip-tease and other flowers of western civilization. I know you are right. There is much good in the West, too, but Westerners out here don't bring it to our knowledge. Why do people always misunderstand each other?"

"Because they don't learn what they ought to. Education all over the world is disgraceful in this respect. How can a Westerner, having never learned about the cultural background of India, not knowing what a peacock or a lotus-flower or a cow means in this country—and why!—understand what's going on?"

"You know India well, memsahib. Why don't *you* write a book?"

I laugh. "Some day I might, who knows? You'll help me, won't you?"

"I'd love to. But you must promise to write about real India."

"What is real India, Your Highness?"

"Villages. Only in villages do you find India. Cities are corrupt, business life is, palaces are—oh, I do know that, though I can say it only to a Westerner. But in villages, especially in those which have not been in touch with the outside world, you still find the honesty, the courtesy, the courage of India. If you come to a village, you are treated as an honored guest. You would insult villagers by offering them money in exchange for food. However poor, they would never accept it."

"I know. India is her villages, not her towns, after all."

"Yes, but village life gets more and more corrupted. Villagers are so poor! So they drift to town into the mills, become proletarianized and undignified. On their return they corrupt the villages."

"What a lot there is to do in this country! If only women like you could come out!"

"I can't, and nothing can alter it—in my lifetime, at least."

"Who knows! Changes come sometimes very rapidly, Your Highness."

"Not in India! By the way, why do you always address me so formally? Would you do the same in the West?"

"Certainly not, but we are a very informal lot. Here you are used to ceremonial and honors and precedence. There are so many details that escape a mere Westerner, and make him behave with insufficient politeness! That's why I always stick to the formal mode of address. I can't go wrong that way."

"I don't think you'd ever be impolite, whatever you did. But now I ask you to drop formality, at least when we are by ourselves, and call me by my name, Induraja."

"I'd love to."

"And may I call you Mother? Mary Ann has gone; let me be a little of a daughter."

January 17

I am feeling a little queer. If things don't get better, I'll have to take my temperature soon.

Meanwhile nannie, coming back from her morning's ride—she on a horse, Jai on his pony—relates how these rides came about.

"Jai just loves riding. Very soon he had enough of trotting round the garden and wanted to get out on the road. I couldn't let him without the Burra Father's permission, of course. So I wrote to Col. Thurston about it. The reply was that Jai was to ride in the Residency grounds, but not outside. So we go there every morning. The grounds are magnificent, and Jai gets all the galloping he wants. Sometimes the Burra Father and Mrs. Thurston join us. They are very sweet to Jai."

Alone, I reflect upon the various Col. or plain Mr. Thurstons who from their Residencies preside over a great variety of intricate problems. They may be sweet to children or not; personally agreeable or the contrary; loved or unloved. Whatever they may be, it is a fact that they protect a good number of lives. If a legitimate consort and her children don't appear for a lengthy period to visiting ladies, the Resident will not be content with the excuse that she is ill. The Residency will so persistently inquire after her that in the end she will have to be produced—maybe from some kind of imprisonment into which a younger and victorious rival had her relegated. Equally, if it is to be expected that the Residency will inquire after the well-being of a certain child, it is unsafe to have this child disappear.

There are many who say that the Residencies interfere far too little in such matters; there are many who say that they interfere far too much. However that may be, there are certainly some who would not enjoy well-being or even life, were it not for the "Burra Father" putting down his foot at times.

Later

"I'd love to take you to my *guru*, Mother, but he lives a long way from here."

"Tell me about him, if you feel like it, Induraja. All the time it seemed to me that you had spiritual guidance of some kind, but I didn't want to ask you."

"And I didn't dare to begin. Not that I thought you wouldn't understand. But we are not used to talking to Westerners about such things."

"What about Miss Jones?"

"When she comes here for her holidays I never mention my *guru*. You know how I love her. That's, perhaps, why I don't tell her. Her misunderstanding would hurt me too much."

"Yes. Only those whom we love can hurt us. But tell me about your *guru*."

"From the day of my initiation I felt different. My own troubles do not matter any more, as they used to. With my *guru's* help I try to free myself from the fetters of the ego. He possesses very great powers."

"Where is his *ashram?*"

"North of Delhi. Lots of people flock there for initiation. Many rulers are among my *guru's chelas*. Peasants, princes, ministers—we all sit at his feet and listen to his words."

"Are you allowed to travel there? Doesn't your mother mind?"

"How can she? My father takes me. He was initiated two years ago. The first among us was His Highness, Jai's father. He took me to the master for initiation."

"Did you need any preparation? Or can any one be initiated on the spot?"

"It is for the master to say. He looks into the heart of each. Nothing is hidden from him. Some people he rejects, some he tells to wait. Most of those who come to him he initiates. There are a few Westerners among his disciples too. One of them has written a book on the master and his teaching. I can let you have it."

"Thank you."

"Have you ever met any of our great teachers, Mother?"

"Indeed I have."

"I did feel that. It couldn't be you, if you weren't on a spiritual path. Have you a *guru*, Mother?"

"I have."

"He is in this country, isn't he?"

"No."

"You did not find in India a *guru* you could choose for your master? It seems hardly possible!"

"It does sound strange, I admit. Let me explain."

"Perhaps you didn't find the right *gurus*. There are so many who are not!"

"I know. That's why I am on my guard. I flatly refuse to meet any *guru, saddhu* or *murshid* who accepts money or displays his

206

faculties in any way. He may be famous for his powers and have hundreds of thousands of disciples: the fact that he performs feats at all for others to behold, keeps me away from him. I'm not speaking of frauds. I'm speaking of those *gurus* and *faqirs* who perform genuine feats. What I object to is the performance as such. I know that in some cases feats like fire-walking, burial for forty days and so on are performed with the purpose of proving to materialists the existence of higher realms. In itself that seems a good aim; but I do believe that in our epoch such an exhibition is out of place. Why? Because such showing off has nothing whatever to do with a spir-ir al path whose ultimate goal is the realization of God."

"Mother, how is it that you know so much, you, a Westerner?"

"I understand what you are too polite to say. Most Westerners in this country are either downright materialistic or fall for 'miracles' and manifestations of all kinds: rope-trick, fire-walking, ascetics' self-immolation, prophecies, the factual feats of Tibetan *lamas*, burial of the living, etc., etc. They don't care about anything beyond. That's what you wanted to say, isn't it?"

"It is. This crude sensationalism is one of the chief reasons for our contempt of the West. But go on, Mother, please. Tell about the *gurus* you met."

"I met some to whom my whole heart and reverence went out, pure, unselfish, nearing the heights of realization. But they talked to me; they asked questions; they advised. They did not *know*. So I did not return to them."

"Why, Mother? I can't understand."

"You will, if I tell you about the greatest of all I've met in India so far. When his chief disciple brought me in for the first time, the *guru* did not look at me, did not ask questions, did not tender advice. After we had been silent together for some time, he raised his eyes and simply said: 'How very great is your *guru!* I am happy to meet him through you.' Needless to say he hadn't known a thing about me in the ordinary way, just as the others hadn't. He made me tell him about my teacher and couldn't hear enough. Only afterwards did he expound his own teaching, which was worldwide. He had transcended all differentiations and segregations into races and religions. He has the realization of God."

"And the others?"

"Were they not still confined to their own circumference? They had not realized that I had a teacher of my own. They needed to be *told*. He didn't."

"Do you still see him, Mother?"

"We write each other, though rarely. Letters aren't needed."

"And you don't want to meet other *gurus?*"

"Of course I do. *Real* teachers."

"Was Mary Ann with you in all this?"

"She was, though I've tried hard to keep her away from premature inner development. I didn't want *my* path to influence her. She was to remain free to decide for herself later on. When she was twelve and thirteen, she sometimes bitterly reproached me for hiding all books of a philosophic and metaphysic nature from her. She complained that I kept her away from all things spiritual. So I did. Had I encouraged inner development before she could choose for herself, this would have meant interference with her freedom. I'm aware, Induraja, that East and West have different opinions on individual freedom. But let's not go in for it today. I'm a bit feverish."

"Yes, I'll send you to bed at once, Mother. How thoughtless of me to keep you so long. Only tell me, what happened then to Mary Ann?"

"After a spell of materialism—'You know, mummy, people must first have enough to eat before one has the right to talk metaphysics!'—she found her own way."

"Which was yours?"

"Yes, but she had found it without interference of mine, quite on her own. That's what matters. It was worth the separations, under which both of us suffered so much. You see, I was afraid that being always together might mean my influencing her. Not by words, of course, but by many imponderable things. It *was* worth while. She got her own independent will and mind. But now that she has gone—I do at times rebel against those separations. I grudge every month, every day we were not together."

"Mother dear!"

"Sorry, Induraja. I didn't mean to cry. It must be the temperature."

"Now let me put you to bed. Yes, *I* will. Just imagine I am Mary Ann."

I'm down with flu, and can't travel today. Rashid will be home before me, but I can't help that. I've wired that I'll not be able to set out before the 22nd—if then.

⁓ *12* ⁓

I T was quite strange to part from Induraja. We've grown to like each other very much. I wonder how both of us will stand our formal meetings under her mother's eye? We'll grin at times, I'm sure of that.

I still feel rather shaky. As a child, I could stand 103 or 104 degrees of temperature. Now I can't. Even a mere 100 degrees gets me down. I'm looking forward to being properly spoiled for a few days. Cook will feed me up. In Ramnagar food was either Indian, which is far too spicy for me, or English type—vegetables boiled even much longer than in England, taste of any kind strictly excluded. Our cook in Akbarabad is very different. Mary Ann and I taught him Frenchified seasoning. He is proud of his new achievements, and loves to surprise me by experiments. Now that I look a little pale he'll surpass himself. Maharaj and *chowkidar* will bring flowers, and do all sorts of pleasant things. Ismail Khan will be at the station. Best of all, there will be Rashid! It's a real homecoming. Only three—no, two-and-a-half more hours. How lovely!

It isn't lovely at all.

No Rashid, no Ismail Khan! What can have happened? Is Rashid ill?

At last Waliuddin turns up, after my luggage is already on the platform.

"Please excuse Rashid, Mother. He had to leave unexpectedly for

Nullgarh. He couldn't wait for you, since you were much later than expected. He should be back in a day or two."

"Well, it can't be helped. I expect he had to take the car. Is maharaj here for the luggage?"

"No. Brother had to take him along."

Soon we are installed in a *tonga*. But I can't help thinking that *chowkidar* could have turned up to look after the luggage.

However, he helps me down from the *tonga*. He and Ram Pershad take my things inside. There are flowers everywhere. A *sigri* full of burning coals stands under my bed to warm the mattress from underneath.

"There I it put, Mother," says *chowkidar*. "Thou second wantest? Thou tea wantest?"

"No, thanks, *chowkidar*."

"Scrambled eggs wantest? Omelet wantest? I them make can!"

"Thou? No, thanks. Now hungry I not am. For cook's evening dinner I wait. He where is?"

Waliuddin coughs. "I am sorry, Mother. Brother had to dismiss cook the day before he left. We did not engage another yet. We left it until your return."

"Dismiss cook?" My heart stops a beat. "Why?"

"Brother says cook is very stubborn and refused to obey his orders. So he had to make him leave."

"Refused to obey? Cook?" It doesn't make sense. Cook is the gentlest of men, always obliging and polite. How dare Rashid do such a thing in my absence! Even if cook were guilty—which I'm sure he isn't—how dare he? I'm responsible for the house, as he is for the laboratory. I don't meddle with his affairs; he shouldn't meddle with mine. And, above all, this is Mary Ann's cook. She trained him. He stood by us during her illness. How can one dismiss such a man without the most serious of reasons? Mary Ann's cook——

"We shall send your dinner tonight, Mother. You might feel too tired after your illness to come to our place."

"Thanks, Waliuddin, I don't want any dinner tonight. I shall rest. That is all I need."

"Shall we send one or two cooks tomorrow morning for you to inspect?"

"No." I answer thus curtly, because I feel I can't trust my voice.

"But Brother will be angry! He came to us just before he left, to make sure we would find a cook for you in time. He did not want you to be inconvenienced on account of his action."

I don't reply, but Waliuddin seems to draw the right conclusions from my expression.

"You must not mind like that, Mother. A cook can be replaced."

"This was Mary Ann's cook, Waliuddin," I say, unable to keep back my tears any longer. "Please leave me now. I want to rest. Thank you for meeting me. Love to your mother. Yes, I shall call tomorrow."

Alone, I do anything but rest. I am too upset even to remain sitting. Pacing the room forward and backward, I try not to cry. I must ask *chowkidar*. He is sure to know what happened.

"Here come, Tejsingh. Cook what thing did do?"

"Sahib to keys he not did give."

"Which keys?"

"Stores' keys. He said, Mother said he keys not should give Mother's return until. He said letter came."

Good heavens! So it is on account of me and my orders.

"Sahib which thing wanted?"

"Soap. He maharaj asked soap where was. Maharaj said storeroom in was. Maharaj said cook keys had. Sahib him called. Cook said keys he not give can. Sahib angry get. Said cook idiot is, keys he give must. Cook said Mother said not give. Sahib said he house of master is. Keys his are. Cook said Mother's order is keys not give. Sahib cook kicked out. Said cook never house near come shall. If come, great beating shall get."

And so cook went. How utterly foolish not to hand Rashid the keys! And how utterly faithful!

"Lavanyia bai and Ram Chandra bai soon come will," continues *chowkidar*.

I don't want to see anybody. The whole compound is sure to know about the domestic tragedy. Being Easterners, they will perceive my deep hurt at once. Whatever I may be thinking of Rashid's action, I must not let him down in public. But where am I to hide? The ladies can be here any minute.

"*Tonga* call do, *chowkidar*."

He seems disturbed. "Where thou go wilt, masahib? Tomb to too late is. Soon dark is. Animals are."

"Torch I take do. *Tonga* do call. *Quickly!*"

"With Mother son go will."

"House alone is. Thou *chowkidar* art. Here thou stayest."

When he returns with the *tonga*, Ram Pershad, the gardener, is perched in front with the driver. "Tomb to I just set out," he says innocently, *"tonga* in I may also drive?"

They are irresistible. It's a flat lie. Ram Pershad wouldn't dream of walking so late to the tomb. But I can't refuse him the lift.

When we arrive at the gardens in which the tomb lies, the flaming colors of a magnificent sunset are just fading away; the evening star begins to sparkle.

"Dark is, masahib," volunteers the driver. "Bad animals are. Yesterday panther this road on was. Thy tomb's garden in many snakes are, many, many! Now darkness is. Snakes darkness love."

"I torch have."

"I masahib with go do," adds Ram Pershad, dismounting.

The rascal! Now he has got me. I can please myself where only I am concerned; but I can't have him trot barefoot through the high grass of these gardens. I don't mind hyenas and panthers, if any; the torch would frighten them away. But I mind snakes for shoeless people.

In a way, it does not matter. What I wanted was to escape conversation and be by myself. I've got that, sitting alone in the *tonga* a few yards from Mary Ann's tomb. The driver and Ram Pershad are standing further down the road. There is no need to explain why I decided not to dismount. Being Indian, they understand the situation, know my very thoughts before I do, and help me wordlessly with perfect tact to carry things through. Eastern politeness, the saving of another's feelings, is exquisite.

This brings me back with a jerk to Rashid and cook. Rashid did not think of other people's feelings. This is another aspect of the East, a very bewildering one. Once emotions are roused, people just let them govern every other consideration. Rashid was angry, so out cook went. Nothing else counted but his anger.

I can't help remembering my inner struggle on account of the broadcasts. The obvious thing to do would have been to say "Yes." Yet I fussed and fussed, afraid I would hurt Rashid by occasional absence. He doesn't mind hurting me. He hasn't even left a note for me to explain things.

And what hurts me to the core is that he did not think of cook's devotion to Mary Ann. Will he with equal facility and no more provocation discard one after the other of the people or things linked with Mary Ann? If so, why should I remain?

I don't want to be unfair to him. But this really alters things.

"Be calm and patient," Mary Ann seems to say within my heart. "Above all remain true to yourself." That means "Stick it out!" I dare say.

January 25

Of all things to happen the Khan Bahadur turns up today. It is as Akhtari predicted. I mustn't fail her. What a strange and amusing situation!

"Am I wrong to surmise that you met my Lahore friends in Bombay, madam?"

He knows as well as I that I did. But if he pretends, I can do the same.

"Friends of yours, Khan Bahadur? I'm afraid I am not aware of having met any." That's no lie. Akhtari most assuredly is not his friend.

"Didn't you meet Sahebzadi Mumtaz Ali Khan at Dr. Hamidullah's? I believe I heard about some tea party. She was there with Akhtari Begum, her delightful daughter, whom I have had the pleasure of describing to you on my previous visits."

"Was she?" I sound polite, but uninterested.

The blow goes home. Before starting to speak the Khan Bahadur carefully clears his throat.

"I should not have thought that the two ladies would pass unnoticed anywhere, madam."

"Yes, I remember now. We did exchange a few words."

"And what do you think of Akhtari Begum, if I may ask?"

"Aktari Begum? Quite a nice girl, I am sure. Lovely eyes. But nothing out of the common, is she?" Only the thought of Akhtari and her Asaph enables me to be so untruthful and impolite.

"You astonish me, madam. Usually everybody is full of admiration for her beauty and grace."

"I'm sorry, Khan Bahadur. She didn't impress me particularly. But that may be my fault."

"I should have thought a cultured lady of your merits the best judge of beauty and accomplishments."

"You have overrated me apparently. One can't discuss tastes, I'm afraid. Has your drive from Bombay been good? It's the best season for travel, of course. I enjoyed even the train."

Three minutes later he takes his departure. This time I'm certain he won't come again. If only Akhtari gets her Asaph! I shall write to both Sultana and Hamid, thanking them belatedly for their hospitality and asking for news. Sultana will understand.

A letter from Joan Chatterji, who has now for some weeks been staying with her husband's people in a smallish Bengali town. They are wealthy, modern as far as Bengali Brahmans go—they don't object to eating with her—but very old-fashioned as far as Joan's impression of them is concerned.

"If I want to go out by myself, I'm told that ladies of the family can't go unescorted and on foot. So I have to wait until my in-laws are ready to take me for some drive or visiting tour. When Shankar comes home from office, we are practically never alone until bedtime. Lots of relatives are living in the same house. Yes, it's still the joint family system, which is quite jolly in a way since I'm not burdened with housekeeping. In our case, it's a modernized system. My father-in-law is very generous; Shankar need not hand him his salary; we can keep it to do with just as we like. Moreover, his father presented Shankar with a lovely M.G. two-seater, and me with a string of pearls. But somehow I don't feel at ease. There are too many people about. Whatever I do or say is commented upon. The whole house knows what I'm doing in my room. I've never the feeling of being alone and safe. Those servants spy and report everything. It's not as though I had something to hide; but this lack of privacy is simply awful. The other day Shankar and I were standing arm-in-arm on our private veranda after dinner. Maybe my head was even on his shoulder for a moment. After all, we're married! It was dark. Nobody could see us that I knew of. Next day my mother-in-law spoke to me: I ought not to set their daughters a bad example, and make myself a laughing stock into the bargain. She said that dancing, holding hands and kissing might be right for the West, where everybody was divorced many times and didn't mind about a dignified code of life; here it was definitely wrong. *Nautch*-girls might hold men's hands, and do all sorts of things incompatible with chastity, but not a decent woman. To bear her husband sons was the way to show love, not to hold hands in public. I was now a member of the family, and was to behave as such.

"I can't tell you how awful I felt. My mother-in-law had not spoken unkindly; but to me it seemed as though she and the women in the house had pawed me all over. Have these people no sense of shame? Daring to speak about husband and wife holding hands —whose affair is it, anyway?—when they themselves live in open polygamy? Shankar's eldest uncle lives in this house with two wives of his own, who, strange to say, seem to be on the best of terms. Polygamy is shameless; not straightforward love. But people here don't understand such things.

"I am going to have a baby, and that prospect makes me happy. But if I have to stay here under the eyes of all these spying prying people, without a vestige of privacy, without anybody who understands me, prevented even from behaving naturally in my own husband's presence—I know I won't be able to bear it. We must have our own house or I'll go mad. I must think of my baby, too.

"Shankar is a darling about it all, always trying to explain me to his people, and his people to me. I hate having to complain to him. It puts me in such a wrong position. And I get frightened. There is a likeness between him and his family. Sometimes it seems to me that he gets more Indian, more like them every day. I know I'm foolish. I do love him so. But being all alone, without your own people around, you are apt to imagine things. My fear is that some day I will wake to find the Shankar I knew for years, the Shankar I loved and married, gone. There will be a stranger in his place, a member of the joint family, who'll never be mine."

There it is. Poor Joan! But also poor Shankar, poor in-laws! Mary Ann very wisely spoke about the necessity of Joan's scrutinizing herself carefully: "It is not enough to love the boy. She must love India, too, or else she won't stand life out here."

Well, Joan is typical of the western girls who love their husbands but not India. I can understand her rebellion so well; but things would be very different if she also thought about the position her in-laws find themselves in, saddled all of a sudden with a bride from the West. I'll have to write to her about it, I'm afraid. It would have been easier if it had come from Mary Ann.

January 26

Some celebration at the mission, tea, display of the school, warrior and harvest dances by the young people after sunset. Quite a number of club members are turning up, including the collector. People make a subtle but inflexible differentiation between the mission and the missionaries, the Blackwells. The mission is taboo; if they want an additional square foot of ground, if they want anything of any kind, the local authorities will veto their request, just because it's the mission. Everybody is fiercely against the mission as such. Both Hindus and Muslims equally resent missionary proselytizing activities. But they equally like the Blackwells personally, especially the padre who is good at billiards and auction bridge, and never misses the club in the evening.

I left word at home to say where I was, thinking that Rashid was likely to arrive before night.

"Please tell me about this harvest dance, *subha sahib*," I ask the collector. "Is it very old? Does it convey gratitude after the harvest only, or something else in addition?"

"Mother, you astonish me. By now you should know all this better than I do."

"I don't, alas. Moreover, how could I dare to know more than a *subha?* Wouldn't that be a criminal offense?"

While laughing with the collector, I see our car drive into the compound. Rashid is here. Instinctively, involuntarily I turn away.

Then I pull myself together. Do I really want to avoid Rashid, I who until two days ago would have restrained myself with difficulty from rushing up to him, after our separation? What nonsense! Yet I *have* turned away. Instinct is more truthful than self-discipline. I'm amazed to see how deeply I'm hurt.

Here he is, talking to Mrs. Blackwell. I go on talking to the collector, pretending not to have seen the new arrival. Somehow I want to postpone our meeting to the last possible second, to the last fraction of that second. In spite of our deep sorrow—because of it, perhaps—we have had much in common. Now—I don't know. I don't know any more how things will be.

"Rashid! I thought you would come tonight. Had you a good journey?"

"Never mind that. Tell me about your flu. Have you no temperature now?"

Rashid's eyelids quiver, which tells me that he is ill at ease. I must pull myself together.

"Shall we go home, Rashid? You must be very tired. Did you have your bath?"

"I couldn't have shown myself otherwise, Mother. Yes, let's go."

In the car, we don't speak at first. Then Rashid broaches the subject that stands between us. "I'm sorry to hear you did not engage another cook, Mother. I couldn't help dismissing our old one. I can't have a fellow being impudent to me in my own house."

I don't answer, afraid I shall start crying if I do. Rashid misinterprets my silence. "So you want to punish me as if I were a little boy!"

I try to appear quiet. "Of course I don't want to punish you. But this affair came as a great shock to me. Cook has done right, according to his lights. I ordered him twice not to hand the keys to anybody except myself, once before we left, once by letter. Of course I thought I'd arrive with or before you, otherwise I would have said 'except to sahib and myself.' So it is my fault, really, if you want to find a culprit. I admit that cook was not overintelligent in that whole business—but even you can't deny that he was faithful to his orders, stubbornly faithful. How you could kick him out for that—without waiting to ask me what my orders had been—without a single thought what this would mean to me——"

"There you are wrong, Mother. I did think of you, very much so. I wanted to write and explain it all, but it seemed impossible to do so by letter. Now, I'm sorry I didn't try."

"It would have made things easier." Suddenly it seems to me that it doesn't matter any more whether Rashid forgot *me* when dismissing cook; what matters is the wrong he did *him*.

"Don't you see that you did this man an injustice? He didn't do any wrong. But you kick him out as though he were a thief!"

"My dear Mother, I kicked him out not because he obeyed your orders, but because he disobeyed mine."

"That's juggling with words. You know full well that he didn't mean to disobey you. He stuck to his duty as he understood it."

"Why do you stick up for him as you do? What does a servant matter, whether I kicked him out or not? Here you are, meeting me after a long separation. I've looked forward to seeing you so much, but if I'd known what was in store for me, I wouldn't. Reproaching me, making me feel mean instead of happy I'm at home—and all for the sake of a servant!"

Rashid struts about the drawing room, to which we have repaired a good while ago.

Suddenly I remember Mary Ann's and his letter from Nullgarh over their quarrel. Then it was maharaj; now it is cook. What does a servant matter! It's always the same old story.

As if to confirm my thoughts Rashid says under his breath: "And if—even if I had done wrong, you should not mind. You should not take the part of that impudent fool against me. You wouldn't, if you really loved me."

"Rashid! You know I do love you! Haven't I proved it many a time?"

"You were sweet and kind. But to me love means something else. If you love me, you don't mind what I do. You don't perceive if I do wrong—or, if you perceive it, you stand by me against the whole world, and maintain that what I did was right! That's what I call love! My enemies are quick enough to point out my wrongs; my own people, whom I trust and honor, should behave differently."

Realizing that talk is no good, I get up and put my hand on Rashid's arm. Didn't Mary Ann say something about "lots of love" needed in the relations between East and West?

January 28

During my absence a new lady doctor has joined the *zenana* Hospital to help Dr. Cama. She is Dr. Miss Venkataraman from Madras, a graduate of Madras University.

"Have you ever been north before?" I ask her.

"No, madam."

"It's a bit bewildering for you here, I'm afraid. You people from the south are not used to purdah and segregation. So you must be pretty homesick."

"How did you guess, madam?"

"Doctor, do I need to be a detective to find out as much?"

We laugh together, and friendship is established.

Shanta Venkataraman is a lovely girl of twenty-four, with deep-brown color of skin. Slim and graceful as a reed; a figure which takes one's breath away each time one looks at her, a beautiful face, especially when smiling; a long ebony plait hanging down to her knees, shining with fragrant oil and brushing; a low, musical voice—that is our new lady doctor, dumped on Akbarabad. Two younger sisters are with her to keep her company, both missing a term to settle her in. They are not quite so pretty as she is, but pretty enough to make me think what a sensation the three of them would create in Paris. Charming girls!

But their fellow Brahmans—they themselves are Brahmans—have no good word about them. "Pretty? These girls? Why? They are nearly chocolate color! Who would ever want to marry such!"

That superiority of northerners over southerners, of Aryans over Dravidians, of café-crême over café-noir! God help us! Those girls will have an awful time of it. Each woman on the compound basks in a new-found feeling of beauty, simply because she's a few shades lighter!

It is not only between races that color prejudice exists; it is inter-racial as well, a fact which has often puzzled me in India. Of Africa I do not know anything, but I shouldn't be astonished to hear that things were the same there. Here, for instance, a younger sister is sometimes easily married off, while the elder and to your mind more desirable girl cannot find a husband. On inquiring why that is so, you will be told: "But the younger one is whiter!" often with reference to a difference so slight that you haven't even perceived it. I have heard that girls with a lighter coloring need less dowry, that they receive preference in certain schools and so on. Whiter skin is certainly regarded as superior to any other beauty or privilege. It is not a chance happening that Brahmans and Kshattryias (Rajputs), the first two castes, are fairer of skin than any other caste or outcast. When the Aryans conquered India from the north, they subjugated the dark Dravidians and remnants of the equally dark Proto-Indians. They were the lords. The Sanskrit word *varna* means both caste and color. The lords had both. From those remote times until today Indians have preferred fair skin to dark. Sometimes I wonder whether those hierarchic and esthetic prejudices existed equally in pre-Aryan times, whether they are as old as mankind itself. They exist everywhere.

Whatever the background and cradle of these color prejudices, it is certain that they ought to go, wherever they exist. Yes, *wherever* they exist. May it be so!

Having reached the time limit I had given for my reply to A.I.R., I have to tackle Rashid.

He listens quietly, without his usual vivacity. "You would like to go to Bombay for these broadcasts? Of course. Why shouldn't you?"

"I didn't want to decide without you."

"That's sweet of you, Mother, but not at all necessary. You are entirely your own mistress."

"Of course I am. That's not the point. I want to know how *you* feel about it—whether you dislike the idea of my going."

"Why should I if it gives you pleasure to go! I myself am sometimes fed up with this place. You have much more right to be. So by all means, go and have a good time. You'll tell me lots of interesting things on your return."

I don't like the sound of it. Rashid does not speak out frankly. However much we both try, the affair of cook still stands between us. He is just pleasant about things, without saying what he really thinks.

Anyway, I'm writing to Bombay to say that I accept. But I can't fix dates as yet. I must feel happier about Rashid before I can undertake good broadcasts.

January 30

I'm copying part of my letter to Joan into my diary. I'll want to reread the things I wrote to her today in some near or distant future; maybe I'll find I've been wrong, maybe additional experience will convince me that I have been right.

"Having explained at length how I sympathize with you in your present plight, let me now try to explain your in-laws' point of view as I understand it. No doubt they would feel that a Westerner couldn't do them justice, which is probably correct; but I'll try my best; besides there is nobody else to tell you—for other Westerners, not having had my opportunities to know Indians well, know still less than I do. Explanations from Indians, on the other hand, would not go home with you, because you'd always feel that they can't understand your predicament properly. If they could, they would understand about your wish for privacy. Wouldn't you say that, Joan dear?

"Now let's get down to brass tacks. Whenever a western girl marries an Indian (or a Chinese) she does feel somehow that she is being very brave, that by her step she takes upon herself a rather difficult job. I'm not denying that she does, far from it. But what I want to point out is that she feels rather superior and altruistic in forgoing all sorts of comforts as well as the freedom of action she enjoys in the West as a matter of course. This is but natural; in marrying an Oriental she *does* forgo much of the freedom western women have, as well as many other advantages the West has to offer —for instance the privacy you do miss so much.

"So she comes out determined to make the best of a difficult job. She resolves—if she belongs to the best type of western girls—not to feel or show superiority; not to betray any dismay if bathing and sanitary arrangements, food, service, table manners, and the like are very different from what she is used to; not to ask for things which in the West are taken for granted, but in East are 'the impossible.' Yet while carrying out these good resolutions in letter and spirit, she can't help being aware of her constant effort, vigilance and self-denial. She *can't*, because she has to concentrate on it. If she didn't, her face might show amazement or even disgust when her in-laws use their fingers instead of cutlery, and lick all ten of them after dinner—which is not done, however, by well-bred Indians, who always carefully wash their hands and rinse their mouths as soon as they rise from eating, and think we are entirely lacking in common cleanliness if we do not do the same. Or she might show her distress at certain sanitary arrangements. So she has to watch herself carefully, not to appear superior. That means that she is constantly aware of what she misses, dislikes, has to overcome, and so on. What *she* has to overcome!

"Does she ever think of what her in-laws have to overcome, where she is concerned? Perhaps in very rare cases. Mary Ann did, at times. But on the whole, I think one can safely assume that she doesn't. Again I don't blame her. Brought up as she is, with nothing in her education to teach her the background of Hindu or Muslim culture as the case may be, how is she to know that there are other standards beside her western ones? How is she to realize that her table manners, her bathing and sanitary customs, her food and, especially, her social habits are just as amazing and repellent to her in-laws as theirs to her? More so, I should say. Hindus think our mode of life much more unsanitary and dirty than Westerners think Indian ways are. I'm sorry to shock you with this statement. But it is so.

"Now, I ought to explain the implications of these words. I ought to explain why Hindus think the use of cutlery disgracefully un-clean—likewise handkerchiefs and bathtubs. But if I did, this letter would not be one, but two, volumes in size. Let Shankar explain all this to you; and if he tries to be casual about it, saying that he doesn't know much of anything about old customs—many Indian boys pretend they don't, just to show how modern and westernized they are—hold him to the task. You need to know about these things, for you'll always come up against them. If Shankar fails you, go to some western woman who knows; you'll find that type among missionaries who have spent all their lives in Indian surround-ings. By the way, I remember one elderly Scotswoman, the picture of tailored neatness, who dumfounded a British audience by describing an Indian house with 'The living room, spick and span, all nicely cleaned with cow-dung'—! Many of these women *do* know India, nobody can deny that.

"So I don't want to go in for the description of Hindu customs today, or at any later date. I leave that to others. What I want to draw your attention to is, that a bride from the West is to Indians not the unmixed blessing she thinks she is. She thinks the sacrifice is all on her side. This is not so.

"Just think for a moment of what the eldest son's bride means to a joint household. As you know—we talked about it in Bombay—a Hindu bride leaves her own family for good and becomes part of her husband's family. The eldest son's bride will be a very im-portant part indeed! Some day, when she has given him a son or sons, when he and she are at the head of the joint household, or at least of the elder generation at its head, it will be she who will manage the whole establishment—distribute, guide, permit, decide. Through the exalted position age holds in India, members of the family, be they young or middle-aged, will look up to her for everything. Retainers and servants will do the same, of course. Will it be a pleasant, peaceful home or one in which quarrels rend the air all day long? Will she understand and minister to the complex needs of every one, or will members of the joint family have to do without the things they consider their due? Will she have an open hand, or a closed fist? Will she uphold the dignity of the family, respect and tend the threads that bind it? Will she be easy to get on with, kindhearted, forgiving, or like a dark thundercloud, looming on the family horizon? Will she be thrifty, however wealthy the family, always mindful of the joint family exchequer? Or will she spend on herself and hers, or on unnecessary luxuries, so that the exchequer will be unable to fulfill necessary requirements? All depends on her.

"It is, therefore, understandable that in India, as in other oriental countries, marriage is not considered something that concerns only two individuals, but something that concerns the bridegroom's family even more. If the future life of the whole clan is bound to improve or suffer through the bride now entering it, it is for the whole clan to decide through its elders who that bride is to be. In the West a wife will influence only the lives of her husband and children; her great-nephews and brothers-in-law are usually not immediately affected by her good or bad qualities. Here conditions are different.

"For a son to bring home a western bride means to upset the intricate pattern of the joint family system. It means that the clan is being presented with a *fait accompli*, without having been consulted; that the family's future will some day be in the hands of a woman nobody knows anything about; and a woman with no idea of her present and future duties, no inkling of the working of a Hindu joint household with its many ramifications.

"Moreover, the union lacks the secure basis of stellar conformity. The first thing Hindu parents do after having received a proposal for their son through a go-between, is to compare his and the girl's horoscope. Do they coincide or are they opposed, in which case the marriage would be an ill-fated one and should not be permitted. If the astrologists say that the union is an auspicious one, negotiations are taken up—and only then. Parents have a certain sense of security regarding this sort of marriage. In the case of a western bride, they are deprived of such comfort. Usually their son marries without obtaining or even asking them for their consent—an understandable omission on his part, since he would practically never receive it. But it is they who suffer, thinking that now their son has brought a wife, the mother of future grandchildren, and nobody knows whether by her very horoscope she is not alien to him and the clan. It's no use, Joan dear, to say that *we* in the West don't go by horoscopes, and that Shankar, like all westernized Indians, ridicules the procedure for your benefit. This is the way of Hindus, let alone Brahmans.

"I'm afraid I've not yet finished my enumeration. It has often happened that, when in Europe, Indian students have become infatuated with and married girls of a class not on the same social level as their own. The landlady's daughter; waitresses; salesgirls and so on. You know me well enough to realize that I am not prompted by snobbery in writing these words. What I want to point out is that the boys bring home girls whose education has not fitted them in any way to lead the life of a daughter in a big joint household. They have not read or heard enough to be aware of other cultures, other standards, than the one they are used to. Hence they are intolerant. They look down on everything Indian. It is generally these girls who cannot bear life out here, who loathe India, whose longing is always for the West and who drift home sooner or later. Good Indian families dread these daughters-in-law more than anything else.

"I've kept the most important point to the last: difference of religion. The modern Indian boy doesn't care about it, or thinks he doesn't; his family, however, does. In an Indian house nearly all matters connected with worship are carried out by women. That is what gives them their strong position, however few of what we call 'rights' they may possess. All festivals—this axle around which Hindu life revolves—all its grace and beauty, depend on the women of the house. Much more than any other religion, Hinduism regulates every domain of life, be it worship or food, learning or pleasures. It is the lady of the house who has all this at her fingers' tips. How can a western girl ever master the manifold tasks Hinduism sets her?

"So, all told, Hindus are wholeheartedly opposed to their sons bringing home brides from the West, quite apart from the fact that

224

today national pride prompts Indians to advocate Indian marriages only.

"There are exceptions to this rule, of course. Modern, educated people are very good to a western daughter-in-law. If she adapts herself to life out here, much is made of her. I picture your in-laws of that type. They wouldn't be as generous as you describe, if they didn't like you. They want to welcome you, to make you happy. You must try to understand them from that angle. If your mother-in-law didn't care for you, she would not advise you how to behave: she would simply let things go, hoping that you would blunder enough—from the Indian point of view—to make Shankar realize his mistake, and that you would ultimately betake yourself off where you come from. Try to take her advice or criticism in that sense. After all, this is India, and theirs is a high-class Brahman house, and you are part of the family.

"I can so well understand your feelings about the eldest uncle's two wives. To us polygamy is the worst of things. On the other hand you should realize that the Muslim religion allows a man four wives simultaneously and the Hindu religion any number of them! You knew that before you married. Most cultured Hindus are monogamous, certainly in Shankar's generation. Some are not, either because the first wife is childless or for some other reason. However this may be, Hindus are entirely within their rights in marrying two or more wives. It's permissible within their code of life. We can't expect them to go by our standards. Why should they? Girls from the West have no right to remonstrate. After all, it's not the Indian household that has invited them to become part of it. They came of their own accord.

"I'm sorry to have been so outspoken, crossing the t's and dotting the i's. But that's what you've asked when you wrote, 'Explain it all to me!' I wish I could be with you for a little bit. It's much easier to say things than to write them. I do realize that this letter won't make you any happier, certainly not at first.

"Now to your last sentence, 'Please advise me what to do. I'm all alone out here.' May I really say what I feel?

"Try to learn about the kind of life your in-laws want you to lead. I expect they won't be so unreasonable as to think that you should give up western ways altogether—and Shankar would certainly hate that. But try to do for them what the son's wife is expected to. The more attention you give to the established details of Brahman life, the happier you try to make your in-laws, the more they will let you go your own way. Try to become a real member of the family, in addition to being Shankar's wife.

"If you feel you can't do that—if you've honestly tried and feel you really can't stick things out—then, and only then, follow your latest idea and set up a house apart, which will mean a very serious step for Shankar to take. It's always a difficult thing for a woman to have a man give up for her sake something that matters: career, throne or, in your case, family. There may always come a moment in which he will repent his sacrifice. But if you feel you really can't be happy as you are, then better have a separate house and make up to him for it by being really contented. If you are unhappy you make him unhappy too, make him resentful towards his family and all the rest of it. The usual story of the bride from the West, who upsets everything! I shouldn't like this to be said against you; nor would you like it, I know."

I'm not satisfied with this letter of mine. Neither is it comforting enough, nor did I frankly state my opinion. Joan should not have come out if she couldn't care for India as such. Having come out, she should either have the courage and good will to make the best of things, or she should go home. But this I can't bring myself to say.

I do so hope she'll stick it out.

February 4

Lately Rashid stays out at night, without telling me where he goes. I'd never dream of asking him, of course; but he always used to tell me everything. I wouldn't mind if he were happy. But he isn't, less than ever. He doesn't smile as often as he used to; his jaw is set, his voice gruff; often he sighs deeply. We are very friendly, but there is still a cloud between us.

February 6

I have to get ready for the reception of my first Muslim lady-visitor to stay in the house. Mrs. Hassan Latif will arrive tomorrow for a stay of two days. I've furnished her room in East-West style. If she wants to sit on chairs, she can; if she wants to sit on the floor, there's a big mattress under a carpet topped by a sheet. There is a pan-box with all necessary ingredients save the leaves, which will be supplied fresh every morning. I've planned an entirely Muslim menu, beginning with the rice of welcome, heavy with raisins, ghi and saffron.

The new cook seems quite capable of dealing with the situation by himself. Somehow I don't feel tempted to teach him, as Mary Ann and I used to teach the old one. Provided he puts no hot spices into my food, I don't interfere.

Later

"So the girl's mother comes here, masahib!"

Mrs. Sharma, Mrs. Lavanyia and Mrs. Motilal are cross-examining me.

"Which girl's mother?"

"Masahib! Again secrets! Your daughter-in-law's, of course. We know, in spite of all your secrecy."

"Do tell me what you know, please."

"Well, we know pretty much. You went to Bombay to see a certain girl, but you didn't like her. You had to stay on for a long time to find a daughter-in-law to your liking. At last you did. She comes from a very good family, and her people are anxious to see the house she'll marry into. So her mother is coming tomorrow to Akbarabad. Or is it her aunt?"

"Neither her mother nor her aunt. The girl doesn't exist."

"And who is the lady arriving tomorrow, please? And why did Auntie and Waliuddin sahib and Faizuddin sahib come to dine with you last night?"

"And why did they bring another auntie with them, one who but rarely comes here? It was a big family-council, as should be held on such occasions."

"The whole compound know about it, but masahib still persists in making secrets."

I give up. Let them believe what they like. How disappointed they'll be, poor dears.

February 8

Mrs. Latif has come and gone. Everything is settled. The wedding is to take place soon, about the end of March. The bridegroom being a widower, and the children too delicate to be carted about without necessity, it will take place in Bombay. I've been asked to travel there with the bridal party.

On Mrs. Latif's suggestion and wish, the family decided on a revolutionary step. Sakri is to spend two or three days each week with me, so that I may prepare her for modern life in Bombay. "Though she'll live in strict purdah as I do," said Mrs. Latif, "life will be very different from what it is here. She must know how to use cutlery, how to receive ladies, how to insist on good manners in children and servants. Also she must learn English properly. Do let her be with you as much as possible."

I laugh. "Do you realize how very old-fashioned we are here, Mrs. Latif? Sakri's coming to me may mean to the gossips that she goes to the house of a man. I can't expel my son, can I?"

"But Sakri is related to Rashid sahib and has appeared before him, hasn't she? Doesn't that solve the problem?"

"It is for you to decide, not for me. You are her future mother-in-law. But please tell Sakri's people that this arrangement is your own suggestion, and that *you* insist on its being carried out. I think this is the best way to prevent any future unpleasantness."

"How well you've got to know us, memsahib."

"Oh, by now I should be *mulki*—of the soil."

"I'm glad you will allow Sakri to be with you."

"I love her sincerely. She is all sweetness and charm. Let us hope your son and she will be very happy."

"*Inshallah!* I'm sure they will."

So we parted, excellent friends.

And the compound?

"You could have told us, masahib," said Mrs. Sharma with a sweet-sour smile.

"But you had settled it all beforehand!"

"What else could we do? We must figure out things for ourselves. Whatever we do, you don't trust us!"

February 9

Several times during the last few days I've had the feeling that Rashid wanted to speak to me. But, somehow, he always ended by making ordinary conversation only. Today, at last, he speaks. It is about nine o'clock and we enjoy looking at the starlit sky from our deck-chairs on the roof. Rashid is nothing but a voice, a whiff of cologne and a cigarette.

"Now you've settled Sakri so nicely, Mother, will you give some time and thought to my affairs?"

I can't help laughing. Rashid of all people being jealous of Sakri! And reproaching me for want of attention!

"Don't you know that you always come first? Really——"

"Let's have it all out, Mother. I've been so miserable all these days, longing to speak to you and not knowing how to."

"I was miserable, too. You should have spoken just as you do now."

"I thought you didn't care for me any more."

"Rashid!"

"And that hurt so!"

"And was so foolish!"

For a long time we are silent, content to be together again. At last Rashid speaks. "Listen, Mother dear. While I was brooding, I've come to the conclusion that I ought to marry. As long as I knew you would be at home whenever I come back it didn't seem necessary. But now you'll be going for your broadcasts. Don't think that I grudge your going, oh, no. You should always be free to do whatever you like. But I dread being alone. Easterners are like that."

"Not you. You sit for many hours alone, studying and working away."

"Oh, that's on my job! But in private life I'm like everybody else. I just can't face the thought of being alone in this house."

"If it were only the question of your loneliness, Rashid, I could give up going away. But it seems to me there are other reasons, too, for your decision."

"It's just that, as I told you. I want children. So why not have them as soon as possible? My real love will always belong to our darling. Whether I marry now or later doesn't make any difference in that respect."

"I see. Yes, dear, let's get you married." How these months have mellowed down my original shock at the thought of such early remarriage! People here are like that. I must take them as they are.

"I was wondering, Mother darling—" Rashid does not complete his sentence.

"What is it? Did you think of anybody in particular?"

229

"Yes and no. I thought how Mary Ann and you seem to belong to me, how both of you have understood me better than any one else ever has. So I was wondering whether I should not again marry a European. They are so frank and kind and reliable. No intrigues. With them you know where you are. And——"

"And, dear?"

"There was a girl in England who rather liked me, I think. She came from somewhere in Alsace, and was studying at the Slade Arts School. I didn't love her, we were just good pals on the rare occasions on which we went out together. You can't imagine, Mother, how much I worked; I hadn't time for anything else. So I practically never thought of that girl—her name is Jaqueline—except when I saw her. And then came our darling, and I forgot all about her. But lately, thinking of remarriage, I've been remembering Jaqueline. She was so reliable, so reasonable, so kind. She would understand that I've had my great passion, and that another marriage can mean but quiet friendship for me. And I know her. I dread marrying a girl I don't know. I have become too westernized to marry in the old-fashioned way."

My heart is full of gratitude. "I'm glad you will choose for yourself. Your repetition of 'My mother will decide,' worried me no end. How can one decide for somebody else?"

"So this worry of yours is over now. Which means also the end of the Khan Bahadur's proposal of the Lahore girl, I dare say."

I can't help laughing. "That has already come to an end." Telling Rashid the story of Akhtari and her Asaph, as well as my last conversation with her father's faithful emissary, I reflect how often worrisome problems work out their solution quite on their own.

"You mustn't tell anybody about this, Rashid."

"Of course I won't. I can see how you just loved helping her."

"Indeed I did. Fancy Muslim girls fighting so courageously on their own! It's marvelous."

"Will you help any future wife against me, Mother?"

"If need be! If you behave badly towards her, I will, of course."

"I wish you were less objective! But you're only joking, I know."

"Don't be so sure, burra sahib! Better try not to behave badly to her."

"What about Jaqueline, Mother?"

I am serious at once. "What do you propose to do?"

230

"I thought I might write to her. Somehow I believe she is still free. And when her reply arrives, and all is as I expect it to be, perhaps you could write and explain about things here."

A sharp stab goes through me. Joan! A European girl coming out, knowing and caring nothing about India, only about the man she loves or thinks she loves. How can she understand and stand life out here, be at the head of an Indian house? I wouldn't want Mary Ann's successor to look down on Auntie!

"Has Jaqueline ever been to India, Rashid?"

"No."

"What are her interests? Only painting? She must be promising if they took her at Slade's."

"I don't profess to understand about painting, Mother. I don't think I ever saw—yes, I did see some of her things once or twice. Landscapes, they seemed to me."

"Didn't you ask what they represented?"

"Certainly not. That would have been extremely impolite. I just admired them, without knowing what they meant."

"What a hypocrite!" I picture a young girl in this house, bewildered by Indian life and customs, taking refuge in her art, finding out that her husband does not really care about it, feeling alone in alien surroundings, shocking people through no fault of hers, getting more and more bewildered, feeling like a bird in a cage. No, not with my help, at any rate!

"Do you agree, Mother? Shall I write to Jaqueline? And will you write yourself in due course?"

"It is for you to decide, dear. You know the girl, and you know what you feel for her. She sounds all right in herself. But do you think a European girl, not knowing a thing about India, can be happy here? Bombay is different. Here is 'real India,' as Mary Ann used to say. I don't think you can quite appreciate how bewildered and lost she might feel."

"There would be you."

"I may not always be here. Moreover, marriage should be based on you and her only, not on anybody else. You love your work; you are bound to your country with many threads. What if your wife did not like India? In a way she wouldn't have known what she had let herself in for."

"And what does all this amount to, Mother? Yes or no?"

"It amounts to your writing to Jaqueline or doing just as you please. But I won't be party to it. She might reproach me more than you. Because I am European myself, she would feel I should have known better."

"So you are against my plan?"

"No. I'm only against your marrying a girl who doesn't know what life in India is. Couldn't we have her out for a visit, though? Would that be a solution?"

"You know this is impossible, Mother. The moment she came here, people would start talking, and worse. Everybody would say she is my mistress, and you tolerate the affair."

"And if we met her in Bombay, she wouldn't get to know life in Akbarabad."

"So what?"

"That is for you to say. If you really like the girl, go ahead. But I can't help."

"Do I really like her? Perhaps I should. At least I do know her. This wretched purdah makes it impossible here to see any girl. And then Jaqueline is European, cultured, reading books, having thoughts in her head. If I think of girls like your Sakri—" Rashid grunts in contempt.

"Don't say anything against Sakri! She's a perfect darling, and far too good for you. Moreover, she's engaged to another man and you are not allowed to discuss her. Am I to teach you good Muslim manners?"

"As far as Muslim manners are concerned, you've become far more of a stickler than even my proud ancestors could have been, Mother. But let's go back to our sheep, as the French say. We have two extremes to deal with. There are western girls, who can understand a man and be his helpmate, his friend. But you rightly point out that they would probably be unhappy here. Then there are Muslim girls of good family who've been kept in purdah and ignorance, and can give a man children, but never be his friend. Between the two there's nothing."

"Oh yes, there is!"

"What do you mean, Mother?"

"I mean——"

"Why has your voice become so soft suddenly? What *do* you mean?"

It is then that I tell him all about Maryam and the Liaqatullahs—Maryam, of whom I have thought every day since first I met her.

If the ladies on the compound would *now* reproach me for "making secrets" they'd for once be dead right. These days Rashid and I have been spending nearly all his free time by ourselves. We've driven to the jungle without Ismail Khan, chatted over meals, stayed on the roof until the small hours. We've decided to keep plans strictly to ourselves, like conspirators.

This, briefly, is the situation. Though in India proposals are usually made to men, not vice versa, the proposal shall this time come from our side. There seems equality of status in every respect; the Liaqatullahs are wealthier, but Rashid's is by far the older pedigree. Moreover, they are cultured and modern enough to appreciate science. The one thing that could be held against Rashid—that he is a widower—is to his advantage in the eyes of Mrs. Liaqatullah. Twice she said to me that if a man had been so good a husband that his late wife's mother vouched for his character and kindness, it would be a joy to entrust a daughter to him. These words were clear enough.

But I've insisted that Rashid go to Bombay to see Maryam for himself and make his own choice. At first he said that there was no need; if I said that Maryam resembled Mary Ann, that was good enough for him.

"Not for me," I replied. "I'll certainly not do a thing about it all if you don't see and choose your future wife for yourself. Didn't you say a few days ago that that's what you wanted to do?"

"I did. But at that time you hadn't told me there was a girl resembling our darling."

"Perhaps I'm mistaken and there is no resemblance whatever. You must judge for yourself. Really, I can't understand you at all. If she were in purdah, it would be different. But she isn't. That's your chance. Yet you make no end of difficulties, one more illogical than the other. So like a man!"

"Now that you grumble again at me, Mother dear, I realize that nothing stands between us any more. How lovely!"

I feel the same, but am careful to go on teasing him. Some situations are such that you might easily weep; better laugh.

We've decided that we don't at present need a go-between. Later,

233

when Rashid's suit is accepted, I'll ask Hamid to settle formalities and financial arrangements (a Muslim bridegroom should present his bride with a house mentioned in the marriage contract). At present nobody else is needed, considering Mrs. Liaqatullah's words. I'm writing her a line saying that my son will spend three days in Bombay, and that I hope he may have the pleasure of calling on her and her family. She will understand, I know.

Somehow I'm going about as in a dream. In spite of all the activity and initiative displayed on my part, it seems to me as if this whole business were not happening to *me*, as if I were reading it in a book, or saw it on the screen. And yet, I am palpably in it. Life is extraordinary. So are human beings. I'll never be able to explain what I am doing to friends at home. Sometimes I am still western enough not to understand, myself.

February 14

Trust Indian servants to find out!

Over the packing of Rashid's things maharaj looks up. "Second memsahib come will, masahib?"

"Second memsahib? Oh no!" I laugh convincingly. "Why ask thou dost, maharaj?"

"Thou much time today sahib's things givest, masahib. Before last Bombay journey not thou didst. This tie pressed is? That tie pressed is?" Maharaj imitates my voice to perfection.

I try a reprimanding look. "Much work is, maharaj. Go on in with. Bombay in sahib's things order in must be."

"Very well, masahib. Very well." He busies himself over the suitcase while I am collecting some more things in Rashid's dressing room.

"How many days sahib Bombay in stay will?"

"Three."

"Three days. Nine ties. Six silk shirts. Best shirts are. Much talk masahib with sahib last days in talk did. Four shoe pairs masahib into luggage put do. Three days for."

I hastily turn away, lest maharaj see me smile during this monologue of his.

"Sahib Bombay in business has," I say, as soon as I have my voice and expression under control.

"Glad I am," replies maharaj in different tone. "Glad I am business

234

is. New memsahib we not want. Masahib is. And our memsahib was. Tomb to today I go do."

～ 13 ～

February 15
"Fairfield
"5, Asoka Road, New Delhi
"February 14

"*D*EAR HILDA,

"It's now more than a month since you left Bombay. During this time I've been traveling about quite a lot. Industrial centers and so on. Now I'm staying here for about a fortnight. After that I'm bound for Calcutta, Madras and home.

"I'm staying here with the Griersons, old friends of mine, as you know. Lady Elvira was much interested to hear about your life out here, and sends you kindest regards. She hopes you'll come to Delhi some time or other.

"Though you were very explicit on our last evening in Bombay, I reiterate that I should be happy to escort you home in case conditions have altered and you feel free to return. I'll be ready to sail about the fifth of April from Bombay. But I shall certainly try to adapt my plans to yours, if any.

"God bless you. Do write c/o Lloyds Bank, New Delhi. I'm waiting to hear from you soon.

"Yours always devotedly
"Arthur"

This is truly Arthurian wisdom and *savoir faire*. He says "in case conditions have altered and you feel free to return," not, "in case you have changed your mind," a thing most people dislike to own. As a matter of fact, conditions have altered, considerably so. But Arthur doesn't know that. Or does he with that uncanny penetration of his wherever I'm concerned? I'm glad I've nothing to hide—he would always find out.

Well, I can't go home just now. It would have helped me to be with Arthur on that more than difficult journey, every minute of which will remind me of Mary Ann's radiant presence on the outward trip. But it can't be done. There's Rashid to be settled, Maryam to be welcomed, before I can leave. I must be Mother first.

Later

Dr. Venkataraman comes in for a chat. "Do you mind? I feel so lonely here."

"Of course I don't mind. It's a pleasure. But why lonely, with your two sisters? Or have they left?"

"Oh no. I shouldn't be able to stand life here without them."

"Is it as bad as all that, Doctor? Your chief is a very kind and sincere man."

"My chief? You mean Dr. Ram Chandra? But he isn't my boss, or only very remotely so. I'm in the *Zenana* Hospital. That means under Dr. Cama."

"Is she so bad? She was very kind when my daughter died. Now that I think of it, I remember that some people grumble about her. But others praise her. I should say it's fifty-fifty."

"Oh yes, she is kindhearted. I'm sure she means well. In her way she is even a good doctor. But so terribly old-fashioned!"

"In medical methods?"

"I didn't mean that. She has kept up fairly with her surgery, I must say that for her. But she doesn't care about any kind of social work. When I asked her whether the doctors here were not taking turns in going to the villages she just shrugged her shoulders, and said I should improve my Hindustani rather than think of such nonsense. How is our poor country to progress, if the educated do not help all they can? Am I not right, madam?"

"Of course you are, child. I'm so glad that you go in for social work."

"We all do in the south. Well, perhaps not all, but most young people. I can't imagine what my fellow students would think of someone who shirked it."

"What exactly have you been doing in the social line while studying?"

"We go to the villages, mostly over weekends. Each squad of students has a certain number of villages to visit regularly. There are future agriculturists, lawyers, engineers, teachers, doctors and all sorts of people in a squad. We look after the villagers' health and tell mothers how to care for their babies; we teach the adults to read and write and to keep houses and villages clean; above all we insist on cleanliness of the village well. We explain what anti-malarial, anti-typhoid, anti-cholera measures to take. We try to get the villagers to form buying-and-selling co-operatives. Our students of agriculture teach the peasants new methods within their reach—nothing that needs money, of course, since they haven't any, only debts. We bring newspapers, and at night read and explain them under the *panchayat* tree. We try to get together enough money for occasionally sending round a teacher to look after the cottage industries. We try to take people out of the village money-lender's clutches. There is quite a good co-operative move on. Soon each group of villages will have its own co-operative bank, we hope."

"It's splendid, Doctor! I'm so happy you told me."

"I was afraid I was taking too long over it. In the presence of elders we should not talk too much."

"What nonsense!"

"It's certainly no nonsense in Akbarabad. People are so terribly old-fashioned. They talk about me and my sisters because we're accustomed to walk about by ourselves. In Madras nobody would bother. Is Akbarabad so dangerous, madam?"

"Of course not."

"Do you go walking alone at night?"

"Good gracious, yes! At midnight, sometimes, if my son is out and if I can slip away without *chowkidar's* knowledge. I take a torch in case there are snakes."

"You are not afraid, are you?"

"Afraid? In India? Of course there are rascals and cutthroats all over the world. But ordinary Indians? With them I feel as safe as a child on its mother's lap. Especially in villages. But everywhere else in India, too."

"You do love our people, don't you, madam?"

"I do. How could I help it?"

"Well—" I see my charming visitor visibly swallowing for politeness's sake what she wants to say about Westerners' attitude to Indians in general. I had better take the thing up myself.

"You see, Doctor, my people usually don't know Indians as I do. What we need is knowledge about each other. And patience. And good will. And——"

237

"And?"

"You know what I mean, don't you?"

"Yes, I know. We need love."

After that, I refrain from asking the proud Brahman whether she, or other Brahmans of her squad, also entered the miserable dwellings of the untouchables which, in South India, are usually situated at a certain distance from the village proper. Often the untouchables are not allowed access to any public well or shop; the shopkeeper puts salt or whatever they want to buy somewhere in no-man's land, where the untouchable can pick it up. What is the use of asking such questions? Either she already goes to the untouchables, or she will some day. Her children certainly will. If she and her Brahman colleagues in the squad are still being forced by their elders to avoid pollution by contact with untouchables, she can at least counter that it is easier for the five or six millions of Indian Christians living in the south, and the many Christian missions, to take care of the untouchables than it is for young Brahman students. As an immediate solution that may be adequate—but certainly not in the long run. Only the Brahman caste which, thousands of years ago, outcast those who are nowadays called untouchables, can remedy matters.

I know, of course, that the orthodox twice-born say this is impossible; that, according to them, caste is of divine origin and must be kept undefiled; that the untouchables have been born as such in consequence of former lives of sin; and so on. Yet I am certain that this view will in due course disappear, not only because more and more people will acquire a perspective on pre-Vedic and ancient Vedic times, and will realize that caste as we have it today is of later and man-made origin; but because I trust human nature. More and more young Brahmans will realize their responsibility and duty towards untouchables, just as great Hindu reformers have done at various periods. Brahmans created untouchability; it is for them to do away with it. Nobody else can.

February 17

There's a wire from Rashid "Arriving tomorrow night splendid health love."

This wording is the result of much deliberation. Knowing that we're always news in Akbarabad, we had decided beforehand that "splendid health" would stand for "everything as satisfactory as possible." It sounds strange, but such precautions are needed. A bare two hours after you've got a telegram the whole town knows its contents, even if you have not spoken about it to anybody. One day I had been out for tea, and went straight on to the club without returning home first. Everybody there made congratulatory remarks, spoke of the good news I had received and, when I looked blank, commented on my secrecy. I couldn't make head or tail of things until later, on my desk, I found a wired money-order from my publisher.

Rashid is back. "You were right, Mother. She is like our darling to an inconceivable degree."

Everything has gone well. Rashid saw Maryam three times, once at tea, once during a drive to Juhu and finally at dinner the evening before his departure. He and she have been able to talk to each other freely (bless Mrs. Liaqatullah!). He thinks she likes him. She has asked him many questions about me. "Give my regards to memsahib" were her last words. Her mother, however, was more definite. "Please give your revered mother our best regards. We hope to hear from her soon."

That means "Yes."

They must have liked Rashid. I'm very glad that Maryam had an opportunity of talking to him and judging things for herself. If she had not been willing to consider the marriage, both she and her mother would have behaved differently.

"I'm proud of you, Rashid! You *did* carry the day, really!"

"Nothing to be proud of, Mother dear. I didn't talk much. I didn't do anything in particular. It just happened."

"Do you like Maryam, Rashid?"

"I think I shall like her very much some day. Now there's a tangle within me. From the moment I'd seen her I wouldn't dream of thinking of any other girl, simply because she is so much like our darling. Did you notice the voice? So you can't wonder at my having been spellbound in her presence."

"I don't. I was myself, the first time I met her."

"On the other hand, I somehow resent the similarity. That's illogical, I know, but there it is. I want to cry out, to interfere. I want to say: 'Nobody has the right to that smile, to move about so gracefully, to laugh in sweet trills, nobody but my darling!' Maybe I'm afraid that both smiles, both laughs will melt in one. I don't want to lose the clear recollection I have of our darling."

"Go on, dear. Try to understand what it is you really want."

"I certainly want to marry Maryam, if she will have me. She is the living image of Mary Ann, as far as such a thing is humanly possible. So she is the very best for me. Somehow I'll manage to keep apart within myself indescribably precious memories."

"I, too, think that you couldn't do better than marry Maryam. But I don't want you to do so only because she resembles Mary Ann. That would be grossly unfair to her."

"But how can I prevent being touched and attracted by just that resemblance?"

"Of course you can't. Only don't stop at that. The resemblance was the door through which you entered. Now you must discover and love Maryam for her own sake."

"I am afraid that will take a very long time to happen, Mother—if ever. There is only one woman for me. You know it."

"Rashid, listen. I will not let you sacrifice any girl to the memory of my child. She herself would never want that. Either you marry in the sincere hope of being made happy by your second wife and making her happy, or I won't have anything to do with your marriage. I am very much in earnest. Take it or leave it."

"You are a marvel, Mother. I always knew you were, but only now do I realize to what extent. Fancy your reproaching me because I might not love my second wife enough! You unselfish darling! You're too good to be true."

Though I can't understand his outburst—it's but natural I should think of the girl he'll marry, once I've agreed to help—I'm deeply glad we are together again, all misunderstandings gone.

"It's very sweet of you to say such nice things about me, dear. But what of my ultimatum? I really am serious, do believe me. Do you think that Maryam is the girl who can make you happy? Will you try all you can to make her happy, not only thinking of her as the mother of your children, but for her own sake? Will you, Rashid?"

"I will try. I promise. I honestly think that there is nobody I would prefer to Maryam. Trust me. I'll make her a good husband.

240

If not, there'll always be my darling mother to make me see reason. I know beforehand that you'll only take her side, never mine."

"Indeed I will. In this country women must help each other against the lords of creation."

For a little while we go on laughing and joking before turning in—perhaps in order not to show each other all we feel. I can't get rid of Rashid's "There'll always be my mother."

There won't. I shall go. Maryam is a modern girl. Those two must build up their life by themselves.

February 20

Next evening I come back to another point. "Do think things over once more. What about Jaqueline? Are you really and truly certain that you want to marry Maryam and nobody else? There is still time."

"I'm quite certain, Mother. Already now I feel differently for Maryam than I ever did for Jaqueline, maybe because she resembles our darling. But there's something else, too. You have often hinted at it. It is better I should marry an Indian girl. Now that you've found me one who is not the ignorant, old-fashioned type, one who combines East and West, so to say, I know I couldn't do better."

"No. There's nothing better, in general and in particular, than a combination of East and West, the best of both. But it's rare."

"Which is a great pity. By the way, Mother, here is a note from Sultana bai. I forgot to hand it to you earlier. They all send their salaams, and hope to see you soon."

"They will, at Sakri's wedding."

"Old Mrs. Hamidullah said she wouldn't have believed you could be such a good matchmaker! She added, however, that it was a pity you didn't exert yourself on my behalf as well. I could hardly refrain from telling her."

"I hope you didn't!"

"No. I pulled as uninterested a face as I knew how to. Won't you read your letter now, Mother?"

It brings good news. "Things *do* go well. Akhtari is to marry her Asaph in April! Sultana says the whole scheme functioned like clockwork. Can any one beat *zenana* strategy?"

241

We've been planning everything.

Nobody here is to know. I've written to Hamid to ask in my name for Maryam's hand, and to discuss all details about marriage contract, expected presents and wedding. It is a great pity that we can't phone for fear of listeners-in. Telegrams are also unsafe. There'll be a lot of express letters to and fro, I know.

The funny thing is that I must do everything. A marriage in the East is arranged by parents or guardians; the two people concerned being kept in official—and sometimes actual—ignorance of arrangements. So Rashid must remain entirely in the background. I have to act for him in everything.

At first I was afraid of the task. "How on earth can I ably represent a noble Muslim family, dating so to say from before the Flood? It's highly improper. I'll make all sorts of mistakes."

"If you don't act for me, Mother, there'd only be Uncle Fakhruddin to take your place. Do you think I'd like that? Or the Liaqatullahs, either? They would say 'No' at once, if he came into the picture. The things he would do and say! It doesn't bear thinking about. No, you are my mother. You, and nobody else must act for me."

"And if I blunder?"

"You won't. I can't imagine you blundering. As to Muslim etiquette, you know more of it than I do. The noble family is better off in your hands than in those of any of its members!"

So I find myself a Muslim mother, and a contracting party.

I've suggested, via Hamid, that the wedding should take place in June, at the end of the hot season. When in Bombay for Sakri's wedding in March, I can do all the necessary shopping and hear—again via Hamid—of Maryam's wishes concerning the house and its rearrangement. She—that is, the Liaqatullahs via their go-between, whoever he'll be—will, of course, say that they have no wishes whatsoever, that it shall all remain as it is, or be as I say. That is etiquette. So I—via Hamid—will not ask questions, but will tender suggestions and then listen for the echo.

After shopping in Bombay I'll have April and May to get the house and everything ready.

There's one thing, however, I wrote to Hamid which I have not as yet told to Rashid. Hamid is to let the Liaqatullahs know that soon after the wedding I shall leave Akbarabad. Maryam is not to be burdened with a mother-in-law.

It is 3 P.M. All the servants being safely out of the way until about 4:30, I take out a new batch of magazines which I got only two days ago. *Saturday Evening Post* and *Picture Post, Time, Life, Royal Geographical, Graphic, Tatler*. My friends do spoil me. Now I'll enjoy myself.

But perhaps this morning's walk was too much. I find myself very tired, closing my eyes for a minute. The magazines? No fear. I've plenty of time to read and hide them before anybody turns up. Just five minutes' doze——

It must have been somewhat longer. When I sit up, I see young Dr. Venkataraman, quietly turning the pages of some magazines— *not* the *Royal Geographic*, I'm sorry to note. My movement to take it away—involuntary, of course—doesn't remedy matters. My visitor begins to laugh.

"I didn't know you subscribed to all those magazines, Mother!"

"I don't take them, Shanta. I'm not as rich as all that. Kind friends send them occasionally."

"You never showed them to me. So many all at once! May I ask you to lend me one or two?"

There it is. Publicity! People will see the magazines carried to and fro, or find them on Shanta's table. How utterly careless of me to go to sleep with the whole display about! There is no other way but to tell my visitor the truth.

"You're welcome to read them here, Shanta. But I'd rather you didn't take them with you. People might misunderstand."

"What might they misunderstand, Mother?"

"The photographs. Here things have another meaning than in the West."

"And Indians, being inferior, are not to be shown the ways and customs of their betters, the magnificent white race, lest they look behind the scenes. Isn't that it?"

"Do you really think that I consider Indians inferior?"

"What a beast I am. Forgive me, Mother. Nobody can accuse *you* of despising Indians. But we are used to being looked down upon. That's why we feel things so strongly."

"It's understandable, of course. But I have often been struck by the fact that you take it out on the very Westerners who don't deserve your reproach: those who are at hand just *because* they are closely associating with Indians. I remember, for example, a charming and cultured Brahman family who were on very friendly terms with Mary Ann and me. Suddenly one day they dropped us, sending the explicit message that they didn't want to have anything more to do with us. Why? Simply because somebody in England, I forget now whether a Minister or the Secretary of State, in a speech had said things they strongly disapproved of. Lumping all Westerners together, they took their wrath out on the nearest."

"I'm ashamed of my fellow Brahmans and compatriots for such conduct."

"Yet I can understand it. Easterners think instinctively in terms of groups, either family, caste or race. Individuality is still something alien, if not reprehensible. So if somebody in the West says something or other, people out here instinctively make his whole 'caste'—all white people—responsible."

"You are very understanding and tolerant, Mother. But, being so, why do you object to Indians reading your magazines?"

"Because—" I try to explain again all I've said to Arthur on the subject. Like films, certain photographs in magazines give a wrong impression about the West, as though all western life consisted of nothing but nudes, jazz, divorces and drink.

"But these things *do* exist, Mother—that is how the West *is!* Why do you want to prevent Indians from knowing? We know anyhow."

"Your words do bear me out. You say 'That's how the West is.' But it isn't! That's just the point! Now let's take one or two magazines at random. A visit to the slums in pictures. Vitamins. A new discovery in television. Strip-tease. Juvenile Court Session. Modern nursing. Sports. That's one. But you'll only remember the strip-tease, if you are the ordinary eastern reader, and say: 'That's the depraved West.' "

"Yes, but Mother, do explain. Take Americans. They have developed such marvelous institutions, they are ahead in science and medicine, they are such splendid people except where the Negro question and elections are concerned. We've always admired them and preferred them to Europeans. How is it that they can lead mankind in so many fields—and don't they know it!—while in others they live like savages?"

"What do you mean?"

"I mean their petting and necking parties, strip-tease, their new tunes, the sex life in colleges, and so on. We know all about it."

"Oh, Judge Lindsay!"

"No, not only he. We've our students out there, who have much to say on their return, although, apart from that aspect of things, they like the United States. And we've the *Reader's Digest*. Lots of us read it."

"I see." Well, that's what popularity like the *Reader's Digest's* brings in its stride, I suppose.

"Americans were not always so. They lived very decent lives formerly, didn't they? Almost too much so, if we think of Puritan times. Where has all that decency gone to? Why does modern scientific, social and economic advance mean savagery in morals—what you people call sex life? We, the young generation brought up on modern scientific lines, would like to contradict the current notions of western depravity. We know what great things the West has evolved, we know splendid Westerners who help or teach us to do social work for our poor people. But what are we to reply to our orthodox when they say that where moral life is concerned the West lives in a state of savagery and evil? What are we to reply?"

There is a lot to reply, and I shall do so in due course. But now I can only think of the situation in which I find myself—to be held responsible for whatever the West does. For so it always turns out in the East, whenever contacts are not shirked. The one Westerner present stands for all British and Dutch doings, for every Gallic impetus, for all American "go." He may be a Slav, a Norwegian or an Austrian like myself; out here he counts as British, simply because his skin is white. "*Angrezi*"—English is what every white is popularly called. Educated people acknowledge differences of nationality, of course; yet even so they make you responsible for everything the West does.

Just now it is my turn. I'm facing that modern girl of proudest Indian Brahman stock, full of social responsibility, a medical graduate, a striking beauty. She asks me about the west's "savage" moral life. She is brown, I am white. So she holds me co-responsible.

245

It is one of those moments in life in which we are suddenly confronted by inescapable naked truth.

I hope I live to see a time in which color will not be a reason to hold another human being responsible for this or that—in which we will look at each other as human beings only, irrespective of any differentiation.

March 2

A letter from Kay. She is ailing, and the doctors don't quite know what is the matter. It doesn't sound too good. I only hope there is no malign growth. After the wedding I'll go at once to Madras, but I can't see my way to go sooner.

Hamid will come tomorrow to pay us a flying visit. It seems he is getting fed up with writing letters or, rather, the prospect of having to write them. So far he hasn't overstrained himself. His two or three express letters, written on one small sheet of notepaper, laconically say, "Everything O.K. I shall explain fully next time."

Well, by tomorrow we shall have that full explanation. If Hamid is not too tired we propose to take him for a jungle picnic, *sigris*, kettle and all. While Ismail Khan and cook prepare lunch, the three of us can talk freely. At home there's always the chance of somebody listening. But I wouldn't dare, of course, to lunch those two on cold food. It'll be an elaborate Muslim lunch: two kinds of meat, chicken *pilau*, chutneys, curds and lots of *chappatis*. The West will be represented by vegetables and fruit salad, Rashid's favorite dessert. Cook'll prepare at home what he can. The *chappatis* need at least one hour's work on the spot.

I hope people won't find out the reason of Hamid's visit. I'll suggest that Rashid take his two guns, implying that Hamid wants to shoot a bit. That sounds plausible.

March 4

Maryam is a B.A. with English Honors! I'm looking forward to telling her some day that we hadn't an inkling of her being a graduate, when we asked for her hand.

Hamid tells us over breakfast that everything is arranged satisfactorily, and that only our approval is awaited. "To put things on paper I should have needed days," he says. "So I thought I'd better come myself. Let me first congratulate you, Mother. You couldn't

246

have made a better choice. The family is excellent from every point of view. As for the young lady, she's perfection. I've not seen her now, of course, but once or twice last year. No Indian mother could have done better, if as well."

"Thanks, Hamid. I didn't do anything at all. Rashid saw Maryam and decided for her. I should never have presumed to choose for him."

"And who arranged the meeting, if not you?"

"Anybody could have done that."

"Would the Liaqatullahs have listened to anybody? Come, Mother, you can't get away from it. You did it all."

"God did it, Hamid, if you want to go to the origin. You should know that better than I. Allah is the All-Doing."

"Of course, Mother, of course!" Hamid's expression is a mixture of uneasiness and dignity, the usual thing if God is brought into the conversation by old-fashioned people like myself. "So you want to escape into theology? Well, wait until my mother tells you what she thinks of your qualities!"

"So she knows?"

"Indeed she does. For days she couldn't talk of anything else. Poor lady! She was bent on finding a wife for Rashid herself, thinking that a memsahib could never manage such a thing. Then you go and arrange the best marriage imaginable, all by yourself and not telling anybody!"

That's what the old lady resents most, I imagine! Won't the others here do likewise! And Auntie—no, she will not resent it. She's too kind for that. But she ought to be told. If Mrs. Hamidullah senior knows, why not she?

"Rashid, I think we should tell Auntie and Waliuddin."

"Didn't we agree to keep things secret until your return from Bombay after Sakri's wedding? We'd have no peace and privacy. I've such a lot of work to do just now!"

"Yes, but is this secrecy fair to Auntie? And won't things leak out anyhow, now that Hamid's ladies know?"

Hamid looks up. "As far as my mother is concerned you needn't worry, Mother. I've sworn her to secrecy. Even Sultana doesn't know."

"That settles it," concludes Rashid. "It's ever so much better if we're left in peace for the next few weeks, at least. It'll be worse for you, Mother, you must know that. Everybody will come visiting, and make you waste your time and strength. By the way, Dr. Ram Chandra told me the other day that you should go slow—remedies for anemia and a weak heart can't do everything. Shopping in Bombay and Sakri's wedding will tax your strength quite enough. After that there will be pandemonium, getting the house ready, preparing for the wedding. Let's not start the whole show now by telling people!"

"All right, then. Nobody appreciates being left in peace more than I do. Will the wedding be in June, Hamid, as we suggested?"

"Yes, Mother. I've lots to tell you."

"Not here, please!" Both Rashid and I remember where we are. Only out in the jungle, with cook and Ismail Khan at a safe distance preparing tiffin, do we allow Hamid to deliver his various messages.

Practical as he is—that's why the running of the Science Congress had been entrusted to him—he starts with finances.

"Your daughter-in-law is quite an heiress, Mother. In addition to her dowry and what she will have on her father's death, she inherits from her paternal grandparents, whose favorite she is. They are very rich. Only part of their wealth will be hers, of course, since her father and his brother will inherit with her. But she will come in for about a *lakh*—100,000 rupees. Aren't you lucky!"

"We are lucky because of the girl, not because of that unexpected wealth. In a way this is bad news. We never thought about the financial side of things. We've not been heiress-hunting, but looking for the girl best suited to Rashid."

"I agree with Mother," says Rashid. "This news of Miss Liaqatullah's wealth is unpleasant. She and her people will think we knew about it. This spoils a good deal for us, doesn't it, Mother?"

Hamid starts laughing. "Forgive me, Mother, but you two are incredible! Instead of being thrilled and happy, you pull long faces. If it were any one but you and Rashid, I'd say you were pretending! Being you, I know you are serious. It's unbelievable, it really is!"

"Why?" both of us ask simultaneously.

"Because it doesn't make any sense, if you'll forgive my saying so. Is Miss Liaqatullah less accomplished because she will inherit from her grandparents? Is she less beautiful and learned? She remains what she is, and brings lots of money into the bargain, which will

248

come in very handy for future generations and for Rashid's research too. What on earth are you worrying about? You should shout for joy!"

Both of us remain silent.

"If it were not for the different pigmentation of your skin, nobody could believe that you're not actually mother and son. Fancy such identical out-of-the-way reactions!"

Rashid and I look at each other. We can't help smiling. Really we are very close to each other.

"Is it because both of you give in to each other?" Hamid pursues relentlessly.

"No. Mother and I feel alike, I'm glad to say."

"I too. Now let's proceed. Maryam is much wealthier than we expected, which has both its good and bad sides. Anyhow, we can't alter it. Now tell us more. The first two weeks of the monsoon bring very heavy rains in Bombay, don't they? Wouldn't it be better to fix the wedding for the end of June, so as not to come in for the worst deluge?"

"I'm afraid the wedding will be very different from what you think, Mother."

"How?"

"In the first place the Liaqatullahs regret being unable to celebrate it in Bombay. They'd love to. But they cannot go against the formal wishes of Mr. Liaqatullah's parents. Miss Maryam is their favorite granddaughter. It is at their place in the Central Provinces that the wedding will have to take place. The Liaqatullahs send their apologies, but it can't be helped. I don't see what there's to regret, though. For me, yes; Bombay would have been much more handy. But for you? The place—I think it's called Aishapur—is just near Nagpur. You can drive over in no time."

"I see. The grandparents are old-fashioned people, aren't they?"

"Well, certainly more so than the Bombay Liaqatullahs."

"Which means the wedding will be old-fashioned, too."

"Exactly. That's what I was going to explain. I faithfully transmitted your wish for a small and quiet wedding, Rashid being a widower. The Liaqatullahs said that, were they free to make their own arrangements, they would certainly fall in with your request. They themselves would not like a big show. But since the wedding is taking place in Aishapur, it must be celebrated according to the grandparents' wishes. For years they've looked forward to that wedding, and planned it all. There's nothing one can do."

"I suppose not." I am somewhat disappointed and apprehensive. A regular old-fashioned Muslim wedding takes about three full days. I've seen some; after a time Mary Ann and I refused further invitations, because we could not get used to certain ceremonies. Though carried out in the *zenana* with no man about, we couldn't help feeling embarrassed. The dance of some female disguised as a male bear, with unmistakable gestures—the elaborate preparation of the double bed in great style—! It's a show-bed, prepared in the bride's house; its only use is to seat the bride when the bridegroom is led to the door to behold her for the first time—through a mirror held at the height of his eyes. But to think of three days of ceremonial and feasting! The weddings I've attended took place in noble or modern families, most of whom were widely traveled. If they kept up all these ceremonies—if our sophisticated woman friends who always followed the latest Paris fashions in shoes, lingerie, perfume and jewels, and read the newest books, arranged the bed in view of hundreds of eyes, visibly enjoying the fun—what will await us at a really old-fashioned wedding? Rashid feasted and harangued at the men's quarters; I made much of in the *zenana*, having to witness all the frolic. Neither he nor I can face that for three full days. No, I'm wrong. It's for him only, not for me. I forget that at *this* wedding I shan't be a visitor, but a party to it—a very important one. As the representative of the bridegroom's family I shall have to prepare the real bridal chamber in the house at the door of which I have to welcome the bride. Which house? In Aishapur?

"So it will be an old-fashioned wedding."

"I'm afraid so."

"Listen, Rashid. What about a honeymoon? By June you'll have been on duty for more than a year. Can't you ask for a holiday? His Highness would understand, I'm sure."

"I think so, too."

"Couldn't you go away right after the wedding? Kashmir is lovely at that season. You can catch the express in Nagpur."

Hamid shakes his head. "I'm afraid that'll be impossible, Mother. We've talked it over in Bombay. Don't you see, it's to be an old-fashioned wedding! The grandparents will certainly expect you to take the bride home to Akbarabad first, bridal procession and all.

After that the young couple can slip away on a honeymoon trip. But the procession home must come first. Old-fashioned people consider a big welcome accorded to the bride as a sign of future good treatment. The grandparents will certainly send somebody along with the bride, to report afterwards. The bigger the welcome, the better."

I shudder. "Elephants and all? Town band?"

"I'm sure the Municipality will provide for that."

"I don't mind the providing, I mind the show."

"I too," adds Rashid. "It's entirely out of place in our case. I'd have thought the Liaqatullahs would be more reasonable and considerate."

"But it's not their fault." Though Hamid is *our* representative, he now assumes the role of theirs. "Don't you see, they must do what the grandparents ask. The money is theirs. It's necessary to humor them. The *lakh* your wife will get one day is theirs, after all."

"Now stop it, Hamid!" Rashid has turned white, as always when something seriously upsets him. "I have not asked for that *lakh* or any money. I'd much have preferred my future wife not to be so wealthy as that. Perhaps, had I known, I wouldn't have proposed at all."

"Brother, now thou art getting ridiculous!" Hamid suddenly is talking Urdu. "Not to propose because a girl is rich! Whoever has heard of such a thing!"

"Well, if you don't understand by yourself, I'll have to be plain. It is a wise custom in our community for men to choose their brides from a lower social level than their own. It is said that such a wife will fit easily into her husband's house and life. A bride coming from a higher level than his, will take him away from his friends, will complain about this thing or that, will make him spend more than he can afford. At her worst she will look down on him. That's why Muslim men don't want to marry above themselves."

"Above yourself! Whose family is better than yours, I'd like to know!"

"Yes, my family is good. There was equal status between the Liaqatullahs and myself. But now, all of a sudden, I am to be made aware that my future wife is richer than I. Mother and I are being made to do things we utterly loathe, all in the name of the grandparents' money."

"I never said——"

"You did. Well, let me tell you, I don't want the money. And if I'm to be made its slave, I don't want the girl, either. I've never demeaned myself because of money. I shan't start now. Am I not right, Mother? You are with me, aren't you?"

"Of course I am, as far as your attitude towards money is concerned. But not otherwise. Maryam is the girl we chose, because of her qualities. We both felt that she was the companion most suited to make you happy. These facts remain, whether she is wealthy or not. You and I don't care much for money as such, I'm glad to say; let's not go to the other extreme and give it undue importance. It does not matter one way or the other, if you come to think of it. Maryam is all that matters."

"Yes, but I have my pride!"

"No but's! Just face things clearly. Do you think that she will make you a good wife or don't you? Is she the girl you want to marry?"

"You know she is."

"That's all there is to it, then. I don't think, moreover, that Maryam is the type to let any one feel her wealth. And who knows when it will become hers. You may be married to her for decades before her grandparents die. Meanwhile you'll grow together and be happy in each other, I hope. The money won't make any difference."

"And you may have been awarded the Nobel Prize for Chemistry meantime," Hamid adds good-naturedly, "or have made untold millions with one of your discoveries. Is the incident satisfactorily closed? Then we can go on, can't we?"

"If it's an old-fashioned wedding, how are we to get an adequate house in Aishapur to receive the bride?" After either a Muslim or a Hindu wedding the bride must be taken in procession to the "bridegroom's house," never to a hotel or any other place. Since the bridegroom and his family very frequently do not own property in the bride's village or town, a house is vacated for them to serve as the "bridegroom's house." It is for the bridegroom's family to furnish and staff it.

"The Liaqatullahs say that can be satisfactorily arranged. They have lots of relatives there, all of them with quite nice houses to lend to you."

"We must bring our own furniture, I believe, and lots of carpets and cushions. Also the whole household, including a cook. We'll have to do a lot of entertaining. I dare say we must bring a cook used to big numbers and festivities. Or can we find one on the spot? Also the extra chinaware? It would be such a nuisance to have to cart everything from the hotel there."

"I'm sure you'll find everything in Aishapur, Mother. If not, satisfactory arrangements can doubtless be made. Don't worry. But how is it that you know all our customs so well?"

"Better than we do," adds Rashid. "I'd never have thought of all this."

"Because you are first and last a man of science. I've come to India with the definite intention of studying the country. So it's no wonder that I've paid attention to customs. Now let's go on. What about the presents they expect?"

"There I've come back empty-handed. The Liaqatullahs say you'll know best. Maybe the grandmother will insist on some kind of old-fashioned jewelry like anklets, a thing Miss Liaqatullah won't wear anyhow. If so, they will let us know. There's lots of time for that. But in every other respect you are to do as you please."

"That's great confidence to put in a mere Westerner, isn't it? Now listen, you two. Check my list carefully and correct me where I'm wrong. Have you a bit of paper? Thanks. I better note the items while I go along.

"First, seven saris, two or three entirely of gold and silver tissue, the others with rich gold and silver borders or embroidery. Will you remember, Hamid, to ask whether the Liaqatullah ladies wear Benarsi saris? Some Muslims don't, but an all-gold or all-silver sari comes only from Benares, as far as I know." No, I must not think now of the gold-gauze sari Mary Ann and I bought together. I must think only of Rashid.

"Second, seven blouses to match, if obtainable all of silver or gold brocade, shot with the color of the sari. Do remember, Hamid, please, to ask for a sample blouse. That's how mothers-in-law know how to prepare the blouses.

"Third, seven matching pieces silk for—. We must again ask for a sample, Hamid." I know, and both men know, that I'm thinking of the wide petticoats worn underneath saris, but I can't say so, of course.

"Fourth, seven pairs of gold and silver shoes and sandals to match. Again we need a sample. That's about all, as far as dress is concerned, isn't it? Oh no. There must be a few matching bags, too."

"Mother, you take my breath away. Seven of everything? Wouldn't five be enough? My mother said four or five would do perfectly well. You are planning a very costly and beautiful outfit."

"I'm afraid I've got my knowledge only from big weddings."

"Royalty?"

"I've also seen royal trousseaus and presents, of course. But I wasn't thinking about them, since we are not Royalty. The set of 'seven of everything' I've noticed in good, perhaps very good families. Aren't the Liaqatullahs one? A High Court Judge?" Deliberately I'm not mentioning Rashid's, as well as the fact that both families concerned are of much better standing than Hamid's and Sultana's. "I admit that good old families often exchange much simpler presents than new rich do, because they can't afford great expense. But I don't think that two more saris will ruin us. After all, Rashid and I are different units, and the presents come from both of us."

"As you say, Mother. You make it easy for me. There'll be no recriminations after the wedding, I know."

"I hope not. Do you agree to the classical number of seven, Rashid?"

"Of course, Mother."

"Now for the jewels. That'll be more difficult. As far as I know it's a set of everything for people of our rather limited means: necklace, clasp, rings, earrings, bracelets, with a few additional rings and bracelets. Do find out, Hamid, whether the Liaqatullahs prefer emeralds or rubies. In this country sapphires are considered unlucky, I'm sorry to say. They are so beautiful! So are aquamarines, but nobody here wants them. Pearls would be best as a necklace, but I dare say a pearl necklace will be part of her dowry, probably a much better one than we could afford. Please write down carefully, Hamid: first about the pearls, then about whether rubies or emeralds. Do also inquire about the style of the jewelry she brings. We want ours to go with hers, at least not to clash. We also want to supply what she hasn't got. Maryam is to have pleasure when wearing her jewels."

"You are taking lots of trouble, Mother."

"Of course I am."

"It will need much shopping and selecting."

"I'll do it all in Bombay at the end of this month. I wish I could go to Delhi, to get the saris at Lilarams'. But that's foolish, of course. Bombay too is marvelous for shopping. I'm only wondering about the jewels. I don't want to buy them without Rashid approving. It's his money, and his wife who'll wear them all her life."

"Yes, I'd like to see the jewels, though you would do very well by yourself, Mother. But I'm afraid I won't be able to leave my work, especially if I want to leave in June."

"We'll find some way or other. I'll select certain things and bring them here on approval. We'll always find somebody to take them back, especially if we pay the fare."

"Mother, I'm afraid we must leave at once. I forgot to look at my watch earlier. It's high time I went to the office. Do you realize we've been talking for three solid hours?"

It's so. Lunch and coffee were partaken of nearly unnoticed, though we made it a point to change the subject whenever the servants were near.

Anyhow, we've covered a good deal of ground. Hamid's train does not leave until late at night. We can talk for hours more.

Later

At home bad news of Kay is waiting. She will probably have to submit to a major operation. I'm sending a wire to Frank's office address, asking him to give me details. This is a serious business. Kay is very delicate, and such an operation may well nigh prove fatal. Poor Frank! How he must suffer. They are so ideally suited to each other.

I wish I'd gone to Madras from Bombay.

Later

What a day!

After dinner we are sitting in the courtyard. There is still an hour's time before both men have to drive to the station. All of us feel that we've done a good day's work. Now we talk about all sorts of things. Hamid tells Rashid the latest news and jokes in Bombay's world of science, "Underworld of Science," as he calls it. Poor

Hamid, he *does* deserve some relaxation. Two nights in the train and one tiring day between, all for the sake of friendship!

Suddenly he sits up. "I nearly forgot to tell you the most important part of my message. What a fool I am! *Mashallah*, there is still time. Listen, Mother. The Liaqatullahs say that on no account are you to leave Akbarabad after the wedding. They say——"

"What is this? How dare they take into their mouth Mother's leaving or not leaving? It's not their affair. It's nobody's but Mother's and mine. What utter impudence!" Rashid begins to pace the courtyard, with set jaws and flaming eyes.

"But let me finish my message! You will see how the Liaqatullahs honor Mother. They——"

"I don't want to hear your message! They have no right to decide whether Mother stays in my house or not. Mother *is* my house, my home, my——! And these strangers, daring to interfere! There is only one person who has the right to decide what she is to do or not: Mother herself."

"But that's exactly what she has done!"

"What!"

"I'm sorry, dear." It is with a guilty conscience I speak. "I *did* ask Hamid to tell the Liaqatullahs that I would leave. If I'd told you, you wouldn't have let me."

"Indeed I wouldn't." Rashid has come quite near. "Why did you do that to me, Mother?"

"Because the two of you should build up your life by yourselves. Because Maryam is not to be burdened with a mother-in-law, who isn't even her husband's mother."

"That is western nonsense! Sorry, Mother. Why should my wife and I be less happy with you here? It's just the other way round. She, too, will be happier through your presence, quite apart from me. And besides——"

Suddenly I remember Mary Ann's words that day she made me move here from the hotel. "Oh, you incorrigible western soul! What am I to do with such a mother! An Easterner wants all his folks around him. You are the first and only mother he has known in his whole life. It's all right for us to have our own notions about privacy and noninterference of parents and so on. But we are here. Here people are used to parents' interference. We have to act according to their notions, not ours."

Oh Mary Ann! You always knew.

"I'm sorry to have pained you, dear! Don't worry, please. Now let Hamid deliver his message. Afterwards we'll talk over everything, you and I by ourselves, but not today. Both of us are dead tired. I promise I won't do anything without you."

Sitting close together, as in the first days after Mary Ann's death when friends gathered in the garden, we listen to Hamid's message.

"The Liaqatullahs say that on no account can they accept Mother's leaving Akbarabad. First, it is very much on her account that they have wished for that union. They say that if a western lady of Mother's standing and qualities says of a man he is good, then he is. Mother's presence is considered a kind of safeguard for Miss Liaqatullah's future happiness. Secondly, the bride has taken a great fancy to Mother, and would be very disappointed not to find her in her future home. Third, they say that it would be much held against the bride, and rightly so, if Mother left the house on her account. Everybody knows what Mother has done for Rashid and how he loves her. Everybody would blame a wife on whose account mother would leave. Rashid would blame her more than anybody else. The marriage would start under a bad omen."

This is a serious thing in Indian eyes, I admit.

"Fourthly, Mother has no children and grandchildren. It is but natural that she should enjoy children and grandchildren in the house of him to whom she has proved a real mother. Miss Liaqatullah will honor and cherish Mother all her life, and hopes to be accepted as her real daughter. The Liaqatullahs put it very beautifully; I'm sorry I can't quite remember their wording. Fifthly and summing up, they say that they accepted the proposal on the understanding that Mother would continue to make her home with Rashid. I think that's all. I haven't forgotten anything important."

It is late. Hamid has to be rushed to the station. I'm so tired out that I can't wait up for Rashid. But I put a note on his bedside table "God bless you, dear. Don't worry."

I don't quite know what I mean by those last two words. But I'm too tired even to think.

March 5

This is Rashid's ultimatum, delivered this morning before breakfast: "If my remarriage makes you leave, there will be no marriage at all, neither this or any other. This is final."

"I can't understand. Marriage and children mean a great deal to you, and rightly so. You can't make it dependent on my going or staying. This is now a merely academic question—for I certainly will not leave against your and Maryam's will, at least not at once—but I want to understand you fully. I realize that you are being incredibly sweet to me, but that realization is not enough. Do explain, please. Why do you say 'Either you stay or there is no marriage'?"

"Because I've found out that brutal methods are necessary to deal with you, Mother. If somebody had told me before yesterday that you'd arrange with outsiders about leaving my house—without first telling me, without giving me any hint or warning—I should have thought him both crazy and impudent. When I realized that you'd done that, you could have knocked me down with a feather. No, that's an inadequate expression. I was deeply hurt. I still am. I should never have thought you could do that to me."

"I'm sorry, dear. I meant well, you know that, don't you? I gave you my reasons last night."

"You did, and I know that you meant well. But that doesn't get us any further. Does any decent person ever not mean well?"

"Yes, it's a foolish expression. Don't be hurt any more, Rashid. There's no reason to be. You know what you mean to me."

"I know. That makes the whole thing all the more incomprehensible. How can a mother suddenly say, 'Off I go!'? I hope you will not now reply that you are not my real mother."

"No, that would be a foolish reply. But what I do say is that we Westerners are used to leaving young couples by themselves."

"We've been over that, haven't we? We here think differently— I admit, not in every case. But I want you to realize what I feel towards you, since it seems you don't comprehend without being told. Physical ties don't mean everything. We have gone through so much together, you've stood by me, defended me, helped me, made life bearable for me, as only a real mother could. You *are* my mother. I look on you as such. So you'd better face that fact."

When he leaves for the office, I don't start pottering about the house as I usually do at this hour of the day. I want to think things over. It is marvelous, this feeling of his. It makes me both proud and humble.

Yet I shall leave—though in due course only—in spite of what he said today. I'm sure it'll turn out that way. Today he knows my companionship, and nothing of his own future. If he is happy with Maryam—and I am as sure of it as one can possibly be in advance—life will be so full and rich that he will let me go. I still maintain that they should build up their life by themselves. That's as it should be. A real union is better without a third, however loved he is. That is what I hope for. I can always come back for a while, to rejoice in their happiness.

～ *14* ～

*A*N express letter from Frank in answer to my wire. The operation is fixed for the tenth or eleventh. There is every reasonable hope that Kay will win through, but there might be complications. Kay knows how things are. She has twice mentioned that she would like to have me near—"It would be like home"—but that they couldn't ask such sacrifice of time from me. Without her knowledge, Frank asks me to come.

I'm going, of course. It means, probably, giving up Sakri's wedding. But that can't be helped. The wedding will proceed just as well without me, while Kay needs every care and Frank all the bucking up he can get.

Rashid understands, and is full of sympathy. "Of course you must go, Mother. Don't worry about me, please. Stay as long as you want to. I'll drive you to Retgarh tonight, so you can catch the connection with the Madras-Mail, without having to lose a full day."

It's six hours both ways. He's so kind.

I don't know what to do first. Settling the house, packing, breaking the news to Sakri and her people. On top of it just this morning I had all my and Mary Ann's luggage brought into my dressing room, to have a three-day session of repacking, doing the cupboards and so on. Bedroom and dressing room are littered with things, for I'd just begun when Frank's letter arrived.

It's impossible to clear up in time. I think I'll leave everything

just as it is, covering the chaos with sheets, locking the two rooms
and entrusting the keys to maharaj (this time with orders to hand
them on request to Rashid!). Both rooms can be made moth-and-
cockroach-proof, as though they were cupboards. Maharaj will take
good care, I know.

Later

"I must go to my friend. There is no other way, Sakri. She is a
sister to me. She may die, and she is all alone but for her husband.
You are going to Bombay with many relatives, and you are going
to happiness. Please understand."

"I do, Mother. You must go. But my heart is heavy. I'm so afraid
of the big town and of the strange people, all of them knowing
more than I do, and looking down on me because I'm so ignorant
of their ways. You would have told me what to do. Now I will
be a disappointment to my mother-in-law. She will be ashamed of
me. And I will not know where to turn. Mother also does not know
the ways of the big town. I'll disgrace myself, and I'll die of shame."

"These words and thoughts are not right, Sakri dear. Every
bride is downcast before leaving home. You know that, don't you?"

"I do, Mother. But not every bride goes to the big town and a
learned mother-in-law."

"Now, listen. It is true that Mrs. Latif knows more than you do.
What does it matter? You are young. You will learn. Now look at
things from *her* point of view. Theirs is a home without joy. Her
son has no wife to love and cherish. He studies and works all day,
and there is nobody to brighten his life. This saddens his mother's
heart. She wants to see him happy. Then there are the little girls.
She wants them to have a mother when one day God calls her away;
she wants them to have a young mother, who can make them happy.
But it must be a mother who will be good and sweet to them not
only now, but also later when she has children of her own to bring
up. So your mother-in-law searched and searched. In her mind she
asked: 'Where shall I find my future daughter? Where is a Muslim
maiden with a pure, loving heart who will keep the All-Merciful's
law, give joy to my son by her sweetness and beauty, and be a good
mother to the children as well as a good daughter to me?' She
searched and prayed. Then she found you. From that moment her
search was ended. She knew she had found the girl she had hoped

for. Doesn't that knowledge make you glad? To bring joy and love to all of them, to fulfill all their hopes and desires—isn't that a marvelous task in front of you? Don't think of the big town and your ignorance of its ways. Think of what you bring into your husband's house, all your love, all your prayers, all your sweetness. Be proud, Sakri, of what you bring. You will be a blessing in their lives."

"Shall I really—can I—?"

"Of course you will make them happy." It is so necessary to buck up Indian girls. Auntie's generation of old-fashioned womanhood doesn't know any doubts; Sakri's doesn't know security any more.

Oh Sakri, image of everything that is sweet, warmhearted and good in the ancient traditions of eastern women, my love goes to you as to nobody else. I want to protect you as one wants to shelter children and ailing people—you and the other girls of your type, the sweetest I've ever met anywhere. It is of the past. But I'm sure that Indian women will be able to carry at least something of its fragrance into the future, also.

Later

"Again thou goest, Sister. This time without Rashid."

"I have to, Sister. It is not my choice. Illness has spoken."

"So Rashid remains by himself. Is there nothing thou wantest to tell me, Sister?"

There it is! Auntie senses the engagement. What am I to do? I want to tell her the truth, of course. But Rashid was so emphatic about keeping things secret yet for a while. I can't go against his explicit wish.

"Is there nothing, Sister? Really nothing?" she repeats.

"Nothing I can say to thee now. But soon I will."

Whereupon I get up to take my leave. I can't trust myself much longer. It's an unjust and unfair situation. Why should I know and not she?

En route, March 9

On the train I'm dealing with my correspondence. Who knows if and when I'll have time to write in Madras while Kay is in the hospital!

One letter to Hamid, giving him my Madras address. There'll

always be things we have to discuss, especially, as it seems, I shan't be able to attend Sakri's wedding on the twenty-fifth. I shall proceed to Bombay as soon as I can for the shopping, but when will that be? Perhaps it would be better to travel straight there, instead of going to Akbarabad first.

One letter to Arthur. I can't now quite remember his dates, but he did say he'd be in Madras some time this month. Perhaps we can meet before his sailing for home.

One letter to Shanta Venkataraman, asking for her people's address in Madras. I had no time to say good-by to her. One letter to my bank, asking for lots of money, much more than I should. But now is not the time for economizing. I must be free to dash across country at a moment's notice, and see that Maryam gets her presents all right. After Rashid's wedding I'll go slow, and spend only what is strictly necessary. One letter to Rashid to say I'm fine, and he should take care of himself. One short note to Induraja to let her have my address. I'll write her more fully from Madras.

And now I'm going to rest, in anticipation of restless days and nights.

Hill House
Mylapore, Madras
March 13

Thank God, Kay will recover.

It was touch and go. The operation took much longer than the doctors had expected. Frank and I were sitting in the waiting-room of St. George's Nursing Home for nearly three hours before we were told that Kay had been taken back to her room. It was then that Frank fainted.

I'm now allowed to sit in Kay's room. The doctor caught the smile she gave me after regaining consciousness, and suggested himself I should do so. I'm not talking to her, of course. She is far too exhausted to take interest in anything, far too exhausted and drugged. But from morning to evening, from evening to morning, I can discern some improvement or other.

March 16

Kay has had a slight reverse these past three days. Frank has given up sleep almost altogether. At first I scolded him, saying that it was his duty to keep his strength up for Kay's sake. Later I gave in. If he can't sleep, he can't. This is the first great sorrow, the first great upset of an otherwise ideally happy life.

Every night we talk into the early hours, sitting on the terrace or even out in the garden after it has been combed for snakes. We look over the moonlit sea, inhaling the sweet scents of jasmine intermingling with the queen of the night's fragrance. Sometimes we don't say anything for hours; sometimes we do continuously. But never do we try to keep up a conversation. That is the blessing of long-standing friendship.

"Do you really think that she is better, Hilda?" Frank keeps on asking. "Or do you only say so to give me courage?"

"Of course she is better. Didn't you see how today for the first time her color was nearly normal?"

"Yes, but she didn't seem to take her food properly."

"Can you wonder after all she's been through, and all the remedies she has to take?"

"Yes, I know. I expect I'm fussing too much."

"Indeed you aren't. You're a model of self-restraint; I'll always bear witness to it."

"It was sweet of you to come."

"It was natural."

"You see, Hilda, I wanted you very badly. It's not only because you remind Kay and me of home, and because the three of us are old friends; it's because of what you've been through yourself. Richard—Mary Ann—and yet you are so brave!"

I don't reply.

"Is it very hard to bear, Hilda? Even for people like yourself, to whom death doesn't mean complete separation?"

"Yes, Frank, it is. Terribly, terribly hard. In spite of my not feeling separated from my dear ones, in spite of my knowledge that we shall meet again, that we *are* together, daily life without them is so hard to bear that words fail to describe it. I wake in the middle of the night out of a happy dream about Mary Ann, eager to tell her about it, eager to see her. Only after a few minutes do I realize that here on earth I can't tell her, that she has gone, that I am alone, that it is 'now.' It's about eight months since she went. It is not true, Frank, that time is a healer, that the sense of loss decreases. I feel it

263

on the increase. In years to come I'll miss Mary Ann only more than now, not less."

"I'm so sorry! I should not have asked you!"

"Nonsense! Do you suppose I think of Mary Ann only if reminded by somebody else? I'm glad you did ask. Why? You'll now believe in my genuine conviction about Kay's recovery. If I thought you might lose her, I'd never have told you what I did just now. Do you see that?"

"I do, Hilda. Thank you."

"And don't you think you can make up your mind to try sleeping for a change, now that I've convinced you?"

"I will do my best. I've been a beast. Compared to your loss, my worries are but small. Sorry. I should have realized that fact."

"Make up for it now by having a real sleep. You'll see Kay will be better tomorrow, and you must look your best."

March 18

Kay is better, there's no mistaking it this time. She talks, enjoys her food and begins to look, however faintly, her own dear self. Now it's only a question of time. The doctors say that in about two weeks and a half she'll be home.

"And so I will," she comments. "Fancy your staying at Hill House, and my not being there to be your hostess! I'm sure they don't treat you properly."

"Don't worry! Everything is perfect, food, service and all. Your servants are so well trained that even in your absence things run smoothly."

"I don't know whether this is a real compliment or not!"

"Of course it is, you vain old thing." What joy to hear Kay joking again! "In your house I'm simply basking in well-being, fussed over by everybody and given scones and crumpets for tea. The first day I thought I was dreaming. Involuntarily I looked for the familiar drizzle and grayness to go with scones. But outside there was the blue sea, the sun and a perfect maze of glorious flowers run riot."

"You've sometimes such a picturesque way of putting things, Hilda. One can just *see* them. Why don't you write that book on India Peter is so keen about?"

"Because I know too little."

264

"Aren't you pretending ignorance?"

"Kay, you're getting too much for me. The moment you are better, you come down on me! The martial blood of the Mackenzies speaks in you. They were marching with whom? Or did other clans march with them? Good heavens, I've forgotten what little Highland knowledge I may ever have possessed, just now when I'm being fed shortbread and scones. What a shame!"

"Your side-stepping won't help you. We're talking of India, not of my ancestors."

"We're now talking of your having a good rest, and not tiring yourself out before Frank's arrival. But I promise to stand for a fight over that book the first day you're allowed three hours out of bed."

March 19

Dear letters from Rashid, which I take in only now. During the days of worst anxiety I read them without understanding a single word. He says everything is all right, and I shouldn't worry about him.

Arthur'll be here in a few days.

Later

Now Frank's anxiety has gone, he's again his collected, mature, inquisitive self.

"Let's talk about India, Hilda. You have been intimately connected with places I don't know anything about."

"How long have you been out here, Frank?"

"Well, it's twenty-one, no, twenty-two years already."

"How many vernaculars do you know?"

"Really, Hilda, I've not counted them."

"But you would say they exceed ten?" I know perfectly well he knows nineteen; but I also know his English passion for anonymity and understatement.

"Well, they might be round about ten."

"And you want to hear from me about India? From me who've been here such a short time? I can just manage a little bit of Hindustani, that's all. Really, it's ridiculous. You have spent nearly a lifetime in the I.C.S., up and down the whole country, studying and knowing conditions intimately. Which one can tell the other about India, you or I?"

265

"Listen, Hilda, I didn't mean to get statistics out of you. If I want those, I need only ask for them in the office. What I want is to compare notes. I excel in quantity and you in quality. After all, even if I lived here another decade or two, I'd still have to live on western lines, muffins and all, as you put it the other day. You, on the other hand, do *live* among Indians. They've accepted you as one of theirs, even if your Hindustani is faulty. Oh yes, we've a number of Indian friends, and sit on the floor at their dinner parties, and don't commit too many breaches of etiquette. But that's not the thing. In my younger days, when I was on tour practically nine months in the year, I had close contact with the people. Sometimes I didn't meet another European for months. I was always with my Indian staff of *babus* and surveyors. Sometimes, when camping near a village, I sat at night in the market place with the elders, and we had a good heart-to-heart palaver. Those were the days, though I was without Kay then. Now I've nothing but office work, and lots of dinners to attend and to give, but I'm cut off from the people. What is the sense of being here, if I've lost my contacts with those for whom I work?"

"That's so everywhere in the exalted realms of high official jobs, Frank. Don't forget you can do a lot for India, holding high office and deciding important issues, knowing the needs of the people well, even if you don't sit any more with them under the *panchayat* tree."

"There's something in that. But I hadn't finished my say. As it happens, I've never worked in the north except for a short period as a youngster. After that it has always been Madras or Bombay Presidency; hence my knowledge of southern languages and vernaculars, of which you wrongly make so much. Well, there is no purdah in the south, nor are there all the communal problems of Central and Northern India. These are things you know better than I, so just make up your mind to answer my questions."

"If I can! What is it you think about, Frank?"

"There are, for instance, many Westerners—the blimp-minded, but they've influenced even the others—who maintain that the moment you break down the barriers, the moment you really make friends with Indians, they start despising you. Is that so, in your experience?"

For a moment I don't reply.

266

"Why don't you answer?"

"I'm trying to think. Do you remember that passage from the *Forsyte Saga* which says that old Jolyon despised his own club for the simple fact that it had admitted *him?* To him only those clubs seemed the real thing which were beyond him. Such is human nature. Yet on the whole I should certainly answer your question in the negative. In my experience Indians appreciate kindness, trust and friendship more than anything else, and respond at once."

"That has been my experience, too. But it's difficult to explain these things to fellow Westerners. There are so many misunderstandings and misconceptions to fight!"

"Aren't there!" I'm remembering the vexed problems of moral depravity, purdah, truth, cleanliness, privacy and so on, on which East and West hold such different opinions.

"The other day a junior colleague, rather new to the service, complained about his head clerk. 'I can't ever get a clear yes or no from him, never a truthful opinion, damn his hypocrisy. He will slavishly agree to all I say, though he knows local conditions better than I do, and should warn me of certain things. He just grins and agrees. You can't get a true word out of these people!' "

"The old story of politeness versus blunt truth!"

"That's what I've tried to point out to him. I said that to Easterners politeness meant much more than to us; that if truth was hurting another's feelings, it could not be uttered. This was part of the religious code of hospitality of the East, extended into not hurting others by pointing out possible defects of thought or action. I further explained that Indians *do* convey unpalatable truths, but in a veiled form. If he'd care to study the slight differentiations in his head clerk's answers and smiles, my young friend would soon know whether the answer meant yes or no."

"Did you succeed in convincing him?"

"Not at first. He said he'd come out to India to do his job, not to solve riddles. Whereupon I became demi-official, and after that it was plain sailing. It's a pity that officials nowadays don't live under canvas when on tour, as my generation did. They go by car, and are back for dinner in their own bungalows, instead of talking to the villagers at night. A few persist in touring on horseback even now. They are the salt of the earth. That boy is not among them, hence his misunderstanding nearly everything."

"We mustn't forget that it is extremely difficult for mere Westerners to distinguish between such subtle nuances as confront us here. At first I thought Indian music merely repeating itself endlessly, without reason or rhyme as far as I was concerned. Later on I learned that each repetition brought a tiny variation of the main theme, and that that very variation conveyed a great deal to listeners. Even now, after having heard quite a lot of Indian music, I usually can't find that subtle change for myself. Rashid lifts his brows or smiles at me in the crucial moment, and then only do I know."

"But that politeness-versus-truth business accounts for many East-West misunderstandings."

"Yes, Westerners often think people here are untruthful when they're only trying to be polite. When maharaj—that's our *chaprassi;* you remember him, don't you?—for the first time told me that he wanted to go to the fair, I was clumsy enough to point out that there wasn't any on. Now I know that this was merely a polite, considerate way of indicating that I'd kept him after his working hours."

"Then all the misunderstandings regarding food customs! It cuts both ways. Indians think we never wash before meals, because we have no ceremonial for it."

"Well, to be quite frank, *does* every Westerner wash immediately before meals?"

"You've got me there."

"There's another thing that comes into my mind. When Rashid's Muslim friends first came to the house ordering our servants about for chairs and glasses of water in our presence, Mary Ann and I thought them terribly ill-mannered. But we were wrong. People of the same caste or community not only call each other 'brother,' but feel as such. The house of one belongs to the other while he visits it. So it is but natural he should order servants about, thus proving that he feels at home!"

"Was it always easy for you and Mary Ann?"

"Not always. We misunderstood and were misunderstood in turn. But misunderstandings don't matter, really, if there's good will. Indians are extremely generous in acknowledging the slightest bit of it. I must have committed countless breaches of etiquette or of religious

268

law, but these lapses were never held against me, simply because people saw I *tried* to do things correctly."

"Can't you give some concrete cases?"

"Dozens. You know the *Divali* festival. Well, though Rashid is a Muslim, all the Hindus working on the compound or in the Laboratories came to us to give us their *Divali* wishes. Rashid warned me in time; he said there'd be about three hundred in all, and that they would come to the bungalow to honor *me*, since to honor him they'd merely go to his office. I took expert Hindu advice on everything, and had lots of the right kind of *Divali* sweets in readiness. To each person I gave two hands full of sugared rice and a yellow and a white piece of *Divali* toffee, each the size of a palm. By etiquette the white has to come last. I had arranged with maharaj that, if the callers were poor or had many children, he was to give me a nod. Then I would try to give them more sugared rice by plunging not only my hands but even my arms deeply into the huge bag, thus getting out some additional rice on and above my wrists. I couldn't plunge more than once, or else dealings would have looked unfair. There had to be the same procedure for everybody.

"Well, everything went smoothly, as always when maharaj is in charge of something. About two hours had gone, we'd had nearly three hundred callers—*chowkidar* was checking up, so that we knew how far our supplies would take us—when at last Rashid returned. By then the sweepers were coming to wish *Divali*. Of course they didn't mount the steps to the veranda, as the others had done, but I handed out rations to maharaj, who dropped them neatly into the bit of her cloth the sweeper-women held up for the purpose. He urged me to give them double rations, since nobody would now see that I did. By the way, I've often seen him or other high-caste Brahmans do kindnesses of some sort to the untouchables. They don't allow them to approach wells lest the water be polluted; but they don't hesitate to toil in order to fill the untouchable's pitcher."

"Yes, that is so. What happened then, Hilda?"

"Well, Rashid joined me, while I was dealing with the last untouchables. 'Why do you take all that trouble, Mother? Maharaj could finish things off.' I felt full of righteous indignation. 'If I've worked for the castes, I'll jolly well work for the outcasts, too!' Rashid's face grew suddenly serious. 'Mother, do you mean to say

269

you've handed out the sweets to every caller?' 'Of course I have.' 'But then the three first castes, perhaps even the fourth, not only cannot eat the sweets, but have been polluted by touching them! Remember, you and I are also untouchables!' And suddenly he burst out laughing. 'Bless you, Mother darling, what *did* you do!'

"In a split second I realized the enormity of my *gaffe*. 'It's your fault. Why weren't you here to tell me?' I said, woman-wise.

"I was terribly ashamed of myself, especially when I remembered how even the first-class Brahmans had accepted the sweets out of my hands without flinching, smiling at me and thanking me, without warning off their relatives who happened to come later. What poise, what dignity, what genuine courtesy! Any one in the West would naturally have said frankly: 'I can't accept this, for such and such reason. You don't mind, I hope?'

"Later I admonished maharaj. 'Why didst thou not tell me? Thou knowest!'

" 'Who son is Mother to tell! People glad were Mother's hands from sweets to get. They say: Mother good is. They say sweets always are, but Mother not always is.'

"I reproached the lady whom I had asked for advice about the sweets, an ultra-strict Brahman. Why had she not warned me? Before her eyes I had measured the rice, had asked her whether what my two hands could hold was enough! She replied: 'It was your wish. I should never have dared to interfere. Your good will means more to people than the sweets.'

" 'But some of them are so poor! Sweets *do* mean lots to their children!'

" 'Your kindness means more. The children will tell of it to their own children. Fancy a memsahib doing what you have done!' "

"Hilda, I wish you'd write that story down."

"In a way I ought to. Can you beat such tact and politeness? I commit a *faux pas*, the worst you can commit in India. Not only do they not resent it or interfere—but they manage to turn it into something praiseworthy. What incredibly gentle-natured people! I'll often feel cold and homesick in the West, I know."

March 12

Now that Kay is beginning to see visitors, I'm beginning to take in Madras, which I have not seen since our first journey. Frank took me to the lighthouse for a good view of the town, after which we drove along the Marine. Another day I went by myself to the old quarters, on still another I had tea with Shanta's parents, very modern-minded Brahmans. Shanta's mother is on the Town Council, and does lots of work among women and destitutes. No need to ask where her children get their sense of social responsibility.

Madras is a lovely garden-town, mostly of independent bungalows with spacious compounds. To my mind its position and Marine cannot compare with Bombay's; there are no hills round the city, let alone Bombay's graceful outlines of Malabar Hill and of the Backbay Reclamation. The nearest hills are the Nilgiris, more than three hundred miles away.

Nevertheless Madras has a charm all its own, with its many gardens and white-clad inhabitants. People here are very quick on the uptake, full of interest and vitality. Both Hinduism's and Christianity's most spirited and spiritual achievements have had their home in South India, which holds some of the treasures of Hindu architecture. The temples of Madura and Trichinopoly must be seen to be believed. In South India there are many Hindu sages of great repute and merit, as well as many millions of heart-Christians —not the *rice-Christians* who get themselves baptized at one time or other to get either food or job or both. Apart from the Himalayas, Benares and some other holy places in Northern and Central India, it is held that only in South India does one come across real spirituality.

To me the charm of staying in Madras or, rather, Mylapore, consists mainly in its connection with St. Thomas the Apostle, called the Twin. Here he is supposed to have met his martyr's death. The Cathedral of St. Thomé is erected over his supposed tomb. There have been some schools of historical thought which have denied the possibility of his ever having been here; many others have furnished proof of it. His remains are traceable to Edessa in Shapur's Persia, whence they were taken to the island of Chios and, lastly, to Tortona. Many are the descriptions of his actions on Indian soil. He is the Apostle of India, with a strong tradition dating back to the first century A.D. The so-called Thomas-Christians have kept it alive for nearly two thousand years.

I've always had a special love for Thomas the Apostle, not because of his erstwhile doubts—they rather put me up against him

271

—but because of his words, "Let us also go to Jerusalem to die with Him," and in addition, the beautiful things we learn about him from the Apocryphal Gospels. I wish I could remember them clearly, now I'm here. But it's decades since I read that English edition of the Apocryphal Gospels.

One of the deeds performed in India by St. Thomas I do remember, even though I may have forgotten details or chronological order. I've often thought of it when worried unduly about worldly possessions. I love to think about it sitting at the desk of Kay's best guest room, overlooking the sea on which the saint must have traveled many a time, and the soil into which his blood flowed.

This is the story. When Thomas landed, he soon was brought before the Indian King in whose lands he happened to be. So greatly impressed was the King by what he had heard of Thomas' ability as a builder, and by what Thomas told him about the One God Who is Three, and His Son whose disciple Thomas had been, that he presented the Apostle with much gold, silver and jewels, requesting him to use them to erect a place of worship to his God. If he wanted more, his requests were to be granted at once. So Thomas departed toward the distant hill on which he was to build his church, taking with him the valuable cargo and promising to finish the building in a year or two. But nothing happened. For about three years the King got no news from the church-builder. Finally he sent out messengers, who returned in due course, reporting that there was neither church nor house nor gold. Thomas had spent everything on the poor, to whose needs he ministered.

Furious, the King sent for the saint, intending to put him to death. But Thomas spoke again of his teacher, of the Son who was leading mankind to the Father. And again the King was pacified, and sent out the disciple once more with a caravan of precious loads.

But after a further two years, messengers came back empty-handed. Again gold and jewels had gone. Again there was no building of any kind. This time the King did not listen to Thomas. Too great was his anger. The execution was to take place at dawn in the presence of the whole court.

That night the King could not sleep. For a long time he lay awake, till at last he got up to meditate during the silent hours of the night. Arising out of his meditation, he had a vision. The heavens opened before his astounded eyes. He beheld their glory, dazed and mute in presence of their radiant light. Then a voice said to him, "Look up!" He obeyed, and saw the most beautiful building he had ever visualized in his boldest dreams. It was made of massive gold, and its columns were sheer ruby, and the door was two huge emeralds. Inside the building everything was made of diamonds, which reflected the radiance of heaven while radiating into heaven their own luminance. There was so much light, so much radiance, that the King had to lower his gaze, which fell into his own heart. It was then that he realized what he had seen.

Here was the gold he had given to Thomas. Here was every precious stone he had given, multiplied a hundredfold by the fullness of God. Every tiny morsel of bread the saint had handed to the poor was now here in heaven, transformed into diamond and ruby, whose splendor would shine into all eternity. The church of God *had* been erected.

Next morning there was no execution. Instead, the King and his courtiers knelt before the saint, asking for his blessings and teaching.

I often wonder whether the saint spoke of Christ Jesus as his *guru*, and of himself as His *chela*. It would be the natural thing to do. In India everybody, certainly every educated man or ruler, was following the guidance of a spiritual teacher as his disciple. In Palestine, Thomas and others had done the same. They had followed the Master. The Hebrew expression for "master" is *rabbi;* the Sanskrit is *guru*. So the King must have known instantly what the stranger was talking about: his master's power and message. Had the King gone to foreign lands, he would have probably done the same: proclaimed *his* master, as best he could.

Assuming this, it is but natural that the King was anxious to learn more about the stranger's master, and asked him to erect a building to his God.

This tradition is taken from the Apocryphal Gospels. But I've often found that the East teaches us a new understanding even of the four canonic Gospels. They have come to us from the East; they describe eastern conditions, customs and mentality. Events, expressions and wordings which we've known all our lives, but which never did make any sense to us—had we had the courage to say so—become at once understandable and logical if we face them in the light of everyday eastern modern life and mentality.

Unfortunately we don't know that fact. Or, if we do know, we often forget. Or, worst, we think Christianity is entirely "of the West."

It is a pity. It is wrong.

Thinking about *gurus*, I remember my last talk with Induraja. I've been uneasy ever since, because I said either too much or not enough. I should have told her that to me the wholesale initiation given her by *guru* meant something very different than to her. I should have said that my own teacher had led me to deeper understanding of Christ; and that the great initiate I had described to her had at once realized that fact.

On the other hand, it is not good to say things the other person is not asking for. It's a kind of interference with his freedom. If Induraja wants to, she'll ask me herself some day.

March 22

A cryptic wire from Rashid.

"If possible prepare departure await express letter nobody ill everything all right love."

What can that mean? If nobody is ill and everything all right, why am I to hurry home?

I give it up. The letter will reach here at the latest the day after tomorrow. Until then I must be patient. Meanwhile I'm preparing for departure by having long talks with Kay and Frank—though I have not told them my reason as yet.

March 23

"You know what I want to ask you, don't you, Hilda?"

Why pretend ignorance? "Yes, I think I do know, Arthur."

"And what is your reply? Will you marry me? It is the second time I have asked you. The first was three years after Richard had gone. You said then you couldn't yet face remarriage. I waited for five more years. You can't say I haven't been persevering. Will you now have me?"

The staccato sentences, the obvious uneasiness, the distance from which he speaks, touch me more than I can say. Where is his usual self-assurance?

"Thank you for all your patience, Arthur. You are my dearest friend."

"That means I'll never be more."

"Hear me to the end, please. You are my dearest friend, for you have understood without any reproach, you have waited without any impatience. If ever I were to remarry, it would be you only."

"This is a great step forward, Hilda. I should be grateful. I am. But I want more. Now tell me why you say 'if.' Is it still because of Richard? Or is there another reason?"

"Both. It is difficult to imagine saying 'my husband' and not meaning Richard. On the other hand I know he would like you and me being together, with you looking after me, I know that."

"And your other reason?"

"I wonder whether I could remain myself as your wife."

"I can't follow. Why shouldn't you? Do you think I'd be fool enough to want you different?"

"I didn't mean that *you* would do something to alter me. But you see, Arthur, what I undertake I do wholeheartedly, whether it's in my personal line or not. If I were your wife, I'd try to be a good one, and in so doing, I'd lead more and more your life; mine would go to the wall."

"Can't you explain a little more in detail?"

"I'm an all-round kind of creature. I've bonds of various description, to rich and poor, religious-minded and atheists, East and West. I'm friends with lots of people to whom you'd have nothing to say, and whom you'd make awfully uneasy in return. I'd hate that. So I would more and more conform to pattern, be the squire's lady—sorry, I shouldn't have said that!—see less and less people outside your own circle. That means I wouldn't be true to myself. This is my reason for not coming to you. I know myself. My only security lies in remaining free, responsible only to my conscience."

"Listen, Hilda. There's a good deal in what you say. But I've not waited for you eight years in order to make you conform to county pattern, have I! I could have had that pattern many times and without waiting. No, if I want you, I want you as you are, with all your many affinities and broad-mindedness. I'll try to make friends with any friends of yours; and if I feel I'm a spoilsport, I'll clear out to let them enjoy your company by themselves. And if you say you'd prefer to be with me or the parish instead, I simply won't let you!"

"You're a dear, Arthur."

"So what is your reply?"

"Give me a little more time, please. I must settle Rashid first. After his wedding I'll consider myself free, though I'll always come back to visit him if he wants me to."

"Am I to sail home without your answer?"

"I'm afraid so. But—since you've told me you'd even use force to make me remain myself——"

"Hilda!"

March 24

I don't know whether I'm dreaming or waking.

Here is Rashid's letter.

"My darling Mother,

"Maybe you will think me crazy when you read this. But I am not, only worried how to break the news to you.

"Mr. Liaqatullah's brother, he who stays with the grandparents in Aishabad, is very ill. He must go for treatment to Europe, and will sail on April 5, accompanied by some relatives. He is very keen to attend the wedding, since he feels he may never return; but Hamid says that those who really insist on his being present are the grandparents. They want the wedding to take place at once, fixing it for the 29th. All Hamid and I could do was to say that, subject to your approval of the whole plan, we could not have it earlier than March 31. It was impossible to refuse.

"What worries me is yourself. You'll have to rush home, you'll want to have the presents and everything ready, you'll make yourself tired and ill.

"But there's one blessing in disguise about a hurried wedding: it cannot be elaborate. The grandparents agree to a simple ceremony, preceded by an afternoon reception and followed by dinner. We'll be spared all the ceremonies both you and I have been dreading.

"Please wire at once your approval or disapproval. If you approve —I know you will—you can be here at noon on March 26. Until you come, I shall tell nobody.

"Please travel first class, if you can't find good accommodation in the second. Lie down as much as possible. You will need all your strength.

"God bless you, Mother dear. Take good care of yourself.
"Your loving son,
"Rashid."

"I must leave tonight, Frank. Please get ticket and reservation for me. I'm terribly sorry, but it can't be helped."

"I'm sorry, too. I can't talk you round, I'm afraid. But need you hurry so much? Can't you shop here? My whole overdraft is at your disposal."

"How sweet of you, Frank! But Madras is Hindu and Christian. There's no catering to Muslims. If I knew whether Maryam would wear Benarsi and Madrassi saris, I'd buy them here like a shot. But I don't know. It's the same with jewels. I can't give a Muslim bride Hindu earrings."

"You *are* well-versed in things Indian, I must say!"

"I should be by now, shouldn't I? Now we'd better get going. I want to be with Kay all I can."

"Shall I let Arthur know you're off?"

"Arthur—yes, do. Perhaps he can come to the station."

We've had our talk. Arthur knows how I feel. Nothing more is needed. Now I must think of Rashid only.

⚬ 15 ⚬

I AM alone in my compartment, but I can't rest. I can't see how I'll manage in time. This is not the West. It needs no end of time to find matching blouse and petticoat material here. I could travel to Bombay, of course, taking the train tomorrow night, returning two nights later. On the other hand, the house must be put in order. Who knows how many guests we'll bring back from Aishapur, in addition to the whole of Akbarabad! I must also provide for entertaining in Aishapur. There are Rashid's and my clothes to think about and a hundred other things. The back of the courtyard must be painted. All the servants need new clothes. I must arrange about the bridal procession. How many elephants? We haven't got enough crockery. I have to buy another zinc tub. Ram Pershad must be told exactly about flowers. Cook will lose his head, especially since I won't be there to help him. I'll have to prepare an Urdu hour-to-hour schedule, if we are to find a proper meal on our return from Aishapur, Maryam's first meal in her new home. I can't have it a flop. No, Bombay is out of the question.

It's all very well for Rashid to say that a hurried wedding needn't be elaborate. But there are the grandparents to consider; they don't seem to be the kind of people to make allowances. Why should they? After all, Kay or no Kay, uncle or no uncle, this *is* Maryam's wedding. She has a right to her proper presents and her festive entry into our house.

If only Hamid had let me know in time the answers to my many questions. If only Rashid had reminded him. But both of them forgot—just like men.

The sample slippers, the sample blouse! I hope I find them ready for me in Akbarabad. But I don't believe I will. It'd be too good to be true. Thank God I bought a few good bags in Madras. That's something.

I hope Rashid got Ismail Khan a new uniform and cap, all in white. That's how he should be clad, if he is to drive the bridegroom.

Dear Maryam! I wish I had time to think of her! But I haven't. I must think of arrangements only.

Today is Sakri's wedding. I wish I were there just for the day.

Auntie! If only I had not listened to Rashid! Now it's too late. She will always feel I deliberately kept her out of things—she, the last person in the world I'd want to hurt.

I've still another seventeen hours to travel. It's exasperating to sit idle with all that work ahead. At times I catch myself bending forward, every nerve strained, as though to will the train into quicker motion.

March 26

Rashid at the station.

"How tired you look, Mother! Didn't you rest?"

278

"Don't worry! Let's not lose time. How are things?"

"We have to be in Aishapur by the thirtieth. The wedding takes place that day."

"Hamid will be present?"

"He'll try to be here on the twenty-ninth."

"Thank God for that. How about here: does any one know as yet?"

"I've told only Seth Chandralal. He has asked the collector and lots of officials to tea at four o'clock today. It is there you will make the announcement."

"I?"

"Who else? It is for you only to make. You are my mother."

"I see."

"I'm not going to the Laboratory today. We must plan everything. Seth Chandralal is entirely at our disposal."

"That's good news. We'll need all the help we can get. But he's a Hindu; he will not know certain details. I'm so afraid I'll not do things properly. Which Muslim can I ask?"

"I can only think of Quraishi. He'll be at the tea party."

"Did you tell Auntie?"

"No, of course not. I was waiting for your return."

"Oh Rashid! She'll feel so hurt! Can't we go just after lunch?"

"We might try. But you must have a rest. I want you to look your best this afternoon."

Oh—my dresses must be pressed at once. It's maharaj's midday break. I shall have to iron one or two myself. After dealing with some tradespeople I turn on the electric iron.

"I it do will," a voice suddenly says.

"Thou? Why not at home thou art, maharaja? Thy free time now is."

"Mother's work son's work is. Much work these days in be will."

I look imperturbable. If the notables and Auntie haven't been told, I can't own up to maharaj. But he knows, bless him. He always did.

I don a nice ice-blue foulard with navy accessories, including even a hat. Akbarabad hasn't seen me wear any, except at official functions. But today is a special occasion and, by instinct, I want to hide my extreme fatigue behind clothes.

"How nice you look!" Rashid always appreciates dress. "I'm so

279

glad you are feeling better now. When you arrived you were so pale."

Bless him! It would never enter his dear head that I, his respectable mother, might use makeup in emergencies.

While sitting near him on the way to Auntie's, I'm suddenly aware of a *faux pas* on my part. To Auntie and her family I'll look a stranger in a hat. They'll feel shy. So I toss it behind. I shan't have a mirror to put it on again before the party; that can't be helped. Better a hat at the wrong angle, than making people I love uncomfortable.

"What about your honeymoon, Rashid? Can't you ask for, say, two weeks' leave?"

"Mother, now you speak of it, I realize I haven't even yet asked His Highness' permission to marry!"

"Rashid! Well, you couldn't. The telegram would have revealed things in town. But we must send the wire *before* the tea."

At Auntie's I ask at once that all children and onlookers be sent away. Soon we are facing only Auntie and her two sons. I begin to tell how all has come about. "Believe me, Sister, we did not know that the wedding would take place soon. I'm terribly sorry that, through that illness in the bride's family, things are now so rushed. But this is not our fault. Please forgive us that our invitation comes only a few days before the wedding. You'll travel with us, won't you? Waliuddin and Faizuddin will have to go by another car, I'm afraid. All that will be arranged. You will like Maryam, I know. She resembles Mary Ann to an amazing degree."

Silence. All three of them sit perfectly still. The sons can't talk, of course, before their mother does. But why doesn't she say anything? Is she too hurt?

At last Auntie rises, coming over to where I am sitting. "Thou art a good mother to Rashid, Sister. His own mother could not have done more by him. The Omniscient be thy rewarder."

Now it is I who cannot talk. Both of us are sitting close to each other, in her favorite position, my head on her shoulder, her arm around me. She knows! She of all is the only one to know how terribly difficult it is for me to carry on, in spite of my brave show. In the pressure of her shoulder against mine, in her firm handclasp, I recognize her mute message of sympathy.

The three men don't talk. Somehow they feel that something beyond them is taking place.

"My heart is full of sorrow for Mary Ann, that ray of sun and moon alike, that flower of paradise that was thy child." Auntie now looks sternly in front of her, but it is obvious that her words are partly meant for Rashid, who has paled visibly. "I did not think of another to take her place so soon. If Rashid had asked me, I should have said, 'Wait for a long while yet, if wed thou must. Wait for a long while yet, for it will break Mother's heart to see another in her daughter's place. She will not let thee know. She will do all a mother should do, and will not let thee see her tears. But I shall know, for my tears will flow together with hers.' This I should have said, had Rashid asked me. But he did not. Sister, thou sayest that the bride from Bombay is good. I believe thee. She will become one with Rashid, she will be, *inshallah*, the mother of his sons, and I shall open my arms to her. But to me and mine, thou and Mary Ann will remain close forever."

There is nothing to say, certainly not on my part. I can only bow my heart in silence before the old Muslim woman, who cannot read books, but whose heart possesses almost more greatness and wisdom than all this world's books contain. I thought she would be hurt and full of reproach. Instead she has in simple dignity stood up for Mary Ann and me.

As for the wedding, Auntie implies that her sons may attend, but that she won't. Her words sound final. She takes me down to the car —that is as far as the purdah entrance—not once looking at Rashid.

"Is it true that you are unhappy, Mother? That I should have waited? You never told me—" His voice sounds strangled.

"Of course not. I told you soon after Mary Ann's leaving us, when we discussed the Khan Bahadur's proposal, that I would help you, though I couldn't understand. Well, I've helped you, that's all. There's nothing you have to worry about. And I like Maryam, you know that."

"Do you suffer, Mother?"

I must end this, once and for all. "I'll soon suffer, if we can't get things ready for the wedding. There's so much to do. Have you invited those of your friends who don't live here?"

"Heavens, no. By the way, you must invite them, not I."

"Letters won't reach them in time."

"We'll have to wire."

"But not now." We're just driving up in front of the post office. "Now we've just time for His Highness. Let's wire by express delivery, so they can't let the telegram lie about for an hour or so." Carefully we draft and redraft the important message, asking for marriage permission and three weeks' leave.

By now it's 4:15. I stick my hat on somehow, powdering my nose as we are already driving into Seth Chandralal's compound. We are the last to arrive. Tea is not laid on small tables as usual, but dinner-fashion, which must be in honor of the great news I'm to break to the gathering. Seth Chandralal thinks of everything.

Soon I'm seated between the collector and the host, with Rashid facing me. All senior officials are there, and those among the juniors who are known to be Rashid's friends, as, for instance, Lavanyia. I'm the only woman, but I've long since given up bothering about such isolation.

Reflecting that the longer I delay, the longer we shall have to stay at the party, I wait until each guest has his cup and plate filled, catch in turn the Seth's and Rashid's eye, and am ready to start.

"May I make an announcement, Subha sahib?"

The collector nods. "What is it, Mother?"

In return I only smile.

"Silence, please! Mother has something to say to us."

At the collector's words I rise. "It is with great pleasure that I have to announce the engagement and forthcoming marriage of my son Dr. Rashid Ali to Miss Maryam Liaqatullah, the only daughter of Mr. Justice Liaqatullah, High Court Judge in Bombay."

What follows next, I can't grasp in detail. Everybody stands, shouting, cheering, shaking hands, patting shoulders.

When guests have again resumed their seats and tea, talk is at its happiest.

"How well Mother and Rashid sahib kept the secret!"

"Nobody knew. Really, nobody!"

There is a pandemonium of excited exclamations.

Then the host rings his glass. "The collector sahib will be good enough to speak to us."

"I've not much to say, my friends. Like yourselves I did not know of Mother's secret. Proper speeches will, no doubt, be made at the wedding itself. Today I want only to express our joy at hearing the glad tidings. Rashid sahib deserves every happiness. We sincerely hope that from now on his life will be protected from cold winds, and will flow on in peace and contentment, with his every wish fulfilled. And now I want especially to speak of Mother."

At this juncture everybody claps and cheers.

"I see you feel as I do with regard to her. We have seen for some time past before our very eyes something we never should have believed possible: the genuine bond of love between a western mother and an Indian son. What Mother has done for Rashid sahib, she has done for each one of us. Our gratitude will be hers forever. But today we have been privileged to hear that she has gone a step further, a step that even to her goodness and love must have been extremely difficult to take. You all know what I mean. I bow in silence to what Mother must have gone through. Let me conclude these few remarks. Three cheers for Mother! Three cheers for Rashid sahib and his future happiness! May it last forever."

After the speech, conversation is so animated that I'm afraid we'll lose too much time. So I confide to the collector that there are lots of things to settle, but that Seth Chandralal has offered his help and advice, and that I'm going to take it. The collector understands at once—isn't he an Indian?—and asks the host to excuse him; unavoidable pressure of work necessitates his premature departure.

His going breaks up the party, which is just what I wanted. Soon the three of us are closeted in the Seth's study, with his private secretary, head accountant and head clerk in the next room in case we need them.

There's so much to settle that we've only a few seconds for every item.

This is the outcome!

I'll chase about the country for two days, trying to collect the presents. One of the Seth's cars will be at my disposal in case Rashid needs ours; and one of his trusted men will accompany me, so I shan't be overcharged in shops I don't know.

We'll ask Hamid by phone to select jewels on approval in Bombay. The jeweler is to send one or two of his own men with them, at our expense.

Seth Chandralal and the collector will arrange for the reception of the bridal procession at the gates of Akbarabad. It will be a civic affair, and there is no need for me to worry about elephants or anything else, though there might be only a few of the majestic beasts available at such short notice.

The Seth will draw up a list of all State officials in the capital or districts who must be invited by telegram. They won't come, but they must be invited all the same, together with the highest officials of neighbor States. The Seth's office will despatch the lot and keep copies. I needn't bother.

As to organizing the bridegroom's party and the drive in state to Aishapur, the Seth declares himself incompetent. "Being a Hindu, I can't interfere in such matters. Make Mr. Quraishi responsible for this part of the program. Or have you no relatives who could undertake this job?"

I look aghast. "Rashid, we've forgotten the uncles!"

"Don't worry, Mother! I'll write and explain."

"Not wire?"

"Better not."

I know what he means.

"So it'll be Quraishi," concludes the Seth. "He is very capable. Make him work, Mother. Make all of us work. Rashid sahib, don't let Mother overtire herself."

"I'll try my best, but you know what she is, Sethsahib. I tell her it doesn't matter if things are not perfect, but she wants them so."

"They'll be far from perfect, I'm afraid. Can't you see that I have to worry much more than an Indian mother would have to? Firstly she would know all that's needed, and not grope in the dark as I do. And secondly, if things went wrong, nobody would attribute the failure to her western indifference and stand-offishness."

"Really, Mother! Who would think of that in connection with you!"

"Let's not argue now. Thanks, Sethsahib, for your great kindness and help. I don't know what we'd do without you."

"Command me, Mother, night and day."

"I'm afraid I'll have to. Come on, Rashid, we must hurry. Love to Sethanisahib. Please tell her the news. I'll visit her as soon as I can.

"We'll write the telegrams to your friends at once," I say when we've reached our garden.

But we don't. The first callers, the first garlands, the first ladies have arrived. There are lots of recriminations about secrecy. Instead of preparing dinner, cook must prepare *pan*, the ingredients of which Ismail Khan's children have to produce from town. The house is full of visitors until almost midnight.

It is nearly 3:30 A.M. when I've finished with the telegrams, and betake myself to my bedroom, which no helpful gnomes have thought to put in order meantime.

March 28

Two days of racing in despair to neighboring towns, after having scanned Akbarabad shops in despair before leaving.

Nothing matches. Hence the despair.

I've got only five good saris with four matching blouses and three matching petticoats. No shoes and sandals! They are all no good. So I've bought gold and silver brocades and leathers; Maryam will have the shoes made up later.

I'm still two saris, three blouses and four petticoats short. I've got the georgette for the saris in view, but one can't get really good borders here; the ones obtainable are but three inches wide. That wouldn't do for bridal saris. Many a lady, melting in later years some of her silver or gold sari borders, acquires substantial silver basins or gold ornaments in the procedure, but then the borders involved are many inches wide. I must get that very type.

It has been tiring to do hundreds of miles by car in two days, especially because of the haunting fear of losing too much time. My heart is bad. Even if I can snatch a few hours' rest, it awakens me from sleep. I evade Dr. Ram Chandra whenever I can. Yesterday he tried to get hold of my wrist, but I escaped.

His Highness sent a very kindly worded telegram, granting the leave and sending congratulations. We've wired to Juhu, the sea resort near Bombay, Mount Abu, the hill-station next to us and to Cotacamund in the Nilgiris for hotel accommodation. At the same time I rang Hamid to ask Maryam—through the go-between, of course—which place she would prefer. If only I could ring her up or her mother! Proceedings would be so much simpler.

The jeweler's messenger will be here tomorrow morning, and will also bring the sample blouse. My tailor is waiting to get it.

Thank God we need not cater in Aishapur. All our entertaining will be done here.

Again ringing Hamid, to ask him to send the two best borders in gold and silver he can get through the jeweler. There'll still be time to have them sewed by hand to the saris, but it'll be a narrow shave.

Today we must send a man to Aishapur, with a sample *chervani, tang pyjamas* and slippers of Rashid's. At his wedding he must wear clothes provided by the bride's family.

Asked how many heads the bridegroom's party would number, I said "Fifty" after consultation with Mr. Quraishi. Now I'm afraid I should have said more. There'll be a lot of offended people, if we don't take all of them. Rashid is at his best when the underdog is concerned; he wants to take all his humbler collaborators. I'm heart and soul with him, of course. On the other hand I have Quraishi and Seth Chandralal warning me not to offend the higher strata.

It's not easy, especially since there's never time to discuss any-thing properly, never time to think, never time to breathe. The house continually full of people. Rashid and I are never alone.

Later

The telephone rings. A trunk call from Bombay. Hamid? No. A woman's voice, speaking remarkably good English.

"Mother? This is Mrs. Raza Ali Khan speaking."

"Who, please?"

"Mrs. Raza Ali Khan. You don't know me. I'm Maryam's aunt, Mrs. Liaqatullah's younger sister."

"But—how kind of you—has anything happened?"

"Nothing at all. Maryam and my sister have heard that you over-work yourself with preparations. They beg you not to. Everybody understands that at such short notice things can't be ready. It's the same on our side. You will have to make many allowances."

"But how extremely kind! Please give both my love and say how much I appreciate their thoughtfulness. I thought the two families were not allowed to communicate directly."

"That is correct. Nobody knows about this call but the three of us. My sister and I are Bombay-born. That accounts for this es-capade of ours. But please don't tell anybody, not even your son. And certainly not the Aishapur family. We trust you, Mother."

"You can. I think this move on your part delightful. May I ask you something?"

"Of course."

"Does Maryam prefer emeralds or rubies?"

"Emeralds."

"Does she wear her own pearls, or would she like some?"

"She brings her own."

"Thanks. How easy everything becomes by direct communication!"

"It does, doesn't it?"

"May I ask something else?"

"Why such a question? I am at your service."

"I can't get all the brocades for blouses up here. I'm short of three. Would you be good enough to get them for me today, one cloth of gold, one cloth of silver, one gold shot with emerald green? The very best you can get, please. You can't imagine what a help this would mean to me."

"Of course. In two hours I'll have the lot, and take them with me to Aishapur."

"Please not to Aishapur. I'll bring the presents already all packed up, and send them on our arrival at once to the bride's house. These three blouses must be wrapped up with their respective saris. Could you have the parcel sent to Dr. Hamidullah's house, before, say four o'clock today, with the request to send it along with the jewels? Then I'll have it by tomorrow. We'll settle accounts in Aishapur. And my most grateful thanks to you."

"What am I to say to Maryam? Will you take care of yourself? She doesn't want you to fall ill on her account."

"Give her my very warm love, please. And tell her that, even if I should be ill, I would recover through her presence."

"How prettily said! May I now take my leave, Mother?"

"Thank you so much for having rung. God bless you."

"God bless you, Mother."

Things are looking a lot better.

March 29

The last day of preparations is over, the jewels are chosen, the bridegroom's party is organized, Rashid is packed off to bed. We start at six tomorrow morning.

I haven't been able to pack the presents before now. Only just before midnight did the tailor bring the blouse and the two saris, complete with borders.

287

Now I'm alone with *chowkidar,* who is helping me to fold the heavy saris. I am wrapping each set in silk of matching color, each parcel being tied with ribbon of real gold or silver. A big suitcase will be filled. The jewels are on top.

I've still not tidied my rooms. Maryam mustn't see them during the twenty-odd hours she will spend here before setting out for Mount Abu, the place she has chosen. I'd be very ashamed if she did.

I'm glad all is still and quiet. But I'm too tired to sleep. Tomorrow, no, today, will be a heavy day.

March 30

"Maharaj and *chowkidar,* house clean be must. Thou to and thou to I everything trust. Painter courtyard finish must. *Pan* four hundred people for prepared be must, *pan* with silverleaf. Here money is it for. Tomorrow night back we are bride with Ram Pershad, many flowers do bring house into. Cook his work knows. Hotel food and waiters will send. Thou and thou I trust."

Now we are off, heading the line of cars which constitutes the bridegroom's procession. The collector's car follows ours, then comes Seth Chandralal's. Ismail Khan is resplendent in his new white outfit. I wanted him to don it only on arrival, but he pointed out that, leading the bridegroom's procession, his splendor was but befitting the occasion.

"Thou still tomorrow beautiful be must, Ismail Khan," I warn.

"Beautiful be I shall. Two new *puggaris*—turbans—with me I have."

Waliuddin and Faizuddin having decided not to attend—why?—Rashid and I are alone. At first we don't talk. Then, when we see Mary Ann's tomb in the distance, it is difficult for both of us not to cry.

I am glad not to have to talk for a while, to be with Rashid and feel that my task is nearing its end. Preparations are over. I feel the peace that finality always brings in its wake.

After an hour or two of silence, Rashid starts to read to me some of the letters and telegrams he has received. As expected, most of the officials from the capital and the neighbor States will not attend. The notice given was too short.

"I didn't know that the Rathgarh Dewan knew you," he says.

"Look, he writes 'your revered Mother's invitation—' I like that wording."

"I don't really know him. I think the wording denotes his perplexity. You see, people can't quite understand me. To them I seem unbelievable. So, to be polite, they say 'revered.'"

"But you *are* unbelievable, Mother! Not because nearly everybody tells me so, but because even I who know you so well, who have been witness to all you did in every phase, cannot even today believe that such action is humanly possible! You are as unbelievable to me as to anybody else. Do you really not mind my remarrying? It seems so, but it is too good to be true."

"I really do not mind. I really am looking forward to Maryam. What I *would* mind is your not making her happy. But you will, I know."

"Who helps you to be as you are, Mother?"

"My religion, if you want to know the truth. Christ. And the thought of Mary Ann."

"Mother—if only—if only I could tell you all I feel——"

"Don't, darling. The only thing I want is for both of you to be happy."

After that, my recollection becomes blurred. As during Mary Ann's illness and funeral procession, events become dreamlike, unreal. Too tired to think, I move like an automaton, taking care instinctively to hide my utter exhaustion.

The late lunch at Nagpur Railway Station—arrival in Aishapur—taking possession of the bridal house *in spe*—despatching Hamid with the precious suitcase to the grandparents' house—dressing for the At Home—meeting innumerable people including Mrs. Raza Ali Khan, smiling, chatting, introducing our party to the Aishapur crowd—returning to "our" bungalow, donning my silver-brocade frock—meeting Rashid, dressed in his cloth-of-gold wedding *chervani*, with a heavy gold *puggari* on his poor head—being alone with him for a bare minute—descending the steps with him to where our ways separate: he to attend the wedding ceremony in the men's quarters, I to join the women in the *zenana*. A last pressure of his hand. Then I walk alone, the only Westerner amidst many hundreds of Indians, at the same time the only one to represent the bridegroom's family. Sensing that I am being watched by many eyes, I walk on, looking straight ahead of me. At the entrance of the *zenana* courtyard the curtains open upon my approach. Through rows and rows of gaily dressed ladies sitting on chairs or squatting on the ground, I go straight to where a shimmering figure is hidden away behind the red wedding veil. Suddenly I feel wide awake.

"Maryam! At last! I am so glad, darling."

"I am so glad you are here, Mother! Are you terribly tired?"

"Not now, when I see you. Are you not hot behind that veil?"

"It is not thick. I can see you perfectly well, but you can't see me."

"I wish I could!"

"Soon, Mother."

"Can I stay here now with you? I'm afraid I don't know the ceremonial. You'll have to tell me."

"You see, I must keep purdah to please my grandparents. So must my mother and aunts. Auntie Mumtaz—Mrs. Raza Ali Khan—slipped out to see you this evening, but she was the only one, because she is not a Liaqatullah. We shall dine here in the *zenana* with all the ladies. You are to dine with the men. They want to do you honor."

"What a shame! I'd like to stay here with you."

"I wish you could."

"Is the marriage over?"

"Yes, the *nikah*—marriage contract—was read outside the purdah just before you came."

"So you *are* already Mrs. Rashid Ali."

"Yes, I am, Mother, I am your daughter now."

She is such a darling. I'm glad to be near her.

Later on everything again becomes blurred. An interminable dinner, at which I'm sitting between grandfather and father Liaqatullah, again chatting and smiling, not knowing what I do or say. Afterwards music. More chatting, more smiles. The bridal procession forming after midnight. The bride's purdah car, the bridegroom's car, my car and then, following, the whole Akbarabad party. We parade the town for about an hour, with me trying not to nod in sleep. Like Rashid I've been put into an open car, and if I should doze off, lots of spectators will see it and say so. At last my car speeds on to the bridal house. I am at the door to receive the bridegroom. He disappears into his room. All servants vanish. When the bride's car drives up, I am alone to receive her, hanging a garland round her neck.

We kiss. Hand in hand we proceed to her room, her two maid-attendants following. The red veil still conceals her face. It is for the bridegroom to lift, before he prostrates himself in prayer for his wife and her future children.

As a Muslim's mother should, I get Rashid and take him to her, smiling at each, kissing each, and firmly drawing the curtains behind me on retiring.

March 30

Everything is more blurred and unreal than ever. In the morning, a visit to Maryam, before her uncle takes her "home." Conferences with members of our party returning to Akbarabad before I do: messages to maharaj, to cook, to Auntie, to the hotel. Visits to Maryam's family. Lunch with the remainder of our party. Now I drive home, alone with Ismail Khan. Maryam travels in her grand-father's car, made purdah, with two woman attendants inside and Rashid next to the driver, for the benefit of the grandparents. There'll be changes afterwards, but until the grandfather's envoys return to Aishapur, Maryam will have to keep purdah.

Others wanted to drive with me, but I asked Rashid for the sole use of our car. I'm too tired to talk.

Halfway we've tea in Maryam's car; on this occasion I note with satisfaction that the maids are now sitting with the driver. When nearing Akbarabad, seats are resumed in their original order.

Civic reception, city fathers, speeches, garlands await us at the entrance of the town. Only Rashid and I are visible, of course, but I make sure that Maryam can see and hear everything.

In procession the bride is taken into town, preceded by cere-monial elephants. Bridal car; Rashid in an open car; I in an open car; the collector and all the others. Many detours are made. People cheer us as we pass along, or raise their hands either in *pranam* or the Muslim greeting. Sometimes they say something, but I can't make it out.

Half a mile from our bungalow I tell the driver to take me home through a side lane. I must receive both of them at our front door.

The house is blazing with light. Hundreds of people are in the garden, with garlands in their hands. When Rashid drives up, they all retire a few steps. I'm alone to receive him. He removes the many garlands round his neck and bends his head to receive mine. Then maharaj brings the purdah sheets. Maryam's car drives up. After inspecting the purdah arrangements I open the door, take her in my arms and then garland her. Between Rashid and me she enters the house and Rashid's room, made purdah.

Outside there is pandemonium. Everybody waits for Rashid to reappear. When he does, literally hundreds of garlands are hung round his neck. Whenever his face disappears up to the ears in flowers, he takes off the heavy load and either hangs them round my neck or deposits them somewhere. But I get my own, too, though not as many as he. Soon there are garlands everywhere. I fling piles of them into Maryam's room, shout to cook that dinner for only the three of us should be served, run out again just in time to catch Rashid who is about to faint under his fragrant burden. I pilot him inside, where he recovers at once, and I return alone to say that Rashid is too tired to reappear. Since practically everybody has got rid of his garland, nobody minds. Soon we are alone. I ask maharaj to dispose of the garlands, and he gathers them in heaps all over the house.

Dinner for the three of us, dinner for the Aishapur party and their servants, sleeping and washing facilities for all of them, arrangements for tomorrow's meals, arrangements for the journey—it is again midnight before I am alone. I can't breathe indoors; my heart is too bad. I'm spending the night on the roof, lying in a deck chair, looking at the stars, thinking of Mary Ann and praying for the happiness of those two dear ones downstairs.

April 1

Breakfast for Maryam and Rashid, breakfast for the Aishapur party.

At seven-thirty the first ladies to call on the bride, look at her jewels and accept bridal *pan*. Maryam, the Bombay-bred, and I, the Westerner, have joined forces to have proceedings modernized; for instance, for her to receive in the drawing room, or at least on the settee of her bedroom; but her Aishapur retinue keep us in order. A proper Muslim bride receives squatting on her bed, and on the bed poor Maryam has to receive.

I'm in and out of the room, introducing the ladies by name, then hurrying into the drawing room which is full of men. Today the visitors from the districts arrive. There are again hundreds of garlands. I'm worrying about *pan*, and send *chowkidar* for more supplies. Six people are preparing *pan* in front of Ismail Khan's quarters at top speed.

I'm sorry I can't stay with Maryam; on the other hand it's nice to escape into male regions, into which the Akbarabad ladies can't follow. While introducing them to the bride, I get enough to hear.

"Mother never told us!"

"She keeps everything a secret."

"Mother does not trust us."

"Mother is very good," Maryam says with authority, already standing up for me.

"She *is* very good! We know that. Only us she does not trust!"

Presents arrive, which I must note down and acknowledge. Visitors multiply. A hurried lunch in Maryam's bedroom while crowds are waiting to be received. Lunch for lots of other people. Packing for Rashid. Ismail Khan will travel with him. I'm continually called away from packing.

For tea Aishapur envoys come to Maryam's room, ostensibly for a little chat, in reality to find out whether we treat her well. That is one of the customs by which the bride's family tries to ascertain how her in-laws behave, and whether they can return, their mind at ease. I can't stay with them. I have to receive all the time; but Rashid attends, as he should.

At about seven P.M.—I've just finished packing—people and servants are turned out, and everything is made purdah. Auntie arrives with her two sons. The meeting is friendly. She is visibly impressed by Maryam's resemblance to Mary Ann, and mentions it.

"Even without it, Maryam is my dear daughter," I say at once.

"So I see. Wilt thou not stay at my house tonight, Sister? It will be sad for thee all by thyself!"

"Thank thee, Sister. Thou art very kind. I shall not be sad. Tomorrow, *inshallah*, I shall call on thee."

Dinner for the three of us. I can't eat. Both Maryam and Rashid worry about leaving me here by myself. They feel very bad about it. As true Easterners, loneliness is something they dislike; they feel guilty of inflicting it on me. In vain do I protest. To be alone, not to see and have to speak to anybody, is the one thing I need.

A few friends have dinner. Hamid draws me aside. "Mother, there's something that'll give you pleasure to hear. You know that everybody is praising you. But the Aishapur collector said something especially nice: 'No Hindu or Muslim mother would have done what Mother did. Only a Christian can be so unselfish.' Now everybody repeats his words."

"Thanks, Hamid. This is indeed a beautiful tribute, but unmerited. I didn't do anything special. Thanks for all your help. Love to Sultana, salaams to your mother."

Drive to the railway station. On arrival a big surprise: all the officials are there, the others in their wake. They *are* doing us proud, really!

Purdah arrangements for Maryam to reach her compartment, since the Aishapur envoys are still present. "When you come back, you'll jump out first, for everybody to see," I say, laughing about today's camouflage.

Farewell to Maryam; farewell to Rashid when he joins her. He holds me close, at first unable to speak. "Promise you'll lie down and do all Dr. Ram Chandra asks you to. I've told him I make him responsible."

Another embrace. Still another. A last kiss from Maryam. I get down. The officials and I are assembled in front of the purdah compartment, with Rashid standing in the open door.

Only he and I speak, which is most embarrassing. It is as though the others did not want to interfere.

"You've promised to rest, Mother. Don't forget."

"Do wire your arrival."

"Of course. Only don't worry, please."

"Don't forget to feed the servants on the way."

"Of course I won't. Take care of yourself."

"I will."

If only the train would leave! As long as I had to run about, I could manage. Now, standing still, my feet don't carry me any more. If only I could take somebody's arm, the collector's or Seth Chandralal's, both of whom are standing near me. But this is India. You can't touch a man not your relative. Moreover, Rashid would get alarmed.

Some words catch my ear. "For Rashid sahib the first of April is not a joke—for him it's a happy reality."

The first of April! Today! Just one year ago that we arrived in

Akbarabad, that we drove to town to fit out the house. A bare year ago—! Mary Ann. Oh Mary Ann! Life is so hard without you.

I can't keep up any longer. I can't. But I must think of Rashid. He is to leave happy.

Thank God, the train is moving at last. Suddenly Maryam peeps out near Rashid. The darling girl! "God bless you, Mother!"

Groping, stumbling, I hurry towards the Aishapur car which is to take me home. No good-by to anybody, however impolite my behavior. I'm at the end of my strength.

Out of the darkness I hear a well-known voice. "I here am, Mother. My hand to take."

Maharaj opens the door, calls to the driver to be quick and jumps into his seat when the car is already moving.

I don't want to cry. Maharaj is discreet, but the Aishapur driver might talk. No, I mustn't cry or let go. When I'm alone, only when I'm alone with the doors locked behind me, can I break down. I want to be alone, like a hunted animal. It is my exhaustion which makes me feel like that. This wedding is my own doing, and I love Maryam. I thank God for her. But I am so tired that I can't think properly any more.

"Thanks, maharaj. Home now do go. Late is. *Chowkidar*, door close do. At once!" I am nearly running towards the courtyard where, I know, my bed will be ready for me. In passing I wonder at the unexpected tidiness. Where have all garlands gone to? And why have I not heard the fastening of the door? Did *chowkidar* not obey? Can't they let me alone?

Then, suddenly, I understand and begin to take things in.

The immense courtyard, including its walls, is sprinkled with water, so I shan't suffer from heat. To the right and left of my pillows, jasmine blossoms and roses are awaiting me in complicated patterns which must have taken Ram Pershad much time and labor to arrange. There is my bedside table and lamp. Outside the light's orbit I see basin and tub full of water; towels, soap, nightdress and kimono are laid out on a chair, instead of waiting in my bathroom. Presumably it was thought I should be too tired to reach it.

Facing the foot of my bed sideways, so that I can look at it without having to turn my head, Mary Ann's enlarged photograph has been set up on a table, surrounded by garlands of roses—not remains from the wedding, but quite fresh ones. The whole table is

295

covered with red roses. Scores and scores of jasmine garlands from the house have been laid out on the ground in the sun-pattern of ancient Hinduism, rising to the table, encircling it in rays corresponding to those of the sun. It is as though flowers rose from the earth in rhythms of the ascending sun, carrying, offering the likeness upwards. There is nothing but flowers and Mary Ann.

No, there is something else, just in front of the photograph. At first I can't make it out; then, taking a step forward, I recognize the object.

There, filled with pale-green flowers—the real *champa*-blossoms so rarely obtainable—stands the handleless cup which Mary Ann took out to the cobra. After her death it had mysteriously disappeared from the pantry. I had thought that somebody had broken it, and had not pressed the point. Now I realize that it must have been rescued from the handling by a Muslim cook, probably by Ram Pershad, the gardener, in whose domain dealing with the cobra belongs.

Seeing my child's sweet face above the flowers, which devotion and love have built up for her, seeing the cup, whose presence means so much in the silent language of the East, I break down at last. Now I can weep. There is no bitterness in my tears, only relief. I'm among my own.

Here they are, appearing silently out of the shadow. Ram Pershad, the Brahman gardener, from whom Mary Ann took leave with a big *pranam*; *chowkidar*, the Rajput, who night and day filled the ice bags for her; the head sweeper, he whom she could not promote one single step higher; and maharaj, the first-class Brahman who changed, while working for her, from slight contempt regarding memsahibs to adoring respect and love—maharaj who did not eat while she lay ill, and who broke down with brain fever after her death. Here they stand. They are no angels; far from it. At times they quarrel, at times they intrigue against one another. But together they have carried out this labor of love, to express their feelings in eloquent silence.

None talks. None expresses his sympathy in words while watching me cry. They stand round me, crying too.

At last I lift my head. "Sit down!" I manage to say. They must be terribly tired.

Before squatting down, however, *chowkidar* puts before me a small table set with food. Shaking my head, I signify that I don't want to eat. But he doesn't remove the table. Why? Has Rajabai again prepared Rajput dishes for me?

I look at the table. Welsh rarebit; stuffed tomato; baked apple. For one moment this seems quite natural to me; then only do I suddenly grasp the implications involved. Who has prepared these western dishes? I have not taught any of them to the new cook.

As though in answer to my unspoken question, our former cook emerges from the darkness. He, whom Rashid had dismissed so unjustly; he whom I had not been able to shield; he, who now works on a monthly salary of only twelve rupees, yet who has refused monetary aid from me—he has prepared in his humble abode the dainties Mary Ann herself had taught him, so that I might find them tonight. I shall never know whether this is his own gift, or whether all of them have clubbed together; I shall never know, and I don't care whether I do. What matters is that all of them have combined their efforts, the wronged Muslim and the proud Rajput, the poor untouchable and the superior Brahmans. There could be no more beautiful, no more adequate, way to commemorate Mary Ann.

I cry again, this time in gratitude. After a time only do I realize that it is past midnight. "Late is. To rest you go must."

Maharaj shakes his head. "Not home we go tonight, Mother. Only cook goes. His house far away is. Stay we do. Thy son *chowkidar* front door outside sleeps; thy son Ram Pershad garden door outside sleeps; thy son sweeper sweeper's entrance outside sleeps; thy son Jagdish north door outside sleeps. So Mother alone not is."

East, west, north, south—they've planned it all.

"No," I say, though I can hardly trust my voice. "Work tomorrow early you do must. Door outside sleep good not is. Soil cold is. Dew is. Snakes maybe are. Home do go. Mother alone not is. *Chowkidar* all doors close does. He alone stay shall. His work is."

"Mother alone is."

"I not alone am. God with me always is."

"Thy God?"

"Our God."

"Yes, God always is."

Again they are standing round me, reassured, but not ready to leave. I must get them to take their more than well-earned rest. They must be tired to death after these last days' overwork.

Suddenly I know what to do. Maharaj, Ram Pershad and *chowki-dar* have time and again asked me in solemn moments to call them "my son." I tried to satisfy them, but I never could. I felt too shy and self-conscious to utter those two words. Even when Rashid once or twice made the same request, I could not bring myself to this direct mode of address.

Now, however, the words come easily. All my western clumsiness seems to have vanished.

"My sons," I say, "go now do. Peace be upon thee, my son Gulam; thy food I shall eat; to me good it do will. My son sweeper, sweeper entrance through thou go do; sweeper entrance me to protection give will. My son Ram Pershad, garden door through thou go do; garden door me to protection give will. My son maharaj, north door through thou go do; north door me to protection give will. You going after *chowkidar* every door lock will. Mother not alone is. God and your goodness Mother with remains."

To cook I perform the Muslim greeting, to the others each a big *pranam*, including the sweeper. They all *pranam* to Mary Ann's photograph, then touch my feet to take the dust from them. Their exit takes place through the north, south, and west doors. After locking them, *chowkidar* leaves by the front door, locking it from outside.

I am alone, facing the flowers and Mary Ann under the starlit sky. I am too tired to think, too tired to feel. I only know that this is India, that I am thousands of miles away from my own people, and yet at home.